CRISIS, HEALTH, AND MEDICINE

CRISIS,
HEALTH, AND MEDICINE

A SOCIAL CRITIQUE

VICENTE NAVARRO

Tavistock Publications · *New York* *London*

First published in 1986 by
Tavistock Publications
in association with Methuen, Inc.
29 West 35th Street
New York, NY 10001
and Tavistock Publications Ltd
11 New Fetter Lane, London EC4P 4EE

Photoset by Rowland Phototypesetting Ltd
Bury St Edmunds, Suffolk
Printed in the United States of America

Library of Congress Cataloging in Publication Data

Navarro, Vicente.
  Crisis, health, and medicine.
  Includes bibliographies and indexes.
  1. Social medicine.   2. Medicine—Political aspects.
  I. Title. [DNLM: 1. Health Policy.
  2. Political Systems.
  3. Quality of Health Care.
  4. Socioeconomic Factors.
  W 84.1 N322c]
  RA418.N38   1986   362.1′042   85-30325

  ISBN 0-422-60580-8
  ISBN 0-422-60170-5 (pbk.)

British Library Cataloguing in Publication Data

Navarro, Vicente.
  Crisis, health, and medicine: a social critique.
  1. Social medicine.
  I. Title.
  306′.46   RA418

  ISBN 0-422-60580-8
  ISBN 0-422-60170-5 (pbk.)

Contents

Introduction: Crisis and its implications in health and medicine

In the last ten years medicine has been one of the social sciences' main subjects of analysis. Never before have there been so many studies of the health of the people or of the knowledge, practice, and institutions of medicine. A frequent theme of these studies has been the phenomenon usually referred to as the *crisis of medicine*, characterized by continuously rising health costs and ever-growing health expenditures accompanied by a relative ineffectiveness of those health care interventions. Not only scholarly papers but also the popular press lament almost on a daily basis these two dimensions of the crisis of medicine: the increasing amount of funds allocated to medicine in our Western societies and the diminishing returns on those expenditures. There does not seem to be a direct relationship between expenditures on medical services, on the one hand, and the health of our populations, on the other.

Why this crisis of medicine? The most frequently heard explanations derive from the analysis of medicine which focuses on the interactions among the different agents (referred to as "interest groups") within medicine, and which concludes that the problems that characterize the crisis are rooted in the dominance that some of those groups (e.g. providers) have over medicine and their ability to optimize their interests by institutionalizing their power through the control of the knowledge, practice, and institutions of medicine. The way these analysts approach the problem, however, prefigures their answers. By concentrating on medicine, they assume that the roots of the problems can be found there.

By focusing their analytical gaze only on medicine, these analysts miss the fact that it is not only the practice and institutions of medicine that are in crisis. Other social institutions such as education, welfare, transportation, as well as many political, economic, and ideological institutions, are also referred to as being in crisis. Themes such as the crisis of the welfare state, of the representative institutions, of the media, and many other related subjects continuously appear in the daily press. Indeed, the whole of our Western world is defined and perceived as in profound crisis. And these societal crises are not the mere aggregate of the different sectoral crises; rather, the *sectoral crises are the sectoral realizations of the overall societal crises.* It is precisely the unawareness of this key point that limits most seriously the explanatory value of most current analyses of medicine. What we have witnessed over the last ten years is the heightening of the internal contradictions of our Western societies in all their economic, political, and civil dimensions and in all areas of life (including health and medicine), with an unraveling of the social tapestry, still sustained by an increasingly challenged dominant ideology.

As Antoni Gramsci indicated, it is precisely in periods of crisis that the relationship between the parts and the whole appears most clearly.[1] Several essays in this volume explain how the part (the crisis of medicine) relates to the whole (the crisis of capitalism). In brief, the crisis of medicine under capitalism is the crisis of capitalism *in* medicine. The crisis *in* medicine takes specific forms, depending on the interrelationships among the forces within and outside medicine. Medicine is, after all, not merely a reflection of outside forces. It has, indeed, an opacity of its own. But how these forces appear, relate, and interact depends on a matrix of power relations defined primarily by the societal whole and not merely by its parts. The crisis in medicine cannot be understood without consideration of its articulation with the crisis of the societal whole.

Another major limitation of many of the studies of medicine is their disciplinary character. Economists, sociologists, political scientists, anthropologists, psychologists, historians, and many others have applied their specific skills to the understanding of medicine.

This disciplinary approach reflects the specific form of knowledge reproduction in our Western academic institutions. Each discipline is supposed to approach the subject from a different angle; the holistic understanding of a subject is perceived as the aggregate of the disciplinary knowledge of it. But the explanation of our reality is more than the mere aggregate of its economic, sociological, historical, and other dimensions. In reality, it is not a question of adding more disciplines but rather producing a different form of knowledge in which the subject of study is seen in its totality and not merely from each of its different angles. Here I am counterposing Marxism—the method of analysis used in this volume—to the methods traditionally used in the various disciplines in social science. The essays in this volume do not use a disciplinary analysis of the components of the social system in order to understand society. Rather, using the Marxist method, they analyze the entire society to better understand the realities in one of its dimensions—medicine. By society, I mean the social arrangements determined by a specific combination of social forces and relations of production, in which power is distributed according to a matrix in which class relations define the form in which those other relations interact and are reproduced. Indeed, and contrary to prevalent ideological positions, I believe that class and class struggle are at the center of the understanding of our realities.

I am aware, of course, that the methods of analysis and even discourse used in these essays are minority ones in today's debate. Terms such as capitalism, class struggle, imperialism, and the like are non-existent in most analyses of medicine or are quickly dismissed, or set in quotes, as if to single them out as subjects of suspicion and of concern only to outmoded ideologues who remain mired in *passé* ideological terrains. The concepts of social class as the determinant of power relations and class struggle as the motor of change are virtually non-existent in most analyses of medicine. This is particularly accentuated in the USA where there is almost complete absence from any established and official discourse—be it academia, government or media—of the concept of class. Class and class power are presented as non-American (and frequently as anti-American) concepts and realities. The USA is assumed to be a "middle class society," a society defined by hierarchical levels of consumption in which the majority of Americans are allegedly in the middle, that is not rich and not poor. Terms such as capitalist and bourgeoisie or working class and proletariat rarely appear in established discourse or are dismissed as ideological baggage.

As a consequence, while the US capitalist class is the most powerful in today's world, its existence is hidden or even dismissed in established discourse. Since it is a non-visible class, it is also a non-target. Its absence from political discourse is not innocent. It is profoundly political. It is propagandistic in the sense of propagating dominant values and interpretations of reality, which reproduce current class power relations. In this non-class discourse, the capitalist class has disappeared. In this (capitalist) theoretical scenario, power is distributed not according to class but rather "interest groups": society, instead of being divided into antagonistic classes, is constituted into groups that compete for power, including state and political power. Analytical categories such as the capitalist and working classes and the state are recycled to become management, labor unions, political parties, government agencies, which each act as interest groups competing for influence. The disappearance of class as a category of power serves the purpose of leaving the class power relations in that society untouched. By "transcending" capitalism, these theoretical positions actually reinforce capitalism. Their ideological dominance, however, is increasingly questioned. As an outcome of the current crisis (the second largest in the history of capitalism), we have witnessed a proliferation of critical analyses of our realities in which the meaning and value of Marxist methods of analysis and discourse have been rediscovered and increasingly perceived as more relevant to the analysis of our realities than the dominant ones. In almost all disciplines and in all areas of theoretical production, there has been in the last ten years a vital opening and flourishing of radical and Marxist analyses that, although initially ignored, have forced a response.

Medicine is not an exception. Since 1976, when I published what was chronologically one of the first Marxist analyses of medicine in the English-speaking world since the works of the late Henry Sigerist, several other volumes have appeared with an increasingly large number of references.[2] Still, the overwhelming conservatism that prevails in most institutions of medicine explains why these critical analyses have been resisted more vigorously in medicine than in other sectors. Witness the review of literature on sociological analyses of medicine prepared by a leading medical sociologist of the USA for the International Congress of Sociology.[3] Not one Marxist reference is even cited.

Nonetheless, alternative explanations to the many subjects and themes that dominate our times continue to be presented. This volume is a collection of essays that present Marxist interpretations of some of the major themes that have appeared in the analysis of medicine in the last ten years, interpretations that aim, as Marx would say, at providing "uncompromising critical evaluations of all that exists, uncompromising in the sense that this criticism fears neither its own results nor the conflict with the powers that be."[4]

Themes of this book

The essays presented in this volume were written in a variety of political and cultural settings. Originally published in different forums, these essays have been pruned to avoid duplication. They have also been written in a variety of tones and styles, although all share the underlying purpose of questioning dominant explanations of health and medicine and presenting alternative ones. They have been grouped thematically under five headings, according to some of the major topics of debate in the last decade.

The first essay (Part I) critically analyzes some of the current interpretations of the crisis of the Western system of medicine and presents alternative explanations for those crises. It indicates that the crisis of medicine—reflected in its ubiquitous problems of costs and limited effectiveness—is due to and reflects the crisis of legitimation and capital accumulation of contemporary capitalism. The essay is divided into six sections: the first two define the specific character-istics of the crisis of Western contemporary capitalism and of its system of medicine, with a critique of current theories which try to explain them. Parts three and four counterpose to these theories a Marxist interpretation of the crisis, tracing its causes to the needs created by the process of capital accumulation and the demands expressed by the working populations. The needs and demands generated by capital and labor are intrinsically in conflict, and are realized in the daily practice of class struggle. The characteristics and consequences of this struggle for health and for the organization, content, and ideology of medicine are analyzed in the fifth part. The class struggle unfolds within a political context in which capital and its social expression, the bourgeoisie or corporate class, have hegemonic—but not exclusive—influence on the organs of the state. The sixth part details how that class dominance is reflected in state responses to the crisis of medicine.

The crisis of the Western system of power also explains the threat that an increasingly diverse world represents for the dominant establishment positions. Both within and outside the USA, the establishment's positions have been questioned more widely than ever before. Within the USA we have witnessed an increased political alienation and mistrust towards the political institutions, with a growing anti-establishment mood among large sectors of the US population. Two of the most articulate conservative theorists in the USA—Professors S. M. Lipset and W. Schneider—concluded a thorough review of public attitudes towards business, labor, and government with the remarkably candid statement,

> "Should the 1980s be characterized by a major crisis, the outcome could very well be substantial support for movements seeking to change the system in a fundamental way. Serious setbacks in the economy or in foreign policy, accompanied by a failure of leadership, could raise greater risks of a loss of legitimacy now *than at any time in this century . . . there are disturbing signs of deep and serious discontent.*"[5]

(emphasis added)

Internationally, the political multiplurality of the world has successfully challenged the dominance of the US establishment in today's world. Thus, in the international ideological debate, massive ideological campaigns supported by that establishment and strengthened both by the Carter and the Reagan Administrations aimed to establish the moral superiority of the US social system over all others. And in that ideological struggle, general features assumed to be in existence in the US society were abstracted as an ideal type and compared and contrasted with the features of other societies, particularly with those that allegedly negate the key feature of our political system, *the existence of human rights.* Thus, an enormous debate has appeared on the national and international scene regarding the nature of human (including health) rights. The second essay (Part II) heading presents an analysis and critique of the prevalent understanding of human rights in US academic and governmental circles. It criticizes (1) the limited focus on only some civil and political components of the original UN Declaration of Human Rights, and (2) the disregard for economic and social rights such as the right to work, fair wages, health, education, and social security. This section discusses the reasons for that limited focus and shows that contrary to what is widely reported in the media and academia, (1) civil and political rights are highly restricted in the USA; (2) those rights are further restricted in the USA when analyzed in their social and economic dimensions; (3) civil and political rights are not independent of but rather intrinsically related to and dependent on the existence of socio-economic rights; (4) the definition of the nature and extension of human rights in their civil, political, social, and economic dimensions is not universal but rather depends on the pattern of economic and political power relations particular to each society; and (5) the pattern of power relations in US society and the Western system of power, based on the right to individual property and its concomitant class structure and class relations, seriously hinders the full realization of human rights in their economic, social, political, and civil dimensions. Nowhere in the Western developed world is the capitalist class as powerful as it is in the USA. And nowhere in the developed capitalist world are there as large sectors of the population without such limited health care rights as in the USA: 32 million citizens and residents of the USA do not have any form of health insurance coverage whatsoever, 88 million do not have any form of catastrophic sickness insurance, 1 million families are refused care for not being able to pay for their services. The list could go on and on. This second essay explains the relationship between capitalism and the denial of human (including health) rights in the USA and abroad.

Another theme, much debated during this period, is the crisis of the welfare state. One of the reasons frequently given for the current crisis of the Western world is the large growth of dependence of the citizenry on the state's social services. In the words of one of the proponents of this position, "people have heightened their expectations too much."[6] This position is usually accompanied by another one that states that the levels of health of our populations depend primarily on what people do for themselves. These positions are dominant in government and academic circles of the Western world. Consequently, one of the main characteristics of major national health strategies in the last ten years has been a focus on changing individual lifestyles. The basic assumption of those policies is that individuals can and should change their ways of living and patterns of consumption. This situation explains the overabundance of studies aimed at understanding the health of the people by looking at their diet, consumption, life-styles, residential patterns and so forth. These studies continue the Weberian tradition, the dominant tradition within Western social science, that sees people as consumers with specific attributes such as income, status, education, all defined in the spheres of exchange, distribution, and consumption rather than in the world of production.

The third essay (Part III) questions these epistemological definitions of the subject—the individual—and presents an alternate approach in which individuals and their health status are considered primarily in terms of their relation to production as workers. The essay in this section is divided into three sections. The first theorizes on the relationship between the elements of the labor process and health. The second analyzes the historical evolution of the labor process and its consequences for health, with a special emphasis on the effect on health of different forms of alienation. The third part examines the changes in the different branches of economic activity and their impact on health, with added discussion of the consequences of the current crisis and the concurrent international mobility of capital on health.

The epistemological importance of defining individuals in terms of their relation to production—rather than consumption—is extremely important for the understanding of not only the relationship between work and health (as explained in Part III) but also the nature of economic, social, and political power in society, including institutions such as medicine. This is the subject of Part IV. Individuals have different degrees of power, depending on the social relations in society, of which the relations of production and the class structure they determine are the key ones. Indeed, and contrary to prevalent mythology, class and class struggle continue to be key categories for the understanding of our realities. One of those realities is the assumed neutrality of scientific knowledge and practice, a key tenet of the dominant ideology. During the 1970s and early 1980s many social movements—labor, civil rights, feminist, and ecological movements—rightly questioned the dominant ideological position of the neutrality of science, including medicine. The institutions of science and medicine indeed are not neutral; their knowledge and practices reproduce class, race, sex, and other forms of power relations. The essay in Part IV analyzes how capitalist or bourgeoisie ideology reproduces capitalist dominance in the spheres of production, politics, and science and medicine. Also, this section explains how class struggle affects bourgeois dominance in the process of production, politics, science, and medicine. Special focus is placed on the analysis of (1) how bourgeois dominance appears in science and medicine; (2) how bourgeois ideology is reflected and reproduced in medical knowledge; and (3) how class struggle determines the nature of scientific and medical knowledge. This essay also includes a discussion of an alternate mode of production of scientific and medical knowledge.

The first four parts of this volume present alternative explanations to the ones that dominate current debate on medicine. The point of the story, however, is not only to explain reality but also change it. How? This is the focus of Part V. But before presenting a strategy for change, there is a need to critically analyze those hegemonic interpretations of health and medicine that carry with them specific operative and normative solutions to current problems. The three essays in this section do that.

The first discusses one of the most acclaimed books in medical history and health policy in the last ten years, *The Social Transformation of American Medicine*, by Paul Starr, recipient of the 1984 Pulitzer prize. This essay analyzes the ideological and political assumptions of Starr's work and his explanations of the past, present and future of American medicine. The future of American medicine, in Starr's theoretical scenario, will be determined by the same forces that have explained its past and present, that is the wishes and wants of the majority of Americans expressed through the market and through their representative institutions. My critique questions these positions on both theoretical and empirical grounds. The future of American medicine under capitalism is seen not as an outcome of majority wants but rather as an outcome of a series of conflicts between classes, races, genders, and other power groupings, within a matrix of dominant–dominated relations, in which dominance is reproduced by coercion and repression rather than merely by persuasion, as Starr believes.

The interpretation that views our realities as the outcome of the desires of the majority is increasingly being questioned. It is recognized that economic and political power is unevenly distributed both within and between societies. The gap between the "haves" and "have nots" is growing rapidly, and with the widening of the gap has come a heightening of the contradictions of the world economic order. There is a need to do something about this situation, a call that has been expressed with a certain urgency due to the fears raised by the current crisis. A dominant position within the Development Establishment has been that there is a need for cooperation and collaboration between the "haves" and the "have nots" to close the gap and resolve the crisis in mutually beneficial ways. Both the Willy Brandt report and the influential WHO-Alma Ata Declaration call for this strategy of collaboration. The second essay in Part V analyzes both these documents within the socio-economic context that determined them and makes a critique of their ideological and political positions. Through a study of what is said and not said, this essay analyzes how these positions appear in the documents. It shows why the understanding of the causes of underdevelopment, the causes of major health and disease problems, and the suggestions for change are faulty. They avoid the key questions. The roots of the problem reside in national and international exploitation of the "have nots" by the "haves," both at the national and the international levels.

The solution to the problem of underdevelopment in today's world requires a break and/or profound transformation of those national and international relations. How to do it? This is the subject of the last essay of Part V, which contains a theoretical elaboration of a strategy of transformation of medicine in both underdeveloped and developed societies. This essay also contains a critique of two traditions within the left that need to be transcended. The first, the radical tradition, typified by the works of Ivan Illich and the Ehrenreichs, among others—much in vogue in the late 1970s and early 1980s—views both the state and medicine primarily as agencies of control. This undialectical vision of the state and of medicine makes it very attractive to the reactionary Right, which can thus present the cuts in social consumption and the reduction of medical interventions as components of a strategy of individual and collective liberation.

The second tradition, the instrumentalist vision of medicine, prevalent among American and European social democratic and many of the Leninist traditions, sees medicine as a useful and neutral instrument whose ends depend on what groups and/or classes control it. Medicine, however, is not neutral, nor is it an instrument. Medicine is a synthesis of social relations, defined within a matrix of power dominant–dominated relations that reproduce those relations within all dimensions of medicine, including its knowledge, practice, and institutions. Thus, a progressive strategy in health and medicine cannot leave those relations unchanged. Socialist medicine is not "neutral" medicine better distributed. It is a qualitatively different form of medicine—an outcome of the struggle not only for change in its priorities and its distribution, but equally important in its production of knowledge, practice, and institutions, a struggle aimed at democratization. The struggle for socialism and democracy are one and the same. The implications of this reality for a left strategy are analyzed in the last essay.

A final word regarding these essays. They represent interventions aimed at providing different explanations to the many themes that appear in current debate on the crisis of medicine. The reader should regard them as diagrams and sketches rather than definitive answers. They are mere pointers on the road to a more humane and just society. They intend to open up new spaces in our asphyxiating environment of "orthodoxy," intolerance and repression, further strengthened in Reagan's USA and Thatcher's UK. Needless to say, this volume will be unpopular in the centers of power, whose upholders will continue to discourage and repress any positions that open fissures in the enormous ideological edifice that sustains a brutal system of oppression. Their great influence over academia and the media explains the continuous exclusion of alternative positions in the realm of current debate. Still, veracity of this analysis will be affirmed not by its "popularity" in establishment circles, which will be nil, but rather on the terrain of practice and history, among those committed to a profound change in our society and its systems of medicine.

Note on tone and style

In these essays I have used a discursive style, trying to avoid the baroque styles prevalent on both sides of the ideological spectrum. Needless to say, terms and concepts have been used that reflect the method of analysis used in this text, a method clearly in the minority today in the English-speaking academic world. It is this phenomenon of being a minority position that explains why some of the terms used in this volume may sound "rhetorical." I would encourage readers who may have this reaction to ask, why do they sound rhetorical? The definition of what is acceptable language and discourse responds to power relations. For example, in explaining why the USA has less federal protective occupational health and safety legislation than Sweden and other developed capitalist countries, Professor Etzioni of the School of Sociology of Columbia University, wrote recently in the *Washington Post*, "We, in the U.S., have chosen productivity over safety." Although this statement may sound straightforward, unideological, and unrhetorical, it is profoundly ideological. It assumes that the US Congress, the federal body which legislates on nationwide occupational health and safety issues, represents the majority of Americans, the "we the Americans." This is an enormous ideological assumption. If I were to say, however, that the US Congress has legislated less protection for the worker than exists in other capitalist countries because (1) the capitalist class has a dominant (but not exclusive) influence over Congress and (2) the class struggle is carried out under conditions of extreme weakness for the working class, it is most likely that in many circles such a statement would be considered rhetorical. Why? The explanation resides in the enormous influence of the capitalist class on the organs of ideological reproduction—including the media and academia —and that makes some terms look suspicious and unwelcome. It is an important task, however, to expose the political nature of the acceptable language and recover the meaning and value of the forbidden one.

Acknowledgements

Having explained the rationale of this volume, its themes, as well as approach, style and discourse, it is fair that I finish this introduction by acknowledging the great assistance provided by many in shaping the positions presented. In more than one way this volume is indeed a collaborative effort. Each essay is the outcome of long and productive discussions with friends and foes alike who helped to shape the ideas presented here. Also, my own practice and that of my friends has taught me a lot.

Written for the most part in the USA during the last seven years, these essays are based on past and current experiences in this and many other countries. Thus, a note of acknowledgement will sound like a list of international and national experiences with a biographical touch.

First, and as always, thanks are due to my parents, family, friends, and comrades in Catalonia and other nations of Spain, whose struggle against fascism I have shared since the 1950s, and in whose struggle for justice and democracy I have also participated during these recent years. Their struggle is a difficult one. And their influence and inspiration for me continues to be very strong.

Also, many thanks to all my friends in all five continents with whom I have shared the extraordinary experience of being part of the International Association of Health Policy, a splendid group of committed scholars and activists from all over the world who dedicate themselves to the betterment of the health of our peoples. I learned much from them and from the specific struggle and projects that the Association has supported and worked for. I owe special thanks to Giovani Berlinguer, Uli Deppe, Finn Diderichsen, Lesley Doyal, Jose Carlos Escudero, Elizabeth Fee, Sally Guttmacher, Cristina Laurell, Najwa Makhoul, Hugo Mercer, Marc Renaud, Malcolm Segal, and many, many others whose listing would become practically the membership list of such an association.

Thanks also are due to my friends of the Americas—North,

Central and South. From those countries to the South of the Rio Grande I owe enormous thanks to a very dear friend and comrade, Juan Cesar Garcia, whose recent death meant an enormous loss for all those who struggle to analyze and change the unbearable realities of poverty and oppression for the largest majorities of that part of the Americas. I owe my understanding of those realities to Juan Cesar, as well as to many other friends who continue to be persecuted because of their belief that the only way of breaking with the underdevelopment of health is to break with the sickness of underdevelopment and the political forces that determine it. I do believe that their enormous sacrifices and the sacrifices of the majority of their peoples will soon be rewarded with the opening of new spaces of dignity and freedom over their lands, lands that have so much wealth to offer to the many, and not just to the few.

From the northern part of the Rio Grande I continue learning from many. As usual, I learned a lot from the unknown folk, those who earn their living from their toil, whose voices rarely appear in official academic, media, or political discourse. I have found the gap between those discourses and those voices to be just overwhelming. The limited ideological diversity that exists in the US establishment institutions also explains the very limited number of voices to which people are exposed. Still, however silent and repressed, other voices do exist. And they compete on very unequal bases for the hearts and minds of our population. These alternative voices, rooted in the repressed progressive traditions of the USA, keep struggling for a future in which solidarity and social justice will prevail. They are the ones who continue the long and heart-breaking history of struggle of our people to recover their past and control their future, a future in which this land will indeed become—as Guthrie used to sing— everyone's land. Among them I want to thank my friends of the East Coast Discussion Group, and to those who in formal settings, in academic settings, have helped me a great deal in understanding the past and future possibilities of our realities. Thanks in particular are due to David Harvey, Rick Pfeffer, Cliff Durand, Linda Zeidman, and Kostis Papadentonakis for their stimulating friendship.

Also, I have benefited enormously from my students, both from those with whom I agree and from those with whom I disagree. They should know that one of the best rewards I ever received was, when, with great generosity, they elected me among the best teachers in our school. I learned a lot from them.

Finally, I want to thank all those without whose work these lines would have never been published. I owe thanks to Debby Sarsgard for editing my English (with heavy Catalan accent) manuscripts, and to Sirkka Lee and Gina Malloney for translating my handwritten notes into readable forms. Their work has been outstanding and splendid.

Also, thanks are owed to those whose work on the production and distribution of this volume will make it possible for the book to be read by you, the reader.

Vicente Navarro

The Johns Hopkins University, June, 1985.

Notes

1 A. Gramsci, *L'ordine nuovo*: vol. 9 1919–1920, Rome: Einaudi, 1954.
2 V. Navarro, *Medicine under Capitalism*, New York: Neale Watson, 1976. See also L. Doyal, *The Political Economy of Health*, London: Pluto Press, 1981, and H. Waitzkin, *The Second Sickness. The Contradictions of Capitalist Health Care*, New York: Free Press, 1982.
3 A. C. Twaddle, From Medical Sociology to the Sociology of Health: Some Changing Concerns of the Sociological Study of Sickness and Treatment, in T. Bottomore, S. Nowak, and M. Sokolowska (eds), *Sociology: The State of the Art*, London and Beverly Hills, CA: International Sociological Association, Sage Publications, 1982.
4 K. Marx, Letter to A. Ruge, 1844.
5 S. M. Lipset and W. Schneider, *The Confidence Gap. Business, Labor and Government in the Public Mind,* New York: Free Press, 1983.
6 E. Ginsberg, *The Limits of Health Reform*, New York: Basic Books, 1977.

PART I
CRISIS AND THE INSTITUTIONS OF MEDICINE

"The crises of the bourgeois order are continuous . . . [they] are due to its intrinsic contradictions . . . These crises frequently heighten in all their dimensions . . . not only in their economic but also in their political and civil dimensions . . . When this occurs, the social tapestry that is sustained and made cohesive by the bourgeois hegemonic ideology starts unravelling and all components are touched upon. . . . It is in these periods of crises when the relationship between the parts and the whole appears most clearly."

(A. Gramsci, *L'ordine nuovo*: vol. *9 1919–1920*, 1954
(my translation))

The Western system of medicine*

Our Western system of power is in crisis. Editorial after editorial
appears in the daily press drawing attention to this crisis and
expressing concern about the future of Western societies. Dailies as
different as the London *Times*, the *New York Times*, and *Le Monde
Diplomatique* have carried, almost simultaneously, a number of
articles on the state of the Western industrial societies, which in all
three papers appeared under the ominous heading, "What has gone
wrong?" The answers to that question are many. However, the one
most frequently given by the bourgeois media and academe alike is
that the pervasive process of industrialization, invading all spheres of
our collective and personal lives, has transformed our societies into
what one of industrialism's main theorists, Ivan Illich,[1] has called an
"engineered hell," an engineered nemesis in which feelings of
powerlessness and alienation have become the main trademarks of
our populations.

And in the overall invasive process, medicine has not been an
exception. Thus, the crisis of our Western system of medicine—
reflected in its ubiquitous problems of costs, ineffectiveness and
inequities—is attributed to its industrialization, by which highly
technological medicine, controlled by the medical bureaucracy and

* Written in 1978.

technocracy, is becoming a source of harm and oppression, rather than, as it should be, a source of relief and liberation.[2]

In view of the overwhelming dominance of this interpretation of our ills, that is industrialization, in explaining the crises of the Western world, including medicine, let me elaborate on the theoretical construct that sustains such an interpretation. Industrialism, the most prevalent conceptual framework used to explain the nature of Western developed societies, suggests that the industrial nature of technology defines social organization in its entirety. Grounded in Max Weber, this construct presumes a technological determinism that shapes the nature of our societies, including our welfare states. According to Galbraith, for example, modern technology compels the adaptation to its requirements of societal structures, whether economic (e.g. the rise of large corporations) or political (e.g. the growing range of state functions).[3] And as stated by two much-acclaimed authors, Wilensky and Lebeaux, in what has been reviewed as the definitive work on the welfare state "[the] technological changes of industrialism lead to changes in the structure of society; these societal changes, in the context of American culture . . . produce or intensify concern about certain social problems, which create a demand for welfare services."[4] And medicine is no exception. Technology is likewise assumed to determine the shape of Western medicine and its crisis. According to Mechanic, an exponent of this position, technology determines not only the underlying assumptions of practitioners and patients, but, most importantly, the organization of medicine and its crisis.[5] In a less sociological, more folksy manner, Illich,[6] Carlson[7] and others have joined the chorus of those expostulating on the industrialized machine which some, such as Bell[8] and Rostow,[9] optimistically call progress, and others, such as Illich,[10] define as a nightmare.

Moreover, according to the theorists of industrialism, industrialization has transcended and made irrelevant and outdated the categories of property, ownership, social class, class struggle, capitalism, and imperialism. Ownership, they argue, has lost its meaning as the legitimization of power. Control is now assumed to be divorced from ownership and to have passed from the owners of capital—the capitalists—to the managers of capital, and from there to the technocrats, those who have the skills and knowledge needed to operate the major social edifices of industrialism, that is the bureaucracies. The new elites, then, are the technocrats and bureaucrats who have supplanted the capitalists. As a result of this evolution, a new social order, based on bureaucracy, has transcended the capitalist order, and capitalist societies have thus become industrial, or post-industrial societies. Capitalism, class struggle, and imperialism are quickly dismissed in introductory notes, where they are usually presented in quotes as a signal to readers that they are indeed subjects of suspicion.

It is the primary thesis of this essay that social class, class struggle, capitalism and imperialism are not, however, out of date as categories, as the ideologists of industrialism postulate, but rather that they are the most important paradigms for understanding the crisis of our Western system of power and its system of medicine. They are indeed, as Neruda would put it, at the very center of things. Moreover, I will try to show that the dominance and hegemony of the ideologists of industrialism do not result from the strength of their arguments—which I believe to be weak—but from their function as apologists for the present pattern of class power relations in our societies, the continuation of which is not weakened, but rather strengthened by the acceptance of such interpretations.

The crisis of Western contemporary capitalism and its system of medicine

Disagreeing with the ideologies of industrialism, which attribute the crises of Western societies and their systems of medicine to their industrialization, I believe that these crises are due to and reflect the crises of legitimization and capital accumulation of Western or contemporary capitalism, and that the crisis of the Western system of medicine is part and parcel of that broader crisis of contemporary capitalism. To expand on that, let me, first of all, outline the main characteristics of Western contemporary capitalism,[11] which are (1) an expansion of the process and pattern of capital accumulation on a worldwide scale; (2) an increasingly global concentration of capital, both between and within capitalist countries; and (3) an increased involvement and participation by the state in all spheres of economic and social life of each Western capitalist society. That expansion of the state takes place in many different forms, but one way that is increasingly apparent is the rise in public expenditures. For example, a 1970 Organization for Economic Co-operation and Development (OECD) report stresses the rapid growth of public expenditures in all developed capitalist countries, growth that is particularly accentuated in three main types of state activities: (1) social services (including health, education, and social security expenditures), (2) capital investments of an infrastructure character, and (3) state aid to private industry.[12] Of these three types of expenditures, "the most striking feature [is] the extent to which education, health and social security [are] responsible for the rising share of government expenditures over the period under study in all the countries, 1955–69."[13] And a very large part of this growth can be attributed to the increased employment necessary for the provision of those services. For example, between 62 and 75 per cent of all public expenditures for education and medical care in the USA, UK, Germany, Finland, and Sweden are allocated to pay the wages and salaries of the ever-increasing labor force in those sectors.[14] Actually, this growth of the health labor force has been particularly accentuated in the USA, where the growth between 1950 and 1975 was a staggering 119 per cent, compared with 74 per cent in services and trade and 40 per cent in manufacturing.[15] This growth of the US health labor force, which was already distended in the late 1960s, became most dramatic in the 1970s. In this regard, it should be noted that, while education was the fastest-growing sector in the USA in terms of employment in the 1960s, medicine has become the sector deserving that categorization in the 1970s.

In observing this growth of employment, which is common to all developed capitalist countries, we find other points of similarity, such as (a) the increased specialization and hierarchicalization of the health labor force, (b) a growth in employment most accentuated for low-paying jobs, which, incidentally, comprise the bulk of positions in that force, (c) women filling the majority of those jobs,[16] and (d) the increasing dependency for the provision of services on either members of minority groups (e.g. Blacks in the USA), or, as is the case in Europe, on foreign labor, euphemistically called guest workers.[17] This dependency, again, is more accentuated in the low-paying than in the higher-paying jobs. For example, while much has been said about the great dependence of the British National Health Service (NHS) on foreign-born physicians (e.g. 30 per cent of hospital-based physicians), little note is taken of what is an even greater dependence in the lower echelons (e.g. 45 per cent of all kitchen workers in the NHS are foreign-born).[18] Let me stress that this situation is not unique to the UK. For example, 40 per cent of all hospital personnel in Germany, and 60 per cent in Switzerland, are also foreign-born, mainly from developing countries.[19] Thus, the relationship of dependency established internationally between the metropolises and their dependent economies is reproduced in the womb of the imperialist countries themselves, frequently with the support and connivance of the governments of these dependent countries. The French government, for example, has a long-standing agreement with the Algerian government which provides migrant workers (many working in sanitation) at a price of labor considerably lower than the labor market forces in France would determine.

The role that guest workers play in reproducing the economic, social, and political order in the metropolises is a major one. For example, to focus on France again, the present cost of bringing up a child to the age of eighteen in that country is about 15,000 French francs. Hence, the net increase of 600,000 immigrant foreign workers that was envisaged in the Sixth Four Year Plan in 1969 meant that a subsidy of 90 billion francs was being donated by the immigrants' countries of origin to the French economy. As *L'Usine nouvelle* has said, "Immigration makes it possible for our country to save on educational costs and to balance the nation's responsibilities better." That amount, 90 billion francs, incidentally, represented three times the total cost of French "development aid" to the Third World during the same time period. In that "unequal exchange" so characteristic of imperialist relations, Western medicine is a direct beneficiary. Indeed, many guest workers, as I indicated before, work and labor in the health care institutions.[20] Moreover, the function of these guest workers in Europe is not only economical, but also political. By keeping a large number of workers—the foreign workers—under marginal and "in reserve" conditions, a cleavage is established within the working class that serves a stabilizing function in that social system. Bosquet expressed this function quite clearly when he wrote in *Le Monde*: "Two million foreign workers [in

France] means two million fewer worker votes at election time and two million fewer potential militants in the factories: in other words, a quarter of the working class is 'denationalized,' and its political weight diminished accordingly." As the late Pompidou once said in the French parliament in 1963, "Immigration is a means of easing the situation in the job market and *resisting social pressure*" (emphasis added). A similar situation appears in most developed capitalist countries. And the institutions of medicine, employers of a large number of foreign workers, contribute greatly to this situation. They reproduce within their labor force the pattern of exploitative relations that characterizes imperialism.

The characteristics of the crisis of medicine: Growth and ineffectiveness

We find in most Western capitalist developed countries, then, an increased growth in employment and public expenditures for social services in general, and for medicine in particular. And such growth of expenditures is widely assumed to be a major contributor to the crisis of Western capitalism, since those expenditures are regarded as a major part of social consumption, which diverts scarce capital that, it is posited, could be better used in productive investment.[21] This shift from productive to non-productive consumption is indeed supposed to be one of the major causes of our crisis.[22] And among these social services expenditures, health care expenditures in particular are assumed to be contributing to that crisis because of their high rate of inflation. In that respect, it is worth noting the great interest in controlling what are argued to be out-of-control medical costs. In all Western capitalist countries, measures are being adopted in an attempt to check the rampant increase in medical costs, one of the worst contributors to inflation in many countries, including the USA.

It is worth stressing that the *growth of medicine*, measured either in terms of expenditures or employment, has proceeded side by side with the other assumed characteristic of Western medicine, its *ineffectiveness*. Indeed, an array of reports, editorials, and articles has appeared in scientific and lay publications expressing a concern that the growth of the house of medicine is not being accompanied by a parallel improvement in the health of the citizenry.[23] "In spite of more and more medical care expenditures," an editorial in the *New York Times* indicated, "our population is not getting healthier." This editorial could have appeared in any daily of any developed capitalist country. *Growth and ineffectiveness thus seem to be the two main characteristics of our Western system of medicine.* Why is this so? Why this increasing ineffectiveness and runaway growth?

Many explanations and theories have been advanced to answer this question. But a viewpoint which tends to be quite prevalent in academic forums, governmental circles, and international agencies alike is one that originates in the industrialist theories mentioned before; it attributes both growth and ineffectiveness to the manipulation of the house of medicine by specific interest groups, among which professional groups—the medical bureaucracy—are considered to be dominant.[24] Disagreeing with that interpretation, as I indicated before, I believe that the two main characteristics of this crisis of the Western system of medicine, its growth and its ineffectiveness, result not from professional manipulation, but rather from the *needs created by the process of capital accumulation* on the one hand and the *demands expressed by the working population* on the other. Moreover, these needs and demands, being generated by capital and labor, are inherently in conflict and thus are translated into the *daily practice of the class struggle.* In view of the absence of such categories in most medical sociology in the English-speaking countries, let me elaborate on each of them and their consequences and implications for medicine.

The needs of capital and its effects on the state and on medicine

To begin, I shall focus on the needs created by the process of capital accumulation, a process characterized by economic concentration in which an increasingly smaller number of economic units account for most of the production of each commodity. A primary attribute of this concentration is that it determines a process of production and consumption aimed at serving the needs of that concentration.

SPECIALIZATION AND CONTROL IN MEDICINE

The first of the needs of the process of capital accumulation is for a *division of labor* at the point of production, which brings about a continuous demand for specialization that fragments the process of production and, ultimately, as Braverman has indicated, the producer himself. And this specialization in turn requires increased state intervention to pay the reproduction costs of specialized labor (education) and to guide that reproduction through licensing and regulation.

Let me add here that I am aware, of course, of the prevalent argument that specialization is determined by the needs and requirements of the technological process.[25] Elsewhere, I have debated what I consider to be the fallacies of such explanations, all of which beg the question why technological process takes the form it takes to start with.[26] Rather, I believe, as does Marglin, that the capitalist division of labor and specialization is determined by the need of the owners and controllers of production to optimize their pattern of control over (a) the productive process, (b) the individual producer, and (c) the collectivity of producers, the working class.[27] By means of that process, the workers are:

(a) compartmentalized into narrow tasks, with no possibility of obtaining a broader view of the process in which they are caught;

(b) hierarchicalized by a division of labor that reproduces the class relations in society; and

(c) expropriated of all possibility for creativity and of all possibility and authority to influence or have a say in the design and development of the production process.[28]

These characteristics of the process of production are expanding to all areas of work and everyday life. Indeed, the assembly line type of work, rather than diminishing, is increasing because of a pervasive need, according to the logic of the capitalist system, to optimize productivity by increasing control over producers—the workers. As Gorz has indicated:

"The fragmented, simplified and repetitive nature of assembly line work is well known, but many people will be surprised to learn that about 80 per cent of administrative employees also do nothing but repeat strictly predetermined tasks that, in the majority of cases, preclude any personal initiative; that among white-collar workers in production departments about 60 per cent of all personnel follow a rigidly defined procedure; and, finally, that in sales departments about 60 per cent of the salesmen operate according to a prearranged sales schedule, which lays down all the details for interviews, including what to say, and even what vocabulary to use."[29]

Thus, there is an increasing similarity in the working conditions of blue- and white-collar workers. Consequently, the great majority of employees in our societies are more and more becoming passive participants in a thoroughly rationalized and objectivized economic process.

I believe that this explanation of the division of labor and specialization also applies to medicine. Indeed, studies have appeared that provide more than suggestive evidence that professionalization, specialization and the consequent hierarchicalization of the health labor force are aimed at optimizing the pattern of control over different components of that force, as well as medical knowledge and practice. Moreover, I also postulate that that pattern of control is primarily determined by capital and only secondarily—and very secondarily, at that—by the medical profession. This postulate, of course, is in opposition to that of the majority of analysts of medicine who assume that the medical profession is the dominant force in the house of medicine, that is responsible for the growth and structure of medicine. Those analysts reach that conclusion because they believe professionals enjoy freedom and independence, since within their specialized domains they do not take (or at least not until recently) orders from any immediately recognizable "boss." This sense of autonomy is further reinforced by constant references to the professionals' control over medical science and technology, which they assume is above and beyond any class interest.[30]

But I believe such an interpretation to be both unhistorical and apolitical. Indeed, it ignores the fact that the actual power of the profession has been, from its creation, a delegated power, delegated by the dominant class—the bourgeoisie. That this delegation is not formalized does not imply that the social group in question—the professionals—is not acting on behalf of the dominant class, whose authority the profession shares. The medical profession is a stratum of trustworthy representatives to whom the bourgeoisie delegates some of its authority to run the house of medicine. The concepts of health and medicine have continuously changed and been redefined according to the needs of the mode and social relations of production at each historical conjuncture. A recent example is the change in many Western capitalist societies of therapeutic practice in obstetrics to include the provision for abortion on demand. This change took place, over the medical profession's opposition, because of the need to re-legitimize the capitalist system when threatened by an increasingly radicalized women's movement.

Regarding the assumedly classless nature of medical science, that interpretation ignores the facts that (a) medical knowledge legitimizes the hierarchical division of labor in medicine which follows class, sex, and race lines, and (b) Flexnerian medical knowledge reflects a social class interpretation of health and disease that serves the dominant class interests.[31] Indeed, many references exist today which trace the evolution and genesis of medical knowledge, showing how Flexnerian medicine reflects a bourgeois, individualistic, and mechanistic understanding of health and disease that reinforces the ideological construct of the bourgeoisie.[32]

To sum up, specialization in medicine is aimed at controlling medicine, its knowledge and organization, adding a most important instrument of control to the bourgeois armamentarium. Examples of this are many. Actually, as Berliner has clearly shown,[33] the creation of the medical profession in the USA, via the Flexnerian revolution, triggered and sponsored by the enlightened voices of the corporate establishment (the Rockefeller and Carnegie Foundations), took place at a moment of great social unrest when a powerful populist movement was threatening the corporate centers of power—the hegemonic block within capital. That legitimization of the medical profession by corporate America put into the hands of the upper middle class, the newly defined professionals, the right to heal, a very powerful right, which had previously been widely distributed among popular elements, many of whom were leaders of the threatening populist movement. Thus, the Flexnerian revolution expropriated the many of the power to heal, a power that is now controlled by the few. But equally important, that power to heal was augmented by the power to define normality, that is health and disease. Corporate America knew only too well the value and importance of controlling medicine as an instrument of depoliticizing rebellion by defining rebels as sick or deviant, a function it still has today. None other than that profoundly conservative sociologist, Talcott Parsons, the most influential thinker in English-language sociological literature, describes approvingly this function of medicine, when he says:

> "The primary condition [for a revolutionary movement] is the presence, among the population, of alternative motivations which should be intense enough and distributed widely and adequately . . . This alternate motivation is a prerequisite for the development of a revolutionary movement. But, as such, it is only a potential form, capable of modification . . . Its strength can be dissipated in many ways, by way of fantasies, by defining criminality and *mental and psychosomatic diseases* [emphasis added], just to mention a few possibilities."[34]

And just in case this was not clear enough, the great guru of American sociology adds: "Patients then cannot develop collective solidarity . . . [thus] . . . from the point of view of the stability of the social system, the role of the patient is less dangerous and threatening than other alternatives."[35] As so frequently occurs, leading sociologists articulate quite well the thoughts and needs of the bourgeoisie. Some may say convincingly that this is why they are "leading." And that function of medicine, as an instrument of social control, is more and more evident in today's Western system of medicine. As the well-known Italian Marxist, Berlinguer, indicates, capital increasingly assigns to the medical profession tasks that were previously left to the spontaneous workings of the market forces of selection.[36] Examples are many, but just to mention a few: psychiatrists and psychologists help managers select employees for jobs to make sure they are suitable; psychiatrists and industrial physicians are hired gently to help workers overcome their personal problems of adapting; physicians in factories determine who is entitled to be defined as disabled or sick; and so on and on. These instances show how capital can afford less and less to rely on the spontaneous forces of the market and needs more and more to control the process of production and consumption. Medicine has been and is increasingly used as an instrument of this control.

Another consequence of the division of labor and specialization, both within and outside the house of medicine, is the establishment of barriers to working-class solidarity. The demand for higher productivity and greater specialization, which usually appears during times of social and economic crisis, can also be perceived as part of a strategy to divide the threatening labor force. As a leading trade unionist of the health sector in Great Britain noted, "By dividing health workers into a multiplicity of sections and grades, the management tries to lead them to believe that they have no common interests and that indeed their interests are opposed."[37] In fact, it is not uncommon, in the hospitals of the NHS in Great Britain, to find separate dining rooms for the different staff groupings. At St Bartholomew's Hospital in London, for example, there are no less than five. Needless to say, that hierarchicalization of grades and sections reproduces the pattern of power relations that is determined for different components of the labor force by their social class position and their race and sex composition.

MEDICINE AS A COMMODITY

Another characteristic of contemporary Western capitalism—or what Mandel has called late capitalism—is the invasion of all sectors of our collective and personal lives, including education, medicine, the arts, transportation, etc. by the process of capital accumulation in its search for profits. That invasion follows the logic of capitalism which, as Marx indicated, is to convert idle capital into service capital, while simultaneously replacing service capital with productive capital. In other words, capitalism attempts to replace services pure and simple with commodities that can be bought and sold on the private market. Needless to say, the degree to which capital penetrates the social services depends very much on the distribution of class forces in each country. And the degree of penetration by capital has been most accentuated in the USA, where capital's power is strongest and labor's power weakest. As two astute observers of the American scene indicate:

> "The health care industry [in the U.S.A.] is big business. Last year Americans spent over $130 billion on health care services of which a minimum of $2.4 billion was profit to private investors. Hospitals, alone, employ 2.6 million workers, and over 4.5 million workers find employment in some segment of the industry. As health care facilities have grown and multiplied, a complex of

intermediate, profit making companies producing drugs, medical equipment, and building supplies has benefited from this growth. Hospitals, doctors' offices and pharmacies serve as retail outlets for the products of these industries, selling to a pliant patient population upon the order or prescription of physicians who, in turn, are besieged by a never-ceasing sales pitch from these industries."[38]

In a more recent study, Stevenson shows that 39 per cent of US health expenditures went, in 1975, to for-profit institutions.[39] And that invasion of the house of medicine by capital is not without political consequences. Elsewhere, I have shown the overwhelming influence that financial capital—insurance and banks primarily —has in determining the nature of health legislation in the USA.[40] A recent example is the power it has to practically veto any proposal for a national health insurance in the USA that would be against the interests of the insurance industry. As an editorial in the *New York Times* once said: "To retain [by the US Congress] the insurance companies' role [as administrators and third-party payers for all proposed national health insurance] is based on recognition of that industry's power to kill any legislation that it considers unacceptable."[41]

Besides the insurance industry, there are other components of capital (e.g. corporate capital), such as the drug and equipment industries, that, as Stevenson has shown, are heavily involved in the US health sector, and for whom that sector is quite lucrative.[42] The drug industry has been, for over a decade, among the top four most profitable business sectors, not only in the USA, but in most of the Western capitalist countries as well.[43] And the stock of the hospital equipment industry has been among the "hottest" on Wall Street since the late 1960s. As an editorial in *Fortune* indicated, health is likely to be among the most profitable businesses in the late 1970s and the 1980s.[44]

In other areas of the Western world, where labor is stronger, penetration by the different components of capital in medicine has been somewhat slower. An example of that is the nationalization of the main components of the health care sector in Britain, a victory, no doubt, for the British working class. But, even in that country, sectors of corporate capital, such as the drug industry, have had a not inconsiderable influence in determining patterns of expenditures in the NHS, and their political will has been able to prevent the industry's nationalization, in spite of the fact that this has been part of the Labour Party platform for a long time.[45] Similarly, on the Continent, greater than one-fourth of the health expenditures have been for drugs, whose influence in determining therapeutic practices is overwhelming. In France, for example, over 28 per cent of the total medical expenditures are for drugs (excluding expenditures on medicaments in hospitals).[46] And the economic association of the drug industry with academic medicine, that sector responsible for the formal reproduction of medical knowledge, is well known.[47] Equally well known is the fact that the most important source of support for medical journals is the drug industry.

The influence by the financial and corporate branches of capital, however, is far greater than its immediate and direct profit-making activities within medicine. Indeed, I believe it to be limiting to analyze the extension and influence of capital in social services by looking only at the degree of their penetration by different components of capital and the degree of surplus value or profits they appropriate. These types of studies are greatly needed, but it would be wrong to conclude or assume that, because a sector is nationalized (i.e. in the public sector), the influence on it of capital is either absent or minimal. Such interpretations are clearly faulty. I have shown elsewhere[48] how the capitalist class or bourgeoisie has a dominant influence over the organs of the state. Thus, the influence of the bourgeoisie over the health sector also takes place through the state. And that influence may take the form—as it does today in most Western capitalist countries—of a demand for rationalization of the health sector, that is more control, based on the argument of the need for higher productivity of the medical sector.

In summary, the invasion of the house of medicine by capital, either directly through the private sector and/or indirectly through the state, leads to:

(a) the increasing transformation of the mode of production in medicine from petty-commodity production—cottage industry—to a corporate type of medicine;

(b) the increased specialization and hierarchicalization of medicine;

(c) a decline in the self-employed and an increase in the wage-earning sector of medicine; and, concomitantly,

(d) the "proletarianization" of medicine, by which physicians increasingly lose their professional autonomy and the majority become highly paid managers of the health team, subject to a higher authority, that is the administrators of capital or its organ, the state.[49]

Consequences of the need for capital accumulation under capitalism

What are the consequences, for the health of our population, of the continuing invasion by capital of all spheres of our collective and individual lives? I will focus, first, on the consequences of the process of expansion and invasion by capitalist production into the area of production and, later, on the consequences of that expansion into the world of consumption.

ALIENATION AND MALAISE OF THE PRODUCER

Regarding the former, we can see that the increasingly detailed division of labor determines a greater specialization of the process of production, which is aimed at *depriving the worker of the power of control over that process.* Consequently, the worker and the collectivity of workers feel more and more powerless to shape and determine the process of work. The present dimensions of this collective feeling are well expressed in a 1970 International Labor Organization (ILO) report which indicates that feelings of powerlessness and work malaise are prevalent throughout Western capitalist countries, not only among blue-collar workers, but increasingly also among large sectors of white-collar workers, to such a degree as to be considered a major economic problem.[50] Many of these feelings of powerlessness and malaise are translated into psychosomatic conditions, underlying most of the problems often presented, incidentally, in general practice offices in all Western capitalist countries.[51]

It speaks for the overwhelming power of capital in our society that very few studies have been done on the relationship between the nature of work and health, in spite of the immense and overriding importance that work has for the everyday life of the majority of our citizenry. As Coburn has clearly shown, the evaluation of one's work is the most important variable in the explanation of one's esteem and perception.[52] And the satisfaction with one's work is a most important determinant of well-being. For the majority of our citizens, however, work is oppressive and not liberating. As has been shown, mechanized and assembly line work is increasingly the rule, not the exception, and such routine work deprives the person of the sense of fulfillment to which he or she aspires. Work thus becomes a source of oppression, rather than a source of liberation. The dimensions of this appear quite clearly in the reality that large numbers of assembly line workers in Detroit take drugs while working. They escape into the realm of illusion to avoid unbearable reality. As Charles Levinson, General Secretary of the International Federation of Chemical and General Workers' Union, has said, "Work is an insult to men." Similarly, Bosquet writes,

> "So deep is the frustration engendered by work that the incidence of heart attacks among manual workers is higher than that in any other stratum of society. People 'die from work' not only because it is noxious or dangerous — 8 percent of all working hours are lost through accidents — but because it is intrinsically 'killing.'"[53]

Thus, for the majority of our citizenry, work is not a source of creativity and self-expression, but a means to achieve self-realization in the world of consumption. This is the "ethos" of our consumer society.[54] But that world of consumption and its "life-styles" are primarily determined by the world of production. Here, I am not only stressing what is obvious, that in our consumer society what *you have* depends on what *you do*,[55] but even more important, that one's psychological framework—which determines one's level of expectation and behavior and pattern of interpersonal relations—is very much determined by one's work. Thus, to speak (as do most bourgeois analysts, including the radical bourgeois fringe) of "life-style" without mentioning the environment—including work—that conditions those styles, is to focus on the individual as the genesis of individual ills or well-being. And this has the profound effect of reinforcing the ideological construct of the bourgeoisie, individualism.

Contrary to that bourgeois position, I believe that to present a dichotomy between life-style and environment is faulty, since the former is very much dependent on and determined by the latter. And among the latter, the socio-economic environmental variable— work—particularly the relationship of a man or woman to it, is of paramount importance. It is a condition for capitalism that the majority of our citizenry—the workers—have no control over their work and, thus, over their lives, including their health. To focus on individual life-styles is to assume an independence and freedom of the individual that is an illusion. Let me here end this part by quoting at length from the conclusion of Coburn's study.

"The findings of links between the psychosocial aspects of work and workers' general well-being also contain implications for research and policy-making regarding 'life styles.' Health attitudes and behaviors are influenced by events apparently far removed from the attitudes and behaviors studied. Such relationships, emphasizing the social bases of individual behavior, call into question classificatory schemas which lead to the study of the individual and his environment separately. Such a schema might lead to the same fragmented approach to man and society as earlier mind–body dichotomies did to the individual.

Finally, whether intentionally or not, the current emphasis on lifestyle and health promotion has an individualistic bias. As Beauchamp has noted:

'Victim-blaming misdefines structural and collective problems of an entire society as individual problems . . . These behavioral explanations for public problems tend to protect the larger society and powerful interests from the burdens of collective action, and instead encourage attempts to change the "faulty" behavior of victims.'

If we are really interested in preventing death and disability and in increasing overall levels of well-being we will have to become more radical—radical in the sense of getting to the root of the problem. Since many of our current health problems are embedded in the social structural and value characteristics of our society, to change these will require first, a painful re-examination of the values and interest implicit in current (public) health policies and approaches, and second, a willingness to change."[56]

It could not have been said better. To get to the root of the problem in the *world of consumption*, we have to address the nature, process, and control of the *world of production*. The consequences of this will be many, but one thing that is becoming increasingly apparent is that the former cannot change until the latter has changed. Life-style is indeed determined by the work, economic, and political environment in which one lives. The validity and importance of this point must be stressed over and over again. Actually the oppressive nature of work in our capitalist societies has led to louder demands by many in liberal and radical circles for a decrease in the work week, allowing workers more leisure time during which the individual may supposedly feel free to realize his or her own potential. But that demand forgets that one cannot live like a free being if one works like an ox. As Edmond Maire has said:

> "As long as your work remains boring and distasteful, there can be no real 'quality of life' even if you have two or three days a week of 'culture' and relaxation. As long as the content of work remains unchanged, workers will be content with diversions they would otherwise think unworthy of them."[57]

One can only conclude by saying Amen.

THE NEW EPIDEMICS: DISEASES IN THE WORLD OF PRODUCTION AND THEIR INDICATIONS IN THE WORLD OF CONSUMPTION

Another consequence of the capitalist process of production is the mortality and morbidity that is imposed on the workers at their work-place and appear as occupational diseases, the "new epidemics" of the Western world. Annually, 100,000 people in the USA die from work-related conditions, and 4 million contract occupational diseases.[58] And the situation is not much different in other countries. Two thousand preventable deaths at the work-place occur every year in Great Britain, with 796,000 major injuries added to that damage.[59] In Italy, there have been, since World War II, 100,000 deaths reported and 2 million invalids due to work accidents, yet the true figures are likely to be even higher.[60] According to Berlinguer, the average life expectancy of the blue-collar worker is less than sixty years—shorter than the average for Italians.[61]

And the known damage to the working population at the workplace is just the tip of the iceberg. Recently, there has been an increase in the concern about workers' exposure to lethal substances produced at the work-place.[62] For example, one study carried out in Chicago found that half the workers of a work-force of 1 million had been exposed to "urgent and serious health hazards" on the job.[63] In a survey carried out by the US federal government on occupational and work conditions in the USA, it was found that "while at work, one out of four Americans is exposed to some substance thought to be capable of causing death or disease." Instances of that exposure are many. To quote from the same report:

"83,494 full time workers were exposed to asbestos, 90 per cent of them with no protective equipment or engineering controls; 48,484 full time workers were exposed to benzene, 55 per cent of them with no controls. ... More than three-quarters of all full time and part time workers exposed to benzene did not have periodic blood tests, and approximately the same proportion of those exposed to asbestos did not receive pulmonary functions tests. ... The survey also found that 880,000 employees were exposed to the 17 carcinogens regulated by the government ... many of whom had not been informed of it."[64]

There is indeed a reality of much death, disease and suffering created at the work-place.

And it is a characteristic of contemporary capitalism that the health problems, which exist because of and are reproduced by the process of production, expand and affect the world of consumption as well, *becoming the problems of everyday life*. The toxicity of products for not only the worker, as their producer, but also for the worker-citizen, as their consumer, explains the public uproar about the conditions of consumption and production under capitalism. Thus, the toxicity of the working environment is replicated more and more in the *living environment of the community as well*. Note, for example, the increasing number of scandals about Kepone factories, nuclear stations, etc. Actually, a series of studies carried out at the Johns Hopkins School of Public Health in Baltimore, Maryland, showed this quite clearly.[65] In those studies, it was shown that Baltimore, one of the most industrialized cities in the USA, has one of the highest rates of cancer mortality in this country. These studies also showed that the number of deaths caused by all types of cancer among workers of the Baltimore Bethlehem Steel plant—the largest employer in the city—is 27 per cent higher than the number expected for the equivalent age group in the city of Baltimore.

But what is even less known, as the *Baltimore Sun*, in commenting on those studies, indicated, is that, not only among industrial workers, but also their families and neighbors, the mortality rate is higher than the extremely high rate for the city overall, "adding to the growing evidence of a connection between cancer and the millions of tons of chemicals that move in and out of Baltimore each year."[66] Professor Genevieve Matanoski and her colleagues of the before-mentioned School of Public Health, in studying cancer prevalence, patterns of wind flows, and soil components in residential areas, have found seven "pockets" of cancer in Baltimore, and all—except one—have in common a close proximity to industrial plants.[67] Thus the damage created at the work-place expands into and is reproduced in the community and residential areas.

THE MANIPULATION OF THE WORLD OF CONSUMPTION BY CAPITAL

The previous section has shown the inherent limitations of analyzing and studying the health problems of the world of consumption independently of the world of production, as most Weberian medical sociologists do. As Marx clearly indicated, in any society those who control the means of production are the ones who shape the nature of that society, including its form of consumption. And this reality appears increasingly obvious in contemporary capitalism where the worlds of production and consumption have become intrinsically interrelated, with the controllers of production determining the type of consumption to which we are exposed and from which we can choose. For example, Paul Cornely, a past president of the American Public Health Association, has warned the public about the increasing deterioration of the American diet caused by the expanding power of agri-business in determining a certain type of production and food consumption among the population.[68] Similarly, the absence of concern for the producers' safety also appears in the world of consumption where there is an equal disregard for the consumers' safety. In 1969 it was revealed that General Motors (GM) had spent less than 0.07 per cent of its profits on safety precautions for both workers and consumers—a quarter of the amount it spent making its cars' doors shut with a pleasing sound. Also, GM had previously refused to allow its products to be fitted with safety glass because "there are more profitable ways of spending the money. We are not a charitable organization."[69]

A last note regarding the manipulation of consumption by the controllers of production is that in that ethos of consumption, the population is continuously encouraged to want more, when more is always inaccessible. That reality of "more," which is only accessible to the few, is presented as the illusion for the many. Consequently, competition to reach the unreachable appears to be the trademark of our population, creating much anxiety and frustration in the process. The cost of that race, into which all generations are coerced, is high in human suffering. One-third of the children hospitalized in England, for example, had psychological problems related to anxieties and fears about the competitive examinations at their schools.[70] That "neurosis of the exam" reflects and reproduces a pedagogical system based on competition, control, and authority, the distinguishing features of capitalist education.[71] Incidentally, parallel to this sickening sense of competition, there has been, in the Western media, a eulogy to force and violence, a situation that is seen quite clearly in the most corporate controlled media in the world today—the American broadcasting industry. The populations of North America and—because of the US's cultural dominance—other Western countries are continuously exposed through the media to the presentation and justification of violence by the forces of law and order. Thus, the intrinsic violence that exists in the economic, political, and social institutions under capitalism is complemented by the continuous glorification of violence in the media at the service of the present social order.[72] It has been estimated that there is an average of one killing per minute in all the movies presented on US television, and the greatest number of killings appear in programs for children. The effects of this exposure to violence are many.[73] Professor Belson, in a survey from 1958 to 1971 of 1,500 children in London aged 13 to 16 years, concluded that TV has contributed most substantially to children's perceptions of the world, which they believe to be a violent place where competition and force are natural events in society and their own everyday lives. Incidentally, this survey found that the most violent shows were the ones that glorified the agencies of law and order.[74]

In conclusion, the pressures, stresses, dissatisfactions, insecurities, and fears that appear in the worlds of both production and consumption, and that are also reproduced by the organs of legitimation and information, determine a pattern of behavior in our populations in which emotional stresses and distresses are becoming increasingly common to our populations. According to the US President's Commission on Mental Health, for example, one-quarter of the US population is suffering from severe emotional stress requiring mental health care.[75]

In summary, I have indicated that the needs of capital and the invasion by capital of all spheres of our lives create more and more health problems necessitating a *growth* of the social services in general, and of the medical services in particular. And in that pattern, medicine is assigned the task of doing the impossible, of solving what is created outside its control. This is what determines its *ineffectiveness*. To sum up, then, the invasion by capital of all spheres of our lives determines both the *growth* of medical care services, to solve the increasing problems created by the process of capital accumulation, and their *ineffectiveness*, since medicine is unable to solve those problems. This, then, is the actual cause of medical ineffectiveness, and it is determined by the function of medicine within capitalism. Let me add here that, while medicine is ineffective from that standpoint, this does not mean it is useless. It has a very high legitimization function. Indeed, it creates the false consciousness that what is basically a collective and, therefore, a political problem, determined by the manner of control over the process of production and consumption in capitalist societies, can be solved by individual therapeutic intervention. In this way, medicine depoliticizes what is intrinsically a political problem. Thus, what requires a collective answer is presented as an individual problem, demanding an individual response. This is a main ideological function of medicine, the *legitimization* of the class relations in our society.[76]

The demands of labor: Class struggle, health, and medicine

In the continuing process of capital accumulation under capitalism, the working class is not passive. It reacts and struggles against that harmful expansion, attempting to either ameliorate or change the conditions of exploitation. The form of that struggle—the class struggle—takes many different shapes. I will mention just a few.

AN INCREASING DEMAND FOR SOCIAL (INCLUDING HEALTH CARE) SERVICES AS PART OF SOCIAL WAGES

Social wages have increased in all Western capitalist societies more rapidly than money wages.[77] And part of that increase reflects an expansion in health benefits gained by the working population. This item—health benefits—is not a minor one. The main expenditure at GM, for example, is not for steel or any other material goods, but rather for health benefits.[78] And the working class fights any attempt by capital to strike down, cut back, or reduce the size of those benefits. Note, for example, the 1977 coal-miners' strike in the USA, where one-third—80,000 workers—of all coal miners went on an unofficial strike for several months to protest the cut in health benefits imposed on them by the coal-mining industry and their union leadership.[79] It is worth stressing that that part of social wages which pays for health benefits is used primarily *to ameliorate* and *take care of*, rather than *to solve or cure*, the conditions and diseases that exist among our laboring populations, many of which are, as I indicated before, unsolvable within the present pattern of power relations. This ameliorative function of medicine—to make damage more bearable—is not a minor one, and it is something that the working class rightly perceives is worth the struggle. But that struggle for care should not be considered independently of, or separate from, the more profound strategy for care which requires a change of that socio-economic environment that determines such disease and unease in our population.

A GROWING REBELLION AGAINST THE CONDITIONS OF EXPLOITATION AT THE WORK-PLACE

As Sergio Mallet has pointed out, there has been, in the Western capitalist world, an increased resistance by the working class to the form and nature of the process of work, and this resistance has grown to such a degree that large sectors of capital are seriously alarmed. A leading representative of US capital has asked, "How long can our political democracy stand the 70,000,000 who live the majority of their waking hours in an atmosphere [at their work] that is totalitarian?"[80] The May 1968 revolt in France and the 1969 revolts in Italy saw, on many factory walls, slogans reflecting resistance against the organization of work under capitalism. That rebellion was best expressed on the door of an Italian factory: "Here in the work-place freedom stops. Let's rebel. Let's be free."[81]

And that this phenomenon of malaise at the work-place is now widespread is reflected by the fact that, in a survey of five different countries—Sweden, Finland, Germany, Great Britain, and the USA —it was found that more labor conflicts occur over issues of working conditions, the nature of work, and job safety than over the amount of money wages and fringe benefits.[82] Health and work, then, are being redefined by the working class at the work-place, where health-related issues become an area for class struggle. And, as a Spanish folksong says, it is the aim of those struggles "to create a world where the workers can sing and have joy while working." The intrinsic conflict between labor and capital implies an incompatibility, however, between productivity in the process of capital accumulation and workers' satisfaction. This conflict limits whatever attempts are made to humanize the working conditions of our population, to make their oppression and suffering less unbearable. As a leading progressive labor unionist in the USA indicated, there are no two ways around it: "To enlarge the profit, means to further screw the worker, so the worker will continue resisting."[83]

How does this resistance at the work-place become evident? In addition to strikes as a tool of struggle, this resistance takes many forms:

• One is *sabotage*, by breaking pieces of equipment, slowing down work, etc. Actually, such direct and indirect sabotage is a major cause of lost productivity in the US today.[84]

- Another is *absenteeism* which has gone up immensely in all Western capitalist countries and has been particularly accentuated in the traditional branches of industry where assembly line work predominates, such as the auto industry, light engineering, electronics, etc. As Gorz indicates:

> "At General Motors, Ford and Chrysler absenteeism has doubled in the past ten years, reaching a peak in the last two, and now averages between 5 and 10 per cent. Five per cent of hourly paid workers are regularly absent without cause (i.e., for reasons other than illness, holidays, etc.) at General Motors. On Fridays and Mondays the figure goes up to 10 per cent."[85]

This absenteeism is even higher in French and Italian firms where it reaches 15 per cent. And reflecting the continued leveling and depersonalization of work conditions among all sectors of labor, the growing absenteeism prevalent throughout industry is seen also in large parts of the service and white-collar sectors.[86]

- A third is *turnover*, with workers changing jobs in order to find better or different working conditions. The dimensions of that turnover are clearly reaching problematic dimensions for capital. For example:

> "In 1969 Ford lost 25 per cent of its labor force. These were mostly younger workers, which suggests that the rate can be expected to increase further with entry of a new age-group into production. Some workers, a manager remarked in amazement, leave their job in the middle of the day, without even bothering to collect their wages. At the world's biggest private capitalist employer, American Telegraph & Telephone (AT&T), the personnel managers face a nightmare task just trying to recruit people. They have had to carry out more than 2 million interviews a year in order to take on 250,000 new employees."[87]

How does capital respond to these forms of class struggle? In many ways. One way is by increasing actual physical repression, intimidation, and physical violence. This terrorist regime is very much the order of the day in big mass-production plants. The auto industry is famous for its private security forces—the supervisors at Ford and GM, the "flying squad" at Renault, the members of the scab foremen's union at Simca and Citroen, etc.[88]

Another response has been the "humanizing work" movement in which medicine and medical knowledge have been relied upon to make workers' lives less unbearable. Psychiatrists and psychologists, for example, are called upon to analyze how work can be less oppressive, and how to better fit workers' personalities into jobs. Needless to say, in all these experiments, people have to be adapted to the jobs, not vice versa. Moreover, that humanizing has to take place within a well-defined set of constraints, of which the most important one is, of course, that the optimization of profit not be affected. Human satisfaction is not an end in itself, but rather a means to the higher goal of capitalist societies to optimize profits. No amount of humanizing people's work can change that. As a very interesting study carried out by Nichols and Beynon in a factory which is assumed to be the most humane, progressive, and advanced in Great Britain shows, no matter how much capitalist relations are "civilized," they do not change the nature of work, characterized as "one of sour frustration, fear of unemployment, boredom, resignation, and above all, of non-involvement." The workers fully realized that the factory was not theirs and was not there for their benefit.[89]

POLITICAL DEMANDS FOR LEGISLATION TO PROTECT AND DEFEND THE INTERESTS OF THE WORKING POPULATION

Class struggle has indeed been, as Marx and Engels said, "the main motor of history," and, I would add, of social legislation as part of that history. It is worth stressing this point because, at least in the extensive English-language literature on the welfare state, very little attention has been paid to class struggle as a determinant and explanation of the nature, type, and timing of social legislation. But, before elaborating further on this point, let me make a quick critique of the two main bourgeois theories that have been put forward to explain the creation of the welfare state and its social legislation. One is the theory I will call the "great men theory," and the other one is the "power elite theory."

The great men theory of change

The "great men" (women rarely appear as leaders in bourgeois history) theory assumes that the Rockefellers, Carnegies, Disraeli, and so on, have played a dominant role in the making of history. History becomes the study of the great men who have shaped the opinions of their times. The primary weakness of this school, of course, is that it begs the question about why those ideas were accepted, implemented, or used. In other words, it avoids the key questions of why an idea is reproduced and pushed forward, by whom, and for whose benefit. The basically ahistorical and apolitical nature of such theories appears quite clearly, for example, in the prevalent historical interpretation of the Dawson Report. Published in Britain in 1920, the Dawson Report is generally considered a landmark in the history of organization and planning of health services. In fact, it is frequently presented as the definitive report on regionalization. And in the English-language literature, somewhat unmindful of documents written in other tongues and not always aware of other countries' histories, it is presented as the *first* proposal in the world to call for regionalization of health services. For example, at a most prestigious forum—a Milbank Roundtable— that took place recently, the Dawson Report was not only credited with being the first to enunciate the concept of regionalization, but its assumed pioneering importance was given recognition through its publication as an appendix to the proceedings of the conference.[90] Usually referred to as a most foresighted document, due to the most foresighted mind of Dawson, the first Minister of Health of the Liberal (Conservative) government, led by Lloyd George, its not being implemented in Britain at the period of its publication is interpreted as resulting from its being too far ahead of its time. In this respect, its assumed progressivism is considered to be the cause of its doom.

Contrary to prevalent belief and in opposition to the most frequent interpretation of this report, and as I have shown elsewhere,[91] the Dawson Report was *not* the first report on regionalization of health services in the world, and, far from being the progressive and foresighted document that it is assumed to be, the report was, in fact, a conservative document, produced by a Conservative–Liberal coalition as a reaction to a social movement—the socialist labor movement—that was perceived as a profound threat to the forces and constituencies who brought about and supported the report. Indeed, the lack of historical perspective that is unfortunately so characteristic of most medical care (and, I would add, sociological) literature leads authors and social analysts to consider specific events independently of and separately from the economic and political forces that historically determined them. Not surprisingly, this approach leads to conclusions that are both empirically invalid and ineffective policy-wise.

To correct this historical insensitivity, it is necessary to analyze the Dawson Report in the context of the politico-economic environment that determined it. Thus, let us go back to the period that is under discussion—the beginning of the twentieth century—and try to see how and why the Dawson Report came about, that is what economic and political forces determined its emergence? But before this, a brief note to set the historical record straight. As indicated above, the Dawson Report was not the first report on regionalization in the world—nor even in Great Britain, for that matter. By the time the Dawson Report was published in 1920, the Zemstvo scheme, which was the first regionalized health system in the world, had been in practice since 1860 in Czarist Russia, and Dr Semashko—a close friend of Lenin's—had written a further report on regionalization that was implemented by the Bolsheviks after the October Revolution of 1917.[92] Ideological preferences or dislikes should not interfere—although they very frequently do—with the reporting of history.

Regarding Great Britain, the first report on regionalization was published by the State Medical Services Association (the forerunner of the Socialist Medical Association), whose principles were supported by the majority of the labor movement at that time, and whose potential threat made it necessary for the British establishment to take steps to curtail its growing influence. Indeed, the first decades of the twentieth century were characterized by (1) widespread social unrest on the part of growing labor and socialist movements, considerably influenced by the Soviet Revolution of 1917, and (2) World War I, which required great sacrifices from the working class and, indeed, from the majority of the British population—sacrifices that were extracted on the basis of the promise of a better Britain and a better world after the war. As Lloyd George, that perceptive, subtle and intelligent conservative Prime Minister of the Liberal government, had indicated in 1917, "The working class will be expecting a really new world. They will never go back to where they were prior to the war."[93]

Actually, the dissatisfaction of the labor movement with its working and living conditions was determining a new level of militancy that was a threat not only to the representatives of the upper class and its political arms—the Conservative and Liberal Parties—but even to the political and parliamentarian leadership of the Labour Party. And it was that level of militancy, heightened by the winds of social unrest sweeping all over Europe (and culminating in the Soviet Revolution of 1917), that was responsible for the emergence of the most radical constitution and the most militant and demanding program that the Labour Party has ever had. It was in February of 1918, almost one year after the Soviet Revolution, that the Labour Party, by a nearly unanimous vote, included in its constitution the famous clause 4—still there today—which formally mandates the Party "to secure for the workers by hand or by brain the full fruits of their industry and the most equitable distribution thereof that may be possible, upon the basis of the common ownership of the means of production."[94]

In its program for the December elections of 1918, significantly entitled *Labour and the New Social Order*, the Labour Party demanded the reconstruction of not "this or that piece of social machinery, but of society itself," and advocated the immediate nationalization of the land, railways, mines, production of electricity, industrial insurance companies, canals, harbors, and steamship lines, with the state assuming responsibility for providing every citizen with a minimum standard of health, education, leisure and subsistence, and guaranteeing employment to every willing worker, "by hand or by brain," with social services paid for by progressive taxation and administered by local authorities.[95] The program also demanded the abolition of the House of Lords.[96]

The health branch of that movement, the State Medical Services Association (SMSA), called for full state ownership of hospitals and health facilities, with the establishment of regional integrated schemes in which full-time salaried physicians and other personnel would provide both curative and preventive services at different levels of care. On the first level, there would be "clinical or health centers," where physicians would provide primary and community care and work in close collaboration with the secondary care centers or hospitals, with which they would share staff, laboratories, libraries, and central sterile supply. In summary, the aim was both to nationalize and regionalize the health services, which were programmed to be under the administration of local authorities. An interesting footnote, incidentally, is that in several editorials, *The Lancet*, Britain's oldest and most influential medical journal, but one noted for its radical maverick stands, supported such a program.[97]

All in all, the Labour Party's program in the economic and social sectors represented a clear threat to the British establishment. The political leader of this establishment, Lloyd George, finished up his closing speech in the December campaign by warning the British electorate that "the Labour Party is being run by . . . a Bolshevik group."[98] These were his last words in that speech and in that campaign—a campaign run by Conservatives and Liberals alike with a heavy dose of scare tactics against the supposed Bolshevik threat. The electorate did not heed the warnings, however. Quite to the contrary, it is an indication of the great receptivity to the radical program of Labour, on the part of not only the working class, but also other sectors of the population, that the number of votes for Labour increased from 400,000 in the last election of 1910 to 2.5 million in 1918, representing 22 per cent of the total vote and converting the Labour Party to the largest opposition party in the parliament.[99]

That growth of a party with such a radical program for restructuring Britain was very disquieting to the English establishment of that time. Moreover, the popular mood after the election represented a clear threat to the system, particularly because the government was not even sure it could count on the army and police if things got out of hand. Expressing such doubts early in 1919, the War Office had sent a secret circular to all commanding officers of troops stationed in Britain, asking—*inter alia*—whether soldiers would respond to orders to break strikes and preserve the social peace.[100] The social climate was clearly a conflictive one. And thus, the government had to react defensively to the threat and take steps to beat back the growing influence of Labour. That response in the health sector was the Dawson Report, published in 1920, one year after the Ministry of Health had been established.

The Dawson Report accepted some of the principles and, indeed, even some of the terminology of the SMSA reports. But, in general, it diluted considerably the recommendations of the socialists, and paid great attention to the interests of the medical profession, whose collaboration was considered essential for the implementation of the report. *It was, in summary, the conservative rebuttal to the socialist call for regionalization.*[101]

For example, wherever the initial socialist program spoke of integration, the Dawson Report substituted coordination. It did not speak of integrating curative with preventive services, but rather referred to coordinating these two services and recommended that they continue to be provided by different types of personnel. Nor did it speak of integration of primary and secondary care, as the socialist proposals had, but rather set forth the coordination of the proposed health center, which would be a cottage hospital (with provisions for private beds), with the secondary care center or hospital, to be staffed by part-time consultants paid on a fee-for-service basis (with ample provision for private beds to handle their inpatient private practice as well). Actually, the report sided with the medical profession in its opposition to providing free care and a full-time salaried service, claiming that the latter "would tend by its machinery to discourage initiative, to diminish the sense of responsibility and to encourage mediocrity."[102] In its stead, general practitioners and consultants were to continue in private practice, leaving it up to them and to the financial ability of the patient to determine where, when, and how a patient would be seen.

Last, but certainly not least, it sided against the socialist alternative of integrating municipal and voluntary hospitals into a unified structure, supporting instead the continuation of the two systems—which reflected the two-class system of care prevalent at the time. The report spoke very approvingly of the voluntary system, for which it recommended all types of support—support that subsequently came in 1923 when Parliament granted £500,000 to assist the voluntary, but not municipal, hospitals.[103]

In summary, the Dawson Report represented the response of a conservative government to a progressive and, therefore, threatening trend. And the fact that it was not implemented does not signify that it was ahead of its time, but rather reflects the fact that the progressive wave that determined the need to publish such a report lost its strength and was finally defeated. Thus, the need to implement the Dawson Report's recommendations diminished substantially. Indeed, the pressure that had been building up and that was reflected in the dramatic electoral gains for Labour in 1918, culminated, on "Black Friday" in 1921, in an open confrontation between the labor movement and Lloyd George's government. In February of that year, the Lloyd George government announced that it intended to decontrol the coal-mines, which had been under state control, and restore full responsibility for their management to the owners. The terms that the owners offered included a drastic wage reduction. So the coal-miners, with their other allies in the Triple Alliance—dockers and railworkers—decided to go out on a general strike beginning Friday, the 15th of April—"Black Friday." In response, Lloyd George announced he was calling out the army. Not wanting to face the possible outbreak of a civil war, the trade union leaders called off the strike, and as Miliband indicates, with that decision, the spine of the revolt was broken.[104]

Actually, not unlike other historical movements of confrontation, the leadership of the unions and the Labour Party shifted the *field of battle* from the streets to the Parliament. Heavily influenced by Bernstein's doctrines of gradual and evolutionary change (as opposed to Lenin's strategy of revolutionary change), the Labour Party leadership opposed any expression of "class war," calling instead for the collaboration and brotherhood of all men and women in their quest for social justice. As Ramsay MacDonald, one of the most important figures in Labour Party history, indicated, the leadership of the party always felt that "socialism reflected the growth of society, not the uprising of a class," and that the goals of socialism were to be furthered by "the close collaboration of all men of good will on the basis of conceptions of right and wrong common to all classes."[105] Thus, the call by that leadership was not to class war, but to "common sense and reason"—to be expressed primarily in Parliament.[106] The shift of conflict from the streets to Parliament had the effect, in 1921, of very strongly diluting the threat represented by a nationwide strike. Indeed, the impressive walls of Parliament were able to control and defuse the protest movement far more effectively than the army and police could ever have done. And in that shift, the pressure that had determined the Dawson Report disappeared.

In summary, class struggle was indeed the main force behind the Dawson Report and all major pieces of health legislation in Britain, from the National Health Insurance Act of 1911 to the 1974 reorganization of the NHS. And I postulate that class struggle is also the cause of most social legislation in other capitalist countries as well.

The power elite theory

The other theory to explain the creation of the welfare state, abundant in English-language literature, is that of the "power elite," according to which the conflict among interest groups determines the nature of legislation. The primary weakness of this theory, as I have indicated elsewhere,[107] is the unawareness that those conflicts take place within a set of class relations which determine the boundaries of those conflicts. In other words, to use George and Wilding's excellent analogy, those theorists look at "the skirmishes between pressure groups, rather than the battles between social classes."[108] An understanding of skirmishes is clearly limited, however, in the absence of an understanding of battles. For example, many authors thought the creation of the NHS was a result of *noblesse oblige* on the part of the British aristocracy and that its final structure was a product of the manipulation and the different degrees of influence different groups had over the organs of the state.[109] But a clear reading of British history shows that the much-heralded consensus of capital and labor in creating the NHS, the gem of the welfare state, had nothing to do with the *noblesse oblige* of capital, but rather was related to the state of the class struggle in Great Britain at that time. Labor did not want to go back to pre-war conditions, and capital was worried that labor had become disenchanted with the capitalist system altogether. No matter how important the roles of the different interest groups were in finally shaping the NHS, the development of that social legislation and program took place according to the set of class relations, and was determined by the nature of class struggle, in Great Britain at that time. Power relations, incidentally, that were not changed with the creation of the NHS. The bourgeoisie and the elite members of the professions continued their hegemony in that sector of the state. In summary, and as Harold Laski has said:

> "Social legislation is not the outcome of a rational and objective willing of the common good by all members of the community alike; it is the price paid for those legal principles which *secure the predominance of the owners of property*. It waxes and wanes in terms of their prosperity. It is a *body of conscience offered to avert a decisive challenge to the principle by which their authority is maintained.*"[110]

Class struggle has been, and continues to be today, the main motor of legislation.[111]

AN INCREASING ALIENATION FROM INSTITUTIONS BASED ON
BOURGEOIS HEGEMONY

The process of class struggle can take many forms. Some of them may be categorized as *active* or productive responses by which a class or segments of it react by taking direct action and actively intervening in the processes of production and policy formation, as shown in the previous sections. The response of the working class, however, may also manifest itself in a *passive* form, by withdrawing support for and participation in the political system, a response that can ultimately damage most seriously the legitimacy of the system. One of these passive forms of response is seen quite clearly in the political alienation that has, in some countries such as the USA, reached threatening proportions for capital. Indeed, it is worth observing that, for the legitimization of the Western system of power (reproduced in many countries by the parliamentary system), there is a need to present that power as stemming from the will of the people through universal suffrage. But rhetoric aside, and as a recent powerful commission (including many of the present leaders of the Western world) on Western democracies has indicated, these democracies work best when the citizenry is passive and somewhat apathetic, and when its input into the political process takes place only through a limited electoral system.[112] Thus, the actual function of the electoral system is to legitimize the political process, rather than to secure the people's input into their governance. For that system to operate and maintain its legitimacy, however, there is a need for the working population to participate. When they do not—as is happening in many countries of the Western world—the power of that legitimization declines quite dramatically. Any observer of the last presidential election in the USA could see the panic of most of the bourgeois media that the majority of the population would not care to vote. And the entire media apparatus was mobilized after the election to show that the vote of just a little over 50 per cent of the population was a victory for democracy. That campaign of "optimism" ignored the fact that almost half of the US population did not vote and that the percentage of non-voters has been increasing steadily since 1964.

That alienation is not unrelated to people's perceptions about the political system and its clear dominance by the bourgeoisie. According to a 1975 Hart Poll, 57 per cent of the US population believes that both parties—Republican and Democrat—are in favor of big business and that major US corporations tend to dominate and determine the behavior of public officials in Washington.[113] An even clearer picture appears at the local level, where the percentage of people voting is less than 20 per cent.[114] This phenomenon of political alienation is certainly not unique to the USA, although it finds its strongest expression in that country. Indeed, the crisis of the Western system of power is not only an economic, but also a political crisis, a crisis of legitimization of the sources and mechanisms of social and political power. Even in countries such as Great Britain, which is considered the mother of parliamentarianism, those political institutions show signs of stress, not unrelated to the increasing sense of alienation. A study by Crewe, Särlvik and Alt, which examined British voting patterns from 1964 to 1974, confirms the previous findings of other studies which indicated that (a) there has been growing disenchantment among the electorate about the two-party system of Great Britain, as measured by the level and strength of party identification, and (b) this disenchantment is greater among the young, the working class, and the trade union communities. These authors conclude that the obvious outcome of that trend "would be the destabilization of the party system in Britain."[115] This disenchantment is even more accentuated at the local authority level where there has been a steady decline in voter turnout since 1946, with less than 40 per cent of the electorate presently voting.[116]

This institutional crisis of legitimization affects social institutions as well. And the house of medicine is no exception. The legitimacy that permitted its substantial growth during the past two decades is being eroded by continuous and persistent questioning about, and demands for proof of, its effectiveness. As the London *Times* editorialized in an article on the NHS, the crisis of medicine's authority includes not only the legitimization of its organization, but even of its function.

In summary, then, I have tried to show *how the present crisis of the Western system of medicine, reflected by its dramatic growth on the one hand and its no less dramatic ineffectiveness on the other, is part and parcel of the crisis of contemporary capitalism which is characterized by a crisis of capital accumulation and a crisis of legitimization.* Also, in the course of this analysis, I have tried to show how both crises are determined, to a high degree, by the nature of class struggle in the Western world. To complete this analysis, let me now focus on the nature of the response to those crises, particularly on the type of answers that the bourgeoisie, through its state, proposes to resolve those crises.

The nature of the state's response to the crises of medicine

In order to comprehend the nature of the state's response to the crises of capitalism and its system of medicine, we have to understand that the primary function of the state under capitalism is to reproduce class relations in a social formation that will maintain the bourgeoisie's hegemony over the political, economic and social lives of that society.[117] It is this function of the state which establishes its composition, as well as the role, nature and type of intervention, both within and outside medicine. Domhoff[118] in the USA and Miliband[119] in the UK have shown the predominance of members with bourgeois and petit bourgeois backgrounds in the different organs of the state. Similarly, Tudor Hart[120] in the UK and myself[121] in the USA have shown the great predominance of members from the bourgeoisie and petit bourgeoisie in the corridors of power in medicine.

It is this function and composition of the state that explains the intrinsic bias of the state's response in favor of capital and against labor. That bias appears, for example, when some ideologies and positions which threaten the pattern of prevalent class relations are *automatically excluded* from the realm of explored possibilities. Indeed, as I have indicated elsewhere,[122] to understand the process of policy formation, a study of non-actors and non-decisions may be as important as—if not more important than—a study of the participating actors and decisions in a specific event. What is excluded is as important as what is included in understanding state intervention. For example, while a study on aging, published by the US Congress in 1973, showed that the most important factor in explaining longevity among people over sixty-five years of age was work satisfaction, very little medical research has been done on that subject.[123] Most research on longevity has focused, rather, on diet, exercise, medical care, genetic characteristics, and so on, not on those socio-political factors such as work that are a potential threat to the actual controllers of the work process. Indeed, the primary objective of the work process under capitalism is not to optimize the satisfaction of the producers—the workers—but rather to increase overall surplus and profit. In summary, we find that the exclusion of ideologies and areas of inquiry which question the basic assumptions of capitalism is one of the most frequent mechanisms of state intervention. Here, let me clarify, of course, that this exclusion does not need to reflect a conspiracy or even a conscious effort. The internal logic of the state, as well as the hegemony over it of the bourgeoisie, determine the ideas of those in power who are believers in bourgeois ideology and who consider natural and logical what can only be logical and natural according to the given class relations.

Moreover, in the study of the state's response, we find that the exclusion of alternatives which threaten the present pattern of class relations from the realm of possible types of state intervention goes hand in hand with the inclusion of those alternatives which reinforce them. For example, the overwhelming dominance of bourgeois ideology in the top corridors of power of the major health research institutions explains the heavy emphasis on individual etiology— habits, diet, and the like—as the subject of research, rather than environmental factors—pollutants, carcinogens, etc. An exposé along these lines is the excellent study by Greenberg and Randal which shows that the dominance of corporate interest in the top decision-making bodies of the National Cancer Institute and the American Cancer Society has given rise to a great deal of cancer research on biological and individual behavior, such as smoking and personal habits, but has implied very little attention to the study of environmental factors which are increasingly recognized as the agents most responsible for cancer. As these authors indicate, the American Cancer Society "has shown scant interest in the carcinogenic effects of air and water pollution, drugs and food additives. Its look-the-other-way attitude closely resembles that of the drug and chemical industries, with which many of its directors—all unpaid volunteers—are directly or indirectly associated."[124]

Both authors also show that most of the educational campaigns carried out by these agencies emphasize individual responsibility and behavior, and do not include information about carcinogens that exist in people's work-places, nor in other areas which might antagonize or threaten industry. Even today, when there is increased evidence that most cancer is caused by environmental carcinogens, much research focuses on cures and the study of individual preventive behavior. Actually, that emphasis on individual behavior is one of the trademarks of current national health policies in many Western capitalist countries. The whole ideological apparatus is mobilized to make citizens believe that the greatest improvements in health will come from what individuals do or do not do for themselves. As a 1976 report by the DHSS in Great Britain indicates:

"The primary responsibility for his own health falls on the individual. The role of the health profession and of government is limited to ensuring that the public have access to such knowledge as is available about the importance of personal habit on health and at the very least no obstacles are placed in the way of those who decide to act on that knowledge."[125]

And that call is further legitimized by elements of the scientific community, as expressed by McKeown.[126] As I noted before, this strategy of individual responsibility for self-care assumes that (1) the basic cause of an individual's illness or lack of health is the individual himself, not the system; therefore, the solution must come primarily from him, not from any structural change of the economic and social system and its health sector; and (2) the individual's behavior is independent of and undetermined by that socio-economic system. But, as I have tried to show in this essay, both assumptions are invalid. Still, the reproduction of that ideology, and its current emphasis, has to be seen and evaluated in light of the state's response to socio-economic crisis, that is, its response strengthens, rather than weakens, the ideological construct of bourgeois individualism by which one is responsible for one's wealth or lack of it, for one's work or lack of it, and for one's health or lack of it. Needless to say, this emphasis on individual, instead of collective, responsibility has an ideological function that is useful to those in power. It legitimizes the reduction or absence of the state's support for individual needs. In the words of one of its popularizers in the USA, former President Richard Nixon, "Do not ask what government can do for you, ask what you can do for yourself." The individual is indeed held primarily responsible for his or her health, wealth, and future. Moreover, this ideology absolves the present pattern of class power relations—a pattern that determines the current economic, political, and social environments—from responsibility for creating and conditioning the individual's behavior and for causing much of the mortality, morbidity, disease, and unease to which our populations are subject.

Last, but not least, let me add to this quick review of the responses of the Western system of power to the crisis of medicine, two other answers which appear frequently in the scenario of political responses. First is the cut in social wages and social services that takes place either directly by diminishing the number of fringe benefits for health (e.g. the previously cited United Mine Workers cuts) or the amount of public health services (e.g. cuts in New York's public welfare);[127] or indirectly by not allowing the rate of growth in social and health expenditures to increase as quickly as the overall rate of inflation (e.g., the rate of growth in the NHS is supposed to rise 1.8

per cent per year in the 1977–80 period, the lowest rate of growth since 1948 when the NHS was established, while the rate of inflation in Great Britain is optimistically estimated to be 12 per cent per annum during the same period).[128] And these cuts are presented, in all these instances, as being necessary for reducing public expenditures in order to help the ailing (private) economy in which the bourgeoisie rules. Side by side with these cuts in social wages and expenditures is the demand by the bourgeoisie for the state to increase the centralization and strengthen the planning apparatus of the health sectors. In 1976, for example, a new NHS planning system in Great Britain was introduced because it was perceived as necessary for further centralization in the allocation of resources.[129] Similarly, during the mid-1970s in the USA, an increased centralization of the health planning and regulatory apparatuses took place with the creation, at the regional level, of *ad hoc* planning committees—the Health Systems Agencies (HSA)—which were finally responsible to the Secretary of the Department of Health, Education, and Welfare. All these changes reflect a demand for the increased centralization of the decision-making process in the health sector, a demand that is made primarily by the main components of monopoly capital, the hegemonic force in the bourgeoisie. Indeed, these components of capital are concerned that the escalating costs of medical care will threaten the overall stability of the economy; thus, the ever-louder call for the state, over which they are dominant, to make sense out of the present mess in the house of medicine. Consequently, there is in all Western capitalist societies a lessening of professional influence in the house of medicine and, in its stead, an increase of influence in medicine of the same economic groups and forces that also dominate the organs of the state. We are indeed viewing in the 1970s the demise of professional power and the heightening of corporate power. It is, in other words, the fulfillment of Marx's prediction that late capitalism (the last stage of capitalism) is capitalism in which the hegemonic force, monopoly capital, invades, directs and dominates either directly (via the private sector), or indirectly (via the state), all areas of economic and social life, including medicine.

In summary, I have tried to show in this essay that in order to understand the crisis of the Western system of medicine—reflected in its alarming problems of costs, ineffectiveness, and inequities—we have to comprehend that crisis as part and parcel of the crisis of contemporary capitalism. Such an understanding leads to the realization that (1) the supposedly transcended categories of social class, class struggle, capitalism, and imperialism are not outmoded concepts, but rather they are most important paradigms for understanding the nature of the Western system of power and its medicine; and (2) their dismissal in the realm of debate is not due to their assumed irrelevance but rather to their irreverence for and threatening force over those in positions of power in the bourgeois order. It is this element of threat to that established order that explains the continuous repression of Marxist discourse in the bourgeois press and academe. Indeed, the overwhelming dominance of bourgeois thought in most of the means of information and learning explains the suspicion and even hostility that are displayed towards Marxist positions, which are dismissed as merely "rhetoric," subject only for ideologues, absent of the objectivity that bourgeois scholarship is supposed to uphold. As Marx said,

> "The thinkers of the ruling class (its active, conceptive ideologists, who make the perfecting of the illusion of the class about itself their chief source of livelihood) . . . [maintain this illusion by presenting] . . . its interest as the common interest of all members of society, put in an ideal form; the ruling class will give its ideas the form of universality, and represent them as the only rational, universally valid ones."[130]

The crises of capitalism and bourgeois ideologies are making that claim to universality increasingly untenable. Consequently, strong fissures are appearing in the buildings of orthodoxy, a building made with heavy stones in the case of medicine. It has been my intention, in this essay, to contribute to the breaking of that orthodoxy and that ideological dominance which, as Gramsci indicated, is the silky veil that hides and obscures a reality of exploitation.[131]

Notes

1 I. Illich, *Tools for Conviviality*, London: Calder & Boyars, 1973.
2 I. Illich, *Medical Nemesis: The Expropriation of Health*, London: Calder & Boyars, 1975.

3   J. K. Galbraith, *The New Industrial State*, Boston, Mass.: Houghton-Mifflin, 1967.
4   H. L. Wilensky and C. N. Lebeaux, *Industrial Society and Social Welfare*, Glencoe, Ill.: Free Press, 1965, p. 181. For an excellent critique of current welfare state theories see I. Gough, Theories of the Welfare State: A Critique, *International Journal of Health Services* 8 (1) (1978): 27–39.
5   D. Mechanic, *The Growth of Bureaucratic Medicine: An Inquiry into the Dynamics of Patient Behavior and the Organization of Medical Care*, New York: John Wiley, 1976.
6   Illich, *Medical Nemesis*.
7   R. Carlson, *The End of Medicine*, New York: Wiley-Interscience, 1975.
8   D. Bell, The Post-Industrial Society: A Speculative View, in E. Hutchings and E. Hutchings (eds), *Scientific Progress and Human Values*, New York: American Elsevier, 1967.
9   W. W. Rostow, *The Stages of Economic Growth*, Cambridge: Cambridge University Press, 1962.
10 Illich, *Medical Nemesis*.
11 E. Mandel, *Late Capitalism*, London: New Left Books, 1975.
12 Organization for Economic Co-operation and Development, *Expenditure Trends in O.E.C.D. Countries, 1960–1980*, Paris, 1970.
13 *Ibid.*, p. 56.
14 V. Navarro, Analysis of the Health Labor Force in the U.S., U.K., Germany, Finland and Sweden, Johns Hopkins University, 1979 (mimeograph).
15 U.S. Department of Labor, *Tomorrow's Manpower Needs*, Bulletin No. 1606, vol. 4, Washington, DC: Bureau of Labor Statistics, p. 88.
16 Navarro, *op.cit.*
17 M. Castells, Immigrant Workers and Class Struggles in Advanced Capitalism: The Western European Experience, *Politics and Society* 5(1) (1975): 33–66.
18 V. Navarro, *Class Struggle, the State and Medicine: An Historical and Contemporary Analysis of the Medical Sector in Great Britain*, London: Martin Robertson, 1978.
19 V. Navarro, Analysis of the Health Labor Force.
20 There is an extensive bibliography on the subject of immigration and its impact on European economies. Two excellent references are Castells, *op. cit.* and M. Bosquet, *Capitalism in Crisis and Everyday Life*, Sussex, England: Harvester Press, 1977, p. 105. Data and quotes in this part of the text on foreign workers are extracted from these references.
21 For an extensive bibliography on the effect of the growth of social and medical care expenditures on the crisis of capitalism, see Mandel, *op. cit.*, and I. Gough, State Expenditure in Advanced Capitalism, *New Left Review* 92 (1975): 53.

22   A. Gamble and P. Walton, *Capitalism in Crisis: Inflation and the State*, New York: Macmillan, 1976.

23   A representative reference is T. McKeown, *The Role of Medicine: Dream, Mirage, or Nemesis?*, London: Nuffield Provincial Hospitals Trust, 1976.

24   Mechanic, *op. cit.*, and E. Freidson, *Professional Dominance: The Social Structure of Medical Care*, New York: Atherton Press, 1970.

25   For a critique of this argument, see H. Braverman, *Labor and Monopoly Capital*, New York: Monthly Review Press, 1974.

26   V. Navarro, The Industrialization of Fetishism or the Fetishism of industrialization, *Social Science and Medicine* 9 (7) (July, 1975): 351–63.

27   S. Marglin, What Do Bosses Do? The Origins and Functions of Hierarchy in Capitalist Production, in A. Gorz (ed.), *The Division of Labour: The Labour Process and Class Struggle in Modern Capitalism*, Atlantic Highlands, NJ: Humanities Press, 1976.

28   See the introduction to Gorz, *op. cit.*

29   *Ibid.*, p. 125.

30   Freidson, *op. cit.*

31   For an expansion of this point, see Navarro, The Industrialization of Fetishism.

32   H. Berliner, A Larger Perspective on the Flexner Report, *International Journal of Health Services* 5 (4) (1975): 573–92.

33   H. Berliner, *Philanthropic Foundations and Scientific Medicine*, doctoral thesis, Johns Hopkins University, 1977.

34   T. Parsons, *The Social System*, New York: Free Press of Glencoe, 1964.

35   *Ibid.*

36   G. Berlinguer, *Medicine and Politics*, Buenos Aires, Editorial Curato Mundo: 1975 (in Spanish).

37   M. Taylor, Creating a Health Workers' Democracy, in M. Brown and K. Coates (eds), *Trade Union Register, 3,* London: Spokesman Books, 1973.

38   L. Rodberg and G. Stevenson, The Health Care Industry in Advanced Capitalism, *The Review of Radical Political Economics* 9 (1) (Spring, 1977): 104–14, p. 109.

39   G. Stevenson, Profits in Medicine: A Context and an Accounting, *International Journal of Health Services* 8 (1) (1978): 41–54.

40   V. Navarro, The Political Economy of Medical Care, *International Journal of Health Services* 5 (1) (1975): 65–94.

41   Health Plan Progress, editorial, *New York Times*, April 7, 1974, p. E16.

42   Stevenson, *op. cit.*

43   For an analysis of the drug industry and its practices, see E. Kefauver, *In a Few Hands: Monopoly Power in America*, New York: Pantheon

Books, 1965 and M. Silverman, *The Drugging of the Americas*, Berkeley, CA: University of California Press, 1978.

44 It's Time to Operate, *Fortune* 81 (1): 79 (January, 1970).

45 J. Robson, The Labour Party and the Drug Industry, *Medicine in Society* 3 (2) (1978): 5–9.

46 P. Cornillot and P. Bonamour, France, in I. D. Wilson and G. McLachlan (eds), *Health Service Prospects*, Boston, Mass.: Little, Brown & Co., 1973, p. 67.

47 For an excellent study showing such relationships in Finland see E. Hemminki and T. Pesonen, An Inquiry into Associations Between Leading Physicians and the Drug Industry in Finland, *Social Science and Medicine* (in press).

48 Navarro, *Class Struggle, The State, and Medicine*; also, Social Class, Political Power and the State, in V. Navarro, *Medicine under Capitalism*, New York: Prodist, 1976, p. 183.

49 As Marx and Engels indicated "the bourgeoisie [strips] of its halo every occupation hitherto honoured and looked up to with reverent awe. It [converts] the physician, the lawyer, the priest, the poet, the man of science, into its paid wage labourer" (K. Marx and F. Engels, *The Communist Manifesto*, London: George Allen & Unwin, 1948, p. 123).

50 *Las Condiciones de Trabajo*, Organizacion Internacional del Trabajo, 1970.

51 Introduction in H. P. Dreitzel (ed.), *The Social Organization of Health*, New York: Macmillan, 1971.

52 D. Coburn, Work and General Psychological and Physical Well-Being, *International Journal of Health Services* 8 (3) (1978): 415–37.

53 Bosquet, *op. cit.*, p. 102.

54 Gorz, *op. cit.*

55 See H. Gintis, Alienation and Power, doctoral dissertation, Harvard University, 1969.

56 Coburn, *op. cit.*

57 Quoted in Bosquet, *op. cit.*, p. 103.

58 D. P. Discher, *et al.*, *Pilot Study for Development of an Occupational Disease Surveillance Method*, National Institute for Occupational Safety and Health, US Department of Health, Education, and Welfare, Washington, DC: US Government Printing Office, 1975, pp. 75–162. Also quoted in D. Burnham, Ford Termed Cool to 3 Key Agencies, *New York Times*, January 16, 1976, pp. 1, 26.

59 P. Kinnersly, *The Hazards of Work: How to Fight Them*, London: Pluto Press, 1973 and H. Grundwald, Safety and Health at Work, *Comment* 21 (1973).

60 Berlinguer, *op. cit.*

61 *Ibid.*

62 *The Development of an Engineering Control Research and Develop-*

ment Plan for Carcinogenic Materials, Washington, DC: US Government Printing Office (in press).

63 Bureau of Occupational Safety and Health, US Department of Health, Education and Welfare, *Occupational Health Survey of the Chicago Metropolitan Area*, Washington, DC: US Government Printing Office, 1970.

64 1 in 4 Americans Exposed to Hazards on Job, *New York Times*, Monday, October 3, 1977, p. 1.

65 E. P. Radford, Cancer Mortality in the Steel Industry, *Annals of the New York Academy of Sciences* 271 (1976): 228–38 and J. E. Ploss, Mortality in a Selected Population of Steelworkers, Johns Hopkins University, September 1, 1977 (mimeograph).

66 See F. Swoboda, Killer May Stalk Steel Plant, *Baltimore Sun*, September 12, 1977. Also see Special Report: Scientists Link Industries to City's Higher Rate of Cancer, *Baltimore Sun*, September 11, 1977.

67 G. Matanoski, E. Landau, and E. Elliot, Pilot Study of Cancer Mortality Near a Chemical Plant and Other Industries in Baltimore, unpublished report for the Environmental Protection Agency (EPA-Contract No. 68-01-2490).

68 P. B. Cornely, The Hidden Enemies of Health and the American Public Health Association, *American Journal of Public Health* 61 (1) (January, 1971): 7–18.

69 Quoted in Bosquet, *op. cit.*, p. 10.

70 Cited in Berlinguer, *op. cit.*

71 S. Bowles and H. Gintis, *Schooling in Capitalist America*, New York: Basic Books, 1976.

72 For an expansion of this point see V. Navarro, The Economic and Political Determinants of Human Rights, *International Journal of Health Services* 8 (1) (1978): 145–69.

73 See A. R. Somers, Violence, Television, and the Health of American Youth, *The New England Journal of Medicine* 294 (April 8, 1976): 811. Also, in the same issue, see F. J. Ingelfinger, Violence on TV: An Unchecked Environmental Hazard.

74 J. Cruz, The Violence on TV, *El Pais*, September 9, 1977, p. 25 (in Spanish). Also cited in *The Guardian*, September 7, 1977.

75 Department of Health, Education, and Welfare, *Interim Report of the President's Commission on Mental Health*, Washington, DC: US Government Printing Office, September 1, 1977.

76 For an expansion of this point see Navarro, The Industrialization of Fetishism.

77 See Gough, State Expenditure in Advanced Capitalism.

78 N. Hicks, Soaring Cost of Health Industry Is Debated in Auto Contract Talks, *New York Times*, August 22, 1976, p. 24.

79 Wildcat Strikes Peril UMW, Coal Chief Says, *New York Times*, September 9, 1977, p. A8.

80 Quoted in D. Pigneon and J. Querzola, Dictatorship and Democracy

64 · Crisis, Health, and Medicine

in Production, *Temps Moderns*, September/October 1972 (in French).
81 Turin, FIAT factory, personal observation, 1969.
82 Quoted in Gorz, *op. cit.*
83 Anthony Mazzocchi, Director, Citizenship-Legislative Department, Oil, Chemical and Atomic Workers International Union, personal communication.
84 Gorz, *op. cit.*, p. 65.
85 *Ibid.*, p. 64.
86 Bosquet, *op. cit*, p. 93.
87 Gorz, *op. cit.*, p. 65.
88 *Ibid.*
89 See T. Nichols, and H. Beynon, *Living with Capitalism: Class Relations and the Modern Factory*, London: Routledge & Kegan Paul, 1977.
90 Proceedings reprinted in E. W. Saward (ed.), *The Regionalization of Personal Health Services*, London: Prodist, 1975.
91 Navarro, *Class Struggle, the State, and Medicine.*
92 V. Navarro, Zemstvo Medicine and/or the World's First Attempt to Regionalize Medicine, *Social Security and Medicine in the USSR: A Marxist Critique*, Lexington, Mass.: Lexington Books/D. C. Heath, 1977.
93 Mentioned in Labour and the Old Social Order, in R. Miliband, *Parliamentary Socialism*, London: Merlin Press, 1973, pp. 59–65.
94 In 1929, this clause was expanded to include "the means of distribution and exchange and the best obtainable system of popular administration and control of each industry and service."
95 For a full account and discussion of the Labour Party program and its consequences, see Miliband, *op. cit.*, pp. 60–3.
96 *Labour Party Annual Conference Report*, January, 1918, p. 136.
97 See J. Tudor Hart, Reform and Reaction in Medical Care, *International Journal of Health Services* 2 (November, 1972): 571. Also D. S. Murray, *Why a National Health Service? The Part Played by the Socialist Medical Association*, London: Pemberton Books, 1971.
98 C. L. Mowat, *Britain Between the Wars*, 1918–1940, London: Methuen, 1968, p. 5.
99 Miliband, *op. cit.*, p. 64.
100 W. H. Crook, *The General Strike*, Chapel Hill, NC: University of North Carolina Press, pp. 240–42.
101 Hart, *op. cit.*, and Murray, *op. cit.*
102 Consultative Council on Medical and Allied Services, *Interim Report on the Future Position of Medical and Allied Services*, London: HMSO, 1920, Section III.
103 O. Anderson, *Health Care: Can There Be Equity? The United States, Sweden, and England*, New York: John Wiley & Sons, 1972.
104 Miliband, *op. cit.*, p. 87.

105 F. Bealey and H. Pelling, *Labour and Politics, 1900–1906*, London: Macmillan, 1958.
106 *Ibid.*
107 V. Navarro, Social Class, Political Power and the State and Their Implications in Medicine, *Social Science and Medicine* 10 (9/10) (September/October, 1976): 437–57.
108 V. George and P. Wilding, Social Values, Social Class and Social Policy, *Social and Economic Administration* 6 (3) (1972): 236–48.
109 For an example of that interpretation, see Anderson, *op. cit.*
110 H. Laski, *The State in Theory and Practice*, London: Allen & Unwin, 1934, p. 143.
111 Navarro, *Class Struggle, The State, and Medicine.*
112 Trilateral Commission, *Governability of Democracies. Report of the Trilateral Task Force*, New York, 1975.
113 Complete Hart Poll Results were published in *Common Cause*, September, 1975, pp. 16–17.
114 I. Katznelson and M. Kesselman, *The Politics of Power: A Critical Introduction to American Government*, New York: Harcourt Brace Jovanovich, 1975.
115 I. Crewe, B. Särlvik, and J. Alt, Partisan Dealignment in Britain 1964–1974, *British Journal of Political Science* 7 (2) (April, 1977): 129–90, p. 129.
116 T. Forrester, *The Labour Party and the Working Class*, London: Heinemann, 1976.
117 For further elaboration on this point see Navarro, Social Class, Political Power and the State.
118 G. W. Domhoff, *The Higher Circles: The Governing Class in America*, New York: Vintage Books, 1971.
119 R. Miliband, *The State in Capitalist Society*, London: Weidenfeld & Nicolson, 1970.
120 J. Tudor Hart, Industry and the Health Services, *Lancet* 2 (1973): 611.
121 Navarro, The Political Economy of Medical Care.
122 Navarro, Social Class, Political Power and the State.
123 Report of a Special Task Force to the Secretary of Health, Education and Welfare, *Work in America*, Cambridge, Mass.: MIT Press, 1973.
124 D. S. Greenberg and J. E. Randal, Waging the Wrong War on Cancer, *Washington Post*, May 1, 1977.
125 Department of Health and Social Security, *Priorities for Health and Personal Social Services in England*, London: HMSO, 1976.
126 McKeown, *op. cit.*
127 R. E. Alcaly and D. Mermelstein (eds), *Essays on the Political Economy of Urban America with Special Reference to New York*, New York: Random House, 1977. Also, New York City Special Bulletin, *Health Policy Advisory Center*, 1977.
128 Department of Health and Social Security, *op. cit.*

129 Department of Health and Social Security, *Health Services Management. The NHS Planning System: Planning Activities in 1967–1977*, London: HMSO, 1976.

130 K. Marx, The German Ideology, *Selected Works*, vol. 1, London: Lawrence Wishart, 1962, p. 40.

131 A. Gramsci, *Prison Notebooks*, New York: International Publishers, 1971.

PART II
CRISIS, POWER, AND HEALTH

"Oh, love,
They keep telling me that I have the right to sing,
But they took away my guitar;
They keep telling me that I have the right to love,
But they killed my child;
They keep telling me that I have the right to shop in the market,
But they took away my land.

Oh, love,
But they also keep telling me that I should not shout, hate or
    steal;
These, I should not do."

Translated from an old Spanish folk song

The economic and political determinants of human (including health) rights*

Introduction: The rediscovery of human rights in America

The American system of power is in crisis. And that crisis is apparent in all spheres of our economic and political lives. While the economic news in the daily press hits us with constant references to unemployment, underemployment, inflation, stagnation, and other items of an equally disquieting nature, the political news carries a continuous message of concern about what a *New York Times* editorial has termed "the current crisis of trust of the people towards their political institutions." That crisis of trust, however, is not new or sudden. It crests a wave of distrust and disenchantment with our political institutions that has been increasing rather than declining for some time now. This situation was well reflected in a Harris Poll survey of public attitudes towards government conducted for a US congressional committee, which indicated that:

"the most striking verdict rendered [in the survey] by the American people—and disputed by their leaders—is a negative one. A majority of Americans display a degree of alienation and discontent [with government] . . . Those citizens who thought something was 'deeply wrong' with their country had become a national majority . . . And for the first time in the ten years of opinion

* Written in 1978.

sampling by the Harris Survey, the growing trend of public opinion toward disenchantment with government swept more than half of all Americans with it."[1]

Many events show such political alienation. A recent and meaningful instance was the record low turnout for the 1976 presidential election, when barely over half of those eligible voted,[2] prompting James Reston of the *New York Times* to write that "the real scandal of this election . . . [has been] the indifference and even cynicism of so many of the American people." Let me add that that political alienation is reflected not only in a feeling of mistrust towards the political institutions but also in an anti-establishment mood that does not escape the notice of the establishment's centers of power. Both Carter and Ford, for example, and particularly Carter, ran in the 1976 presidential campaign with anti-establishment slogans, stressing the need "to give the government back to the people" in order to regain the people's confidence in what were supposed to be, at least in theory, their institutions. And once elected, one of the Carter administration's main emphases was—via the attendance of Carter and his Cabinet at town council meetings, the Carter telethon, and informal TV fireside chats in the evening—to convince the American people that his is indeed a people's government.

Accompanying this new image of power has been the stress on the need for a new leadership and a new morality to be provided by the US government, a leadership, incidentally, that is supposed to be asserted nationally and internationally. One strategy for winning that battle for the hearts and minds of our citizens, and for regaining their trust, has been to show the inherent superiority of our system over any other possible alternative. This emphasis on the moral superiority of our system is particularly evident in the international scene. Indeed, at a moment when alternative ideologies are proliferating throughout the world, and at a time when the Western capitalist world is on the retreat, there was perceived to be a need, in the words of Patrick Moynihan, former US ambassador to the UN and current state senator, to pass from the defensive to the offensive, and to establish the moral superiority of our system over all others.[3] And in that ideological struggle and campaign, carried out nationally and internationally, the general features assumed to be in existence in our system are abstracted as an ideal type, and are compared or contrasted with the features of other societies and particularly so with regard to those other societies which have chosen patterns of development that are alleged to negate what are assumed to be the primary features of our political systems, *the existence of human rights.*

Consequently, a great rekindling of debate is taking place on the nature of human rights as a determinant of policy, primarily international policy. And all voices are called upon to propagate, debate, and discuss the concern about human rights, a concern that is presented as the new trademark of the Carter administration. (This concern is also presented as a major trademark of the current Reagan administration.)

Let me then present an alternative and a minority view of the usually presented concern about human rights—my remarks concerning not only the whats, hows, and wheres of human rights, but equally important, the whys of that assumed concern for human rights. Why are significant voices of our political establishment raising that concern today? The first thing to be noticed is that most of the concern, debate, and promotion of human rights, presented by conservative and liberal authors and commentators alike, is limited to its civil and political dimensions, that is civil and political rights as defined by the UN Universal Declaration of Human Rights of 1948.[4] And of those civil and political rights, the ones most frequently —almost exclusively—mentioned are the right to life and the right to freedom of organization and of opinion. These rights to life and liberty are the rights that supposedly characterize our system. Both the executive and legislative branches of our government are on record as upholding the USA's dedication to human rights—as defined above—rights to life and liberty as the standards of morality in our international and national policies.[5]

It is worth stressing, however, that in this strong emphasis by the established center of power in the USA, there is no attention to or mention of the other dimensions—the social and economic ones—of human rights, also defined and included in that Universal Declaration. The rights to work, fair wages, health, education, and social security that are, among others, expressed in the articles of that declaration, are usually never even mentioned in this newly

discovered concern about human rights. Actually, it is characteristic of the current presentation on human rights, that:

(a) those civil and political rights, defined as rights to life and
liberty, exist in the USA;
(b) those civil and political rights can be secured independently
of the achievement of the socio-economic rights; and
(c) human rights, as interpreted in actual debate in the USA, that
is the rights to life, and to freedom of organization and of
opinion, have a universal interpretation, valid in all types of
societies and in all forms of economies.

In summary, these are the main assumptions made in present
debate about human rights, and they establish the parameters on
which basis that discussion takes place. It is the intention of this
essay to question all of the above assumptions and to postulate that:

(1) civil and political rights are *highly restricted* in the USA;
(2) those rights are *further restricted* in the USA when analyzed in
their social and economic dimensions;
(3) civil and political rights are *not independent of* but rather
intrinsically related and dependent on the existence of socio-
economic rights;
(4) the definition of the nature and extension of human rights in
its civil, political, social, and economic dimensions is *not universal*,
but rather depends on the pattern of economic and political power
relations particular to each society; and
(5) the pattern of power relations in our society and our Western
system of power, based on the right to individual property and its
concomitant class structure and relations, is *incompatible* with
the full realization of the human rights in their economic, social,
political, and civil dimensions.

Due to the central importance of point 5 in explaining points 1, 2,
3 and 4, let me now expand on that point. But first, let me stress that I
will have to limit myself to the mere presentation of paradigms,
leaving it to a more extensive bibliography, cited in the text, the
burden of proof for each one, and leaving it up to the reader to judge
whether my explanation has an internal consistency and whether it
helps him or her to explain our realities better than more accepted
ones.

Right to property, political power and the state, and their implications in human rights

The American constitution established the right to individual private property and assigned to the state[6] the responsibility of safeguarding that right. This right to property determines and safeguards a concomitant class structure whereby very few—the members of the corporate class—own, control, and possess most of the wealth and the means to produce it, that is the means of production, and where the many do not control or own much; they—the majority of Americans—own only their capacity to work—their labor power —which they sell. Indeed, contrary to the mythology that we are a people's ownership society, the value of private property owned by most Americans is very limited indeed. And, for the most part, the type of property owned by the majority is consumer goods used for private enjoyment. But the greatest portion and most important type of property—the property of the means to produce those consumer goods—is owned by an extremely small percentage of the population. Less than 2 per cent of the population, for example—the members of the corporate class and the top echelons of the upper middle class—owns at least 80 per cent of all corporate stocks (the most important type of income-producing wealth).[7] In summary, under capitalism, the few control capital and the many sell their labor. And capital and labor exist in a situation of dominance of the latter by the former, a situation perpetuated by the responsibility of the state to safeguard the right to property. As Sweezy has eloquently indicated:

> "Property confers upon its owners freedom from labor and the disposal over the labor of others, and this is the essence of all social domination whatever form it may assume. It follows that the protection of property is fundamentally the assurance of social domination to owners over non-owners. And this, in turn, is precisely what is meant by class domination, which it is the primary function of the state to uphold."[8]

Indeed, assigning to the state and to its institutions the "mere" right to protect property is in theory and practice to assure the nature of class domination. As Engels indicated, to assure the right to private property is to assure the domination of one class—the non-owners—by another—the owners. Thus, to say that it is a primary function of the state to protect private property is equivalent to saying that the state is an instrument of class domination.[9] Actually, this was said and recognized by none other than Adam Smith, when, in his book, *The Wealth of Nations*, he wrote: "Civil government, so far as it is instituted for the security of property, is in reality instituted for the defense of the rich against the poor, or of those who have some property against those who have none at all."[10] And it is that function of the state, to protect the right to property and the class relations that that right determines, that gives it its capitalist character.[11] Indeed, what establishes the state, including its government, as capitalist is not so much that members of the capitalist class predominate in the main organs of the state (e.g. from 1889 to 1961, over 60 per cent of the US cabinet were businessmen),[12] but more importantly, it is their functions which determine (a) that they give primacy not to the interests of specific capitalist groups, but to the interests of the capitalist economy as a whole, where the private ownership of the means of production is assured and its sanctity considered to be above the interests of specific groups, and (b) that when a conflict appears between what are considered to be the needs of the economy and other needs, such as an increase in the satisfaction of human needs, the former tends to take priority over the latter. And those policies respond to the need perceived by governments that the economy, upon whose health we are all supposedly dependent, has to be straightened out before "we can think of other matters." And it is this behavior, and not the specific motivation of individuals or manipulation of groups, which establishes those policies as capitalist policies.

I am aware, of course, of present mythology that indicates that ours is a "mixed economy." But ours is a society where by far the largest and most important economic activities are still dominated by private ownership and enterprise. This is why, agreeing with Miliband, I find that to speak of a mixed economy is to attribute a special and quite misleading meaning to the notion of mixture.[13] In the USA and other capitalist societies, the state owns no more than a subsidiary part of the means of production, and, for the most part, the state intervention in the economic sphere (including nationalization of economic activities) is aimed at strengthening rather than weakening the private sector. The US society is a capitalist society in which the owners and controllers of the means of production have an overwhelming dominance over the organs of the state. Here again, I am also, of course, aware that this interpretation of the state and political power is contrary to prevalent pluralistic interpretations of the state as a neutral and independent set of institutions. Indeed, according to these interpretations, our societies have neither dominant classes nor dominant groups or elites. Rather, there exist competing blocks of interests, with no one having a dominant control over the state, which is assumed to be an independent entity.

In that explanation of our societies, power is thought to be diffuse, with different competing blocks balancing each other and themselves, and with no particular group or interest being able to weigh too heavily upon the state. It is believed, furthermore, that it is this very competition among interests, supervised and arbitrated by the state, that provides the prime guarantee against the concentration of power. A system is thus created that offers the possibility for all active and legitimate groups in the population to get organized and ultimately to make themselves heard at any crucial stage in the decision-making process. And this "being heard" takes place primarily through a parliamentary system in which a plurality of ideas is openly exchanged, complementary to the free allocation of resources that occurs in the market-place and following, for the most part, the rules of laissez-faire. It is, of course, recognized that the system is far from perfect. But, in any case, our society is considered to have already achieved a model of democracy in light of which the notion of "ruling class" or even "power elite" is ludicrous, completely irrelevant, and of concern only to ideologues.

The main weakness of such paradigms, however, is not so much their postulate that competition exists, but more importantly, their unmindfulness that such competition is continuously and consistently skewed in favor of some groups and against others. As the power elite theorists have empirically shown, the different organs of the state are heavily influenced and in some instances dominated by specific power groups. In that respect, the pluralists' failure to recognize the consistent dominance of our state organs by specific groups is certainly not shared by the majority of the US population, who believe, for example, that both political parties are in favor of big business and that America's major corporations dominate and determine the behavior of our public officials and of the different branches of the state.[14]

The members of those power groups are, for the most part, components of the dominant classes—primarily capitalist but also upper middle class—and, when they are considered in a systemic and not just sectorial fashion, they are found to possess a high degree of cohesion and solidarity, with a common interest and a common purpose far transcending their specific differences and disagreements. And one of those common purposes and interests is their support for the *right to own property*.

Let me stress here that the overwhelming dominance of the capitalist class—or in popular parlance, big business—in the organs of the state, including government, is not tantamount to actual control. There is competition between capital and labor realized in the area of class struggle, and defeats of capitalist interests are possible. After all, and as Miliband indicates, David did overcome Goliath. But the point of the story was that David was smaller than Goliath and that the odds were heavily against him.[15] So, it is this set of class power relations that defines the rights of the citizen in society. The individual's rights, in summary, will depend on what class position he or she holds within our class society. Henry Ford and the assembly line worker of his factory have different rights, given by the class to which they belong. And the meaning of those respective rights is not only quite different but also in opposition and conflict. Indeed, none other than Abraham Lincoln once said:

"We all declare for liberty; but in using the same word we do not all mean the same thing. With some the word liberty may mean for each to do as he pleases with himself, and the product of his labor; while with others the same word may mean for some men to do as they please with other men, and the product of other men's labor. Here are two, not only different, but incompatible things, called by the same name, liberty. And it follows that each of the things is, by the respective parties, called by two different and incompatible names—liberty and tyranny.

"The shepherd drives the wolf from the sheep's throat, for which the sheep thanks the shepherd as his liberator, while the wolf denounces him for the same act, as the destroyer of liberty.

... Plainly the sheep and the wolf are not agreed upon the definition of the word liberty."[16]

Within this introduction, describing the nature of class power relations in the USA, let me now focus and further elaborate on the interpretation and definition of those rights under capitalism.

Civil rights under US capitalism

The most frequently mentioned civil and political rights in American debate are the right to life, the right to freedom of organization, and the right of expression of opinion. Let me very sketchily try to analyze the realization of those rights in this USA of ours, particularly in the light of the previous discussion in which I have stressed the different degrees of power that capital has *vis-à-vis* labor in our society.

Let us start with the right to life. Here, it is worth stressing, as Raphael has rightly indicated,[17] that this right assumes not only the right to life but also the right to protection against physical or quasi-physical injury, harm or suffering which is inflicted on someone against his or her will. The ultimate in such harm is, of course, killing someone. But the right to life in a capitalist system clearly conflicts with the right to private property, which gives to capital the right to control the process of production intended, not to optimize workers' welfare and insure protection of life, but rather to optimize the process of capital accumulation. Because of the dominant influence that capital has over the organs of the state, the rights to life and freedom from harm are made dependent and secondary to the rights of capital to pursue capital accumulation. Actually, the overwhelming amount of legislation that exists in our society to protect private property contrasts quite dramatically with the meager and obviously insufficient legislation to protect the workers against loss of life and harm at the work-place.[18] And the dimensions of that harm are enormous. Four million workers contract occupational diseases every year, with as many as 100,000 deaths every year,[19] while the number of on-the-job injuries exceeds 20 million per year and the number of deaths in work-related accidents reaches approximately 28,500.[20] And most of this death, harm, and disease is preventable. Actually, the dramatic dimensions of this harm at the work-place are there for all to see. These appalling conditions are even worse for some types of occupations, such as coal-mining. On the average, one miner is killed every other day in the US coal-mines.[21] And 4,000 miners die every year from black lung disease, with one out of every five working miners being a victim of black lung.[22] This is a tragic picture of the dramatic and overwhelming violations of the right to life of our working population, daily perpetuated for the glory and benefit of capital. And very little is done to correct such violation of human rights. This is, no doubt, due to the overwhelming influence of capital over the organs of the state. As indicated in a memorandum published by the Senate Watergate Committee, a Nixon official promised to the business community that "no highly controversial standards (i.e. cotton, dust, etc.) will be proposed by the Occupational Safety and Health Agency [OSHA] during the coming four years of the Nixon administration."[23] And the records of the Ford and Carter Administrations are not much better either. The legislation to protect the worker's life and safety is extremely meager. This reality is clearly shown in this quote by A. Miller, President of the United Mine Workers of America:

> "If a factory worker drives his car recklessly and cripples a factory owner, the worker loses his license to drive, receives a heavy fine, and may spend some time in jail. But, if a factory owner runs his business recklessly and cripples 500 workers with mercury poisoning, he rarely loses his license to do business, and never goes to jail. He may not even have to pay a fine."[24]

In the first three years of operation of OSHA only two firms were convicted of criminal violations, and the average fine for OSHA violations was twenty-five dollars.[25] The expressed concern by the Carter Administration that the normative functions of OSHA should not impair the functioning of the economy shows a similar set of priorities, that is life and safety has to be subject to a most important aim, to assure the unalterability of the process of capital accumulation. There is, in summary, a clear violation of the rights to life and freedom from harm of many and large sectors of our working population—a violation of human rights met by a deafening silence in both our legislative chambers and in our media.

Here, in this context of violation of human rights, it is worth stressing the definition of violence in our society. If someone stabs and kills another person, it will be defined as an act of violence. But, if someone—an employer—perpetuates death and disease because of lack of protection of his workers against harm, this action is not considered to be *violent*. The rationale for that distinction is that the employer does not personally harm anyone, and, moreover, that he does not intend harm to the worker. Due to the prominence of the two arguments, let me further elaborate on each of them. Regarding the former, that the employer does not harm directly or personally, one must stress that the argument of impersonality as an excuse for crimes of violence was rightly dismissed in the trial for mass murder of Eichmann in Jerusalem in 1961. The fact that Eichmann was a personable, likeable music lover, and personally unable to kill an insect, was of *no consequence* for defining him as a mass murderer. The point of that judgment was that his actions, however impersonal, led to death and harm for masses of people.[26] In that respect, it is worth stressing that, as Priestland has indicated, most incidences of violence and violations of the right to life in the twentieth century have been and continue to be impersonal.[27] Indeed, as Barnet has also attested concerning violence in the twentieth century, "those who plan, do not kill. And those who do kill, do not plan."[28]

The other argument usually made against defining the employer's actions as violent is that the employer is *not aiming directly at the worker with the intention of causing harm.* In other words, he does not intend to kill or maim. But, as the Nuremberg judges rightly indicated, by taking an action involving a risk tantamount to near certainty that people will be killed and injured, the act must be regarded as an act of violence, regardless of the aims of the perpetrators.[29] Coming back to our example, many employers —coal-mine owners and managers, for example—know that the absence of safety in the coal-mines is highly likely to cause death and injury. In summary, then, whether or not the employers, or class of employers, do not *personally* inflict harm or death on others, or whether or not they do not *intend* to kill or injure, does not excuse their actions as nonviolent. They are indeed violent if, as a result of their actions, death and harm are likely to be and are being inflicted on their employees or workers. Consequently, it is correct to define as violent that set of class relations that puts property and the right to accumulate property over the right to life and freedom from harm, however *impersonal, indirect*, and *unintentional* those relations may be. And it is equally correct to define those economic and political institutions that sustain and replicate that set of power relations that violate the right to life and freedom from harm (established in article 3 of the Human Declarations Charter) as violent institutions. Here, let me add a further note: while much is being said, usually with revulsion, about the individual personal violence, not much is being said about the inherent violence of our institutions that sustain and replicate a pattern of violence that affects and harms many of our working populations.

Political rights under US capitalism

I have tried to show how the control of the process of work by the few, and the overwhelming influence that they have over the organs of the state, seriously and even dramatically impairs the civil rights of the many. The overwhelming influence that big business has over the state organs is particularly accentuated here in the USA, where there is no political arm of labor that could balance it. And that overwhelming influence by the property owners and managers of wealth —big business—over our political institutions explains the exclusion from political competition of those ideologies and those parties that question the set of class, power, and property relations in our society. Gerson, for example, has shown the practical impossibility for parties of the Left, parties that question the right to private property, to have any chance in the overall electoral process.[30] The electoral and legislative processes practically exclude from political competition parties different from the two major parties— Republican and Democrat—each committed to the survival and strengthening of the capitalist system. Actually, the exclusion of alternative, anti-capitalist, anti-property voices finds its strongest expression in their actual physical repression. The physical repression of the Black Panthers, and the Communist and Socialist Parties, among others, is the subject of general knowledge and even acceptance among the corporate-controlled media. Infiltration, sabotage, and even physical eradication of the Left are part of the normal political behavior of the American system.[31] The whole furore about

Watergate and the use of such tactics by an over-zealous President Nixon was not because of the novelty of political repression, which has been consistently directed against the leftwing parties, but rather because it was directed against an "accepted" party, the Democratic Party.

But, far more important than physical repression, is the ideological and cultural repression of the Left, aimed at excluding the presentation of alternatives to the American people. Indeed, the USA is a clear—almost asphyxiatingly clear—example of the accuracy of Marx's dictums that "the ideas of the ruling class are in every time the ruling ideas," and that the reason for this is that the

> "class which is the ruling material force in society, is at the same time its ruling intellectual force. The class which has the means of material production at its disposal, has control at the same time over the means of mental production, so that thereby, generally speaking, the ideas of those who lack the means of mental production are subject of it."[32]

This situation determines what Gramsci called the "hegemony" of the dominant class in civil society, defining hegemony as:

> "an order in which a certain way of life and thought is dominant, in which one concept of reality is diffused throughout society in all its institutional and private manifestations, informing with its spirit all taste, morality, customs, religious and political principles, and all social relations, particularly in their intellectual and moral connotations."[33]

Let me stress here that this dominance does not require a prohibition of opposite views, but rather—and more effectively—that the ideological competition be so unequal as to give a crushing advantage to one side over the other. And it is that crushing inequality that profoundly constrains the political rights to both organization and expression of opinion stated in the Declaration of Human Rights. In that respect, there is an overwhelming hegemony of business in the value-generating systems of the US. One of those systems, the mass media, is in the private domain and controlled not only by business, but by big business, with a rapidly increasing concentration of ownership in the press, magazines, book publishing, broadcasting, cinemas, theaters, radio, television, and all other instruments of culture.[34] As the Commission on Freedom of the Press indicated, "the owners and managers of the press determine which persons, which facts, which version of the facts, and which ideas shall reach the public."[35] And all these corporate-controlled media foster a climate of conformity to the business values, not by total suppression of dissent, but by the "presentation of ideas which falls outside the consensus as curious heresies or even more effectively, by treating them as irrelevant eccentricities, which serious and reasonable people may dismiss as of no consequence."[36]

This overwhelming dominance over the value-generating system by corporate class values appears also, of course, in the schools and universities, whose primary function is to replicate the ideology functional to the actual system of power relations. Indeed, a primary function of schools in America is to teach the superiority of American capitalism and the free enterprise system over any other system,[37] to the exclusion of any alternative ideology. At the present time, for example, most states have laws, passed by their business-controlled legislatures, instructing the schools to teach the dangers of communist and socialist ideologies.[38] Organizations such as the American Bar Association, National Education Association, and the American Association of School Administrators, have all passed resolutions encouraging schools to teach the evils of those ideologies, and they have even resolved that it is perfectly legitimate for schools to fire any communists on their staffs. And, of course, the American Federation of Teachers, not to be outdone, found that membership in the Communist Party was incompatible with membership in their union.[39]

A similar, although not identical situation, appears in academia. As Professor Galbraith has indicated, higher education is attuned to the needs of the private enterprise system.[40] In colleges and universities, students are taught to understand the world in ways calculated to diminish rather than enhance their propensity to change it. Consequently, views challenging the set of class power relations in our society are excluded as not meriting serious analysis and debate. Actually, such exclusion of views is usually done more subtly than in the school system. It is usually presented under the ideological tenet that the holders of such unorthodox views are unacceptable deviants from the pattern of academic excellence demanded and required from all scholars. As Marx indicated, "the thinkers of the [ruling] class (its active, conceptive ideologists, who make the perfecting of the illusion of the class about itself their chief source of livelihood)," maintain that illusion by presenting "its interest as the common interest of all members of society, put in an ideal form; it [the ruling class] will give its ideas the form of universality, and represent them as the only rational, universally valid ones."[41] Consequently, there exists a climate of suspicion, if not hostility towards certain positions of intellectual political unorthodoxy that are dismissed as being subjects only for ideologues, positions that are put aside not as a result of prejudice—God forbid!—but rather because of doubts as to the supposed ideologues' scholarship and objectivity. The overwhelming and indisputable ideological discrimination against Marxist scholars in the academic centers of the USA is indeed a consequence of the dominance of bourgeois ideology in those centers, a dominance that is dictated by the function of those universities, to replicate the ideological relations of the capitalist system.[42]

In summary, I have tried to show how the right to property, assumed and granted by the state, perpetuates a pattern of class relations whereby the few—the owners and controllers of the means and process of production—have a hegemony in all spheres of the civil and political lives of the many, limiting and constraining most profoundly and seriously Americans' civil and political rights. It conditions a class bias in the interpretation and extension of those rights, a bias in favor of the owners and managers of capital and its servants, and against the rights of the majority of the US population—the working and lower middle classes.

This class hegemony over our institutions also explains the very serious limitations that US capitalism imposes on the socio-economic rights of the Americans. Let us now focus on these.

Socio-economic rights under US capitalism

As I indicated before, most of the discussion of human rights in the US has focused on the civil and political rights assumed to be existent in the USA. The notes that I presented before indicate a *class bias* in the interpretation and extension of these civil and political rights. But the Declaration of Human Rights of the UN also includes—and in a prominent place at that—socio-economic rights as part of human rights. Among the most prominent are the rights to work, to receive a fair wage, the right to security and retirement, and the right to health and education.[43] Actually, a quick analysis of the situation in the USA regarding each of those rights may, at least partially, explain why we are met with a deafening silence regarding those socio-economic rights. Indeed, the USA does not compare favorably at all in those components of human rights with the majority of other countries, including other capitalist developed countries, in which, for the most part, these rights fare much better.

Regarding the right to work, for example, the USA is the capitalist developed country with the highest unemployment rate (8.5 per cent in 1975), totaling over 7.5 million people. Similarly, regarding the right to fair wages, the workers who, in spite of working full-time do not receive adequate income to provide a decent standard of living, total 7 million workers, or approximately 7.5 per cent of the US labor force. Actually, Professor Gordon, adding with the unemployed, the discouraged workers—able people who would like to work but have given up the hope of finding it—the involuntary part-time workers and the low-paid workers, has found that over one-third of the US labor force is under- or unemployed and underpaid, and thus have had their human rights to work and a fair wage violated.[44] Here again, we find a clear incompatibility between full employment and fair wages and the nature of the capitalist system. Capitalism needs a reserve army of idle and unemployed workers to establish a sense of both insecurity and discipline in the labor force. Let me add, incidentally, that this unemployment is not only in violation of the socio-economic rights of the unemployed, but also of their civil rights, such as the right to life and non-harm. Indeed, unemployment causes and is responsible for much harm and damage. As indicated by a 1976 Congressional Report, every increase of unemployment by 1.4 per cent determines 51,570 deaths (more than all casualties of Vietnam put together), including 1,540 suicides, and 1,740 homicides, and leads to 7,660 state prison admissions, 5,520 state mental admissions, and many other types of harm, disease, and unease.[45]

Similarly, in other areas, such as health and education, the USA is the only one among developed capitalist countries which has not yet accepted that the access to comprehensive health care is a human right. And even regarding education—usually considered a human right in the USA—none other than former President Lyndon Johnson indicated that in 1965, over one-quarter of the Americans—54 million—had not finished high school.[46] And to finish with this quick sketch of the status of the socio-economic rights of our American people, let me finally say that our system of social security is among the least developed in the Western capitalist world. And this underdevelopment of social security is very much a result, again, of the overwhelming political dominance of capital and the political weakness of our laboring population.[47]

The assumed independence of the two types of rights

As indicated before, the current focus on civil and political rights as the primary components of human rights assumes their autonomy, if not independence from, the socio-economic rights. Actually, these two types of rights are considered to be two separate types of rights, that are frequently in conflict. It is generally assumed that the civil and political rights to life and freedom imply a *negative* obligation upon others, an obligation not to interfere with one's own exercise of those rights. On the other hand, the other rights—the socio-economic rights—are assumed to place a *positive* obligation on others, that is something has to be done if they are to be secured for their recipients. These perceptions have led to the interpretation that those two types of rights may not only be different, but actually may be in conflict. Indeed, to provide the *security* guaranteed by the second type of rights, there may be a need to limit the *liberty* guaranteed by the former type of rights. As one theoretician of that interpretation has indicated, "the promulgation of socio-economic rights has brought them into conflict with civil and political rights, for the planning and control essential to the former impinge on some of the freedom of choice and action that had seemed defensible under the latter."[48]

In less elegant but more direct fashion, this was said by the then presidential candidate, Carter, when, in a radio broadcast, he indicated that a primary difference between the socialist countries and us—the USA—was that they have chosen security over liberty, while we—in the capitalist countries—preferred to emphasize liberty and opportunity over security.[49]

But those interpretations of human rights that assume a dichotomy and even conflict between civil and political rights on the one hand, and socio-economic rights on the other, are erroneous both empirically and historically. Indeed, to state the debate in terms of a choice between liberty and security is to avoid the issue of liberty for whom and for what. The analysis presented earlier in this essay shows that the liberty guaranteed the few who control capital constrains and violates both the liberty and security of the many. The civil and political right to vote and choose among political alternatives, for example, is dramatically reduced by the limited alternatives available to the population as a result of big business control over the media and dominance over the organs of the state. And the civil rights to life and to freedom from harm are denied when the rights to employment and fair wages are—as they are under capitalism —denied. Rather than conflict, then, we must recognize that the full realization of civil and political rights cannot be realized in the absence of the fulfillment of socio-economic rights. As Tawney has indicated: "political rights afford a safeguard and significance to civil rights . . . economic and social rights provide means essential to the exercise of political rights."[50] Actually, none other than former President Franklin Roosevelt saw that dependency when, in his message to Congress back on January 11, 1944, he indicated that "necessitous men are not free men." Except in that he should also have included women, this dictum makes the point quite clear, that civil and political rights are not in conflict, but rather require the full realization of the socio-economic rights. And as I have tried to show in this essay, capitalism, the social formation in existence in the USA today, denies the possibility of the full realization of either type of human rights.

Capitalism as an international system and its implications in human rights

The search for profits, the primary motor for capital accumulation under capitalism, does not stop at or respect national boundaries.

And in that search for profits, the particular mediums through which the profits are gained are (1) the extension of markets, (2) the acquisition of raw materials, and (3) the exploitation of new sources of cheap labor. And in that search, the top monopolistic enterprises of the USA take the leading role in the internationalization of capital. Capitalism thus becomes a set of international relations that is dominated by the giant corporations of a few countries, primarily American corporations.[51] In their process of expansion and internationalization, the owners and managers of the top corporations who already have a dominant influence in the economic and political life of the USA increasingly come to dominate the economic and even political lives of other nations. In Chile, before Allende's government, multinational corporations (the majority from the USA) controlled more than 51 per cent of all manufacturing, and in each of the seven key industries of the economy one to three firms controlled at least 51 per cent of the production. In Mexico, global corporations control 100 per cent of rubber, electrical machinery, and transportation industries; and in Brazil, global corporations own 100 per cent of the automobile and tire production, while their share of machinery was 67 per cent in 1971 and of electrical equipment 68 per cent for the same year,[52] and so on. That international expansion of those US corporations is of vital importance for their strength and dominance. US firms' profits earned abroad, for example, represented 30 per cent of the total American corporate profits in 1974,[53] and this figure is continually increasing. And the top 298 US-based global corporations earn 40 per cent of their entire net profit overseas, with their rate of profit from abroad being much higher than their domestic rate. Actually, this rate of profit for these global corporations is even higher in the underdeveloped world, resulting in a huge net outflow of capital from those countries back to the USA. American corporations, for example, made direct investments in the Latin American continent of $3.8 billion during the period 1950–65, while extracting $11.3 billion, for a net flow of US $7.5 billion back to the US.[54] Indeed, this and other information confirms the conclusion of the Declaration of Foreign Ministries of Latin America in 1969 that: "the sums taken out of Latin American countries are several times higher than the amounts invested. The Latin American capital is being reduced. The profits on investments grow and multiply, not in

Latin America, but abroad."[55] It is that situation that classifies the pattern of international capitalist relations as a pillage of the Third World.[56] Actually, contrary to what is said by the defenders of that international order, the diffusion of capital does not go from developed to developing countries, but rather from developing to developed ones. As Frank has noted, the largest part of the capital

> "which the developed countries own in the underdeveloped world was never from the former to the latter at all, but was, on the contrary acquired by the developed countries in the now underdeveloped ones."[57]

And much of this flow of capital goes back to the US corporations. As Sherman, after reviewing all pertinent information, concludes: (a) the rate of profit of US investments abroad is several times higher in the less developed than the advanced capitalist countries, and (b) the less developed countries make a very considerable contribution to US capital accumulation.[58]

And that flow of capital, from developing countries to developed ones, requires an international political order that sustains and replicates the dominance of the international economic order by the major sectors of capital in developed capitalist countries and especially by the major sectors of capital in the US. Indeed, the internationalization of capital is a process that does not take place in a political vacuum. Capital requires direct protection, and the institutions through which it operates must be protected. Thus, the expansion of the areas of operation of capital is always associated with an expansion of the political influence of the state with which that capital is associated. Translated into the realm of foreign policy, the task of the capitalist state is to facilitate and protect the international business activities of its nationals. And this is done by assuring —by all strategies of domination—the commitment of affected and dependent countries to a free enterprise system, where the *right to own private property by international capital supersedes all other rights, including the human ones.* The purpose of exporting democracy and freedom as standards of American foreign policy has meant in most cases the imposition of the right of American capital to own, dominate and control many of the economies, supposed beneficiaries of that freedom. The meaning of this truth is expressed quite clearly in the words of the former Secretary of the Treasury, William Simon, after his visit to Pinochet's Chile.

"The present Chilean regime is clearly in the best interest of the world compared with the Marxist regime of Allende. Chile has been the leader of democratic societies of Latin America, and they could not tolerate the kind of repression Allende brought. It had also taken an economic dimension. So now we are trying to move Chile back to freedom."[59]

"Back to freedom," of course, meant (1) freedom for the US corporations to regain the control of the Chilean economy that they began to lose during Allende's government, and (2) a violent change from a democratic Allende regime to a military regime that has been described as the bloodiest and most repressive regime in today's world and the main violator of human rights today.[60] Here again, we can see that, as Abraham Lincoln said, the meaning of liberty and freedom is indeed different for owners of capital—the managers and owners of capital and its political servants—than for the non-owners of capital—the majority of Chileans. Their respective definitions of freedom are not only different, but in conflict. Indeed, the freedom for the few to control and manage capital has been, is, and will be incompatible with the human rights of the many—human rights defined in all its civil, political, social, and economic dimensions.

The exportation of repression: The abolition of human rights at the international level

A primary role of the federal government of the USA, both in the nineteenth and twentieth centuries, has been to make the world safe for capitalism in general, and for American capitalism in particular. And that role has taken place in many forms, including (1) military intervention, (2) strengthening the apparatus of order, (3) covert operations and direct intervention, and (d) control of international agencies of legitimation, credit and lending. Due to the importance of each in the violation of human rights in the countries subject to US intervention, let me focus on each.

THE AMERICAN MILITARY INTERVENTIONIST POLICIES

Contrary to what is believed by many Americans, Vietnam was nothing new. American intervention abroad in defense of American property and American interests was and is a very typical feature of American diplomacy. From 1789 to the outbreak of World War II, for example, American troops—without authorization from Congress—were sent to foreign countries 145 times.[61] All of them were police actions in situations of unrest that represented a threat to specific American capitalist interests. Whenever an outbreak of nationalist revolutionary activity occurred (Argentina, 1833; Peru, 1835; Argentina, 1852; Nicaragua, 1853; Uruguay, 1855, 1858; Colombia, 1860; Panama, 1865, 1885; Hawaii, 1889; Chile, 1891; Nicaragua, 1894), or a state of insurrection such as a serious riot with political overtones (Panama, 1856; Uruguay, 1868; Colombia, 1868; Haiti, 1891; Nicaragua, 1899), or a civil war in which the USA had an interest (China, 1854, 1855; Japan, 1868; Samoa, 1888; Brazil, 1894), or a coup or an attempted coup (Nicaragua, 1857; Samoa, 1899), American troops intervened. And in all those nineteenth-century interventions, American troops changed the nature of the political events by favoring those sides that supported US interests. Regarding the twentieth century, a similar history and rationale appeared. Maybe the best testimony is the one provided by someone who should know quite well, a leader of those troops, Marine Major-General Butler:

"I spent thirty-three years and four months in active service as a member of our country's most agile military force—the Marine Corps. I served in all commissioned ranks from a second lieutenant to major-general. And during that period I spent most of my time being a high-class muscle man for Big Business, for Wall Street, and for the bankers. In short, I was a racketeer for capitalism . . .

"Thus I helped make Mexico and especially Tampico safe for American oil interests in 1914. I helped make Haiti and Cuba a decent place for the National City Bank boys to collect revenues in . . . I helped purify Nicaragua for the international banking house of Brown Brothers in 1909–1912. I brought light to the Dominican Republic for American sugar interests in 1916. I helped make Honduras 'right' for American fruit companies in

1903. In China in 1927 I helped to see to it that Standard Oil went its way unmolested.

"During those years I had, as the boys in the back room would say, a swell racket. I was rewarded with honors, medals, promotion. Looking back on it, I feel I might have given Al Capone a few hints. The best *he* could do was operate his racket in three city districts. We Marines operated on three *continents*."[62]

Had General Butler lived longer, he would have mentioned, among other instances, Iran in 1953, Guatemala in 1954, the Dominican Republic in 1965, and, of course, Indochina in 1966. Let me clarify here, that those interventions had as their purpose not only the preservation of accessibility to markets and raw materials, but equally important, the maintenance of the power relations whereby no country could leave the capitalist system and no country could change the rules of international capitalism. As McEwan has indicated:

"What is at stake in Vietnam is not just a geographic area but a set of rules, a system. A capitalist government will and must go all out to protect that set of rules. In part, this is a tactical issue: failure to protect the system in Vietnam would lead to further and more effective threats against the system elsewhere. The 'domino' argument is a very real one. One need only look at the impact of the Cuban Revolution in Latin America or the impact of the Russian and Chinese Revolutions throughout the world to perceive the implications of a victory for the socialist forces in Vietnam."[63]

The difference between the intervention in Vietnam and previous interventions was that its objective, to keep that country safe for capitalism, failed, and that that lengthy struggle created a resistance by the American people, making it the most unpopular war in American history. The recent policy of non-military intervention of US forces in Angola and Zaire cannot be explained without the recent history of Vietnam.

STRENGTHENING THE APPARATUS OF ORDER

Increasingly more important than the direct mode of military intervention is, and will be, the *threat* of military intervention[64] and/or the provision of assistance to the military and agencies of order, such as the police, responsible for the maintenance of property relations in those countries that favor the interests of American capital. Actually, such assistance frequently has taken the form of encouraging the direct seizure of power when forces with an anti-capitalist or anti-US capital tone or program have threatened those interests. As a recent article in the *Washington Post* indicated, all military juntas in Latin America, violators of all types of human rights of the majority of Latin American populations, have counted on the encouragement, support, and acquiescence of the US government and of the US corporations involved in those countries.[65] But, while much has been written about the by now well-known support by the US government of assistance to the military in many parts of the globe, not so much is known or written about the support to police and other agencies of order. An agency that took a prominent role in that assistance was the Office of Public Safety of AID whose aims were, in the words of Bell, Director of AID in 1965, the creation and maintenance of an atmosphere of law and order under civil concepts and controls, whereby the US interests could be promoted and protected.[66] The meaning of those US interests appears quite clearly when one sees where that assistance went, to countries where American multinationals were threatened by hostile forces and needed protection, i.e. Southeast Asia, Brazil, the Dominican Republic, Venezuela, Colombia, Guatemala, Zaire, and Liberia. The nature of that support appears quite clear when one reads that the police assistance to Venezuela went to suppress labor agitation at Goodyear and Gulf; to the Dominican Republic to suppress labor agitation at the Western plantations; and to Liberia to actually pay for the training and salaries of the private security police of Firestone Rubber.[67]

COVERT OPERATIONS AND DIRECT INTERVENTION IN POLITICAL AFFAIRS OF OTHER COUNTRIES

The direct intervention of state agencies such as the CIA, with the cooperation of private corporations such as ITT, Anaconda, and others in the downfall of Allende's government, is even a matter of congressional record. But, as the US ambassador to Chile at the time of Allende's downfall, Korry, has indicated, these practices were not new or the result of Nixon policies. They were a continuation of a long and well-established tradition of active participation by agencies of the US government and multinational corporations to intervene covertly in the doings and undoings of other governments. As Korry indicates, Nixon was just following the steps that had been previously taken by Presidents Kennedy and Johnson to support, by all means of covert activities, the interests of multinational corporations in Chile (and many other countries) and to stop—also by all means—the increased power of the Left in these countries. Actually, it is worth noting that Korry mentions that Cyrus Vance, Secretary of State in the Carter administration, and designated to carry the human rights message around the world, was knowledgeable and a participant in those policies when serving in previous administrations. As Korry's testimony concludes, there is an

> "old boys' network—of say, Mr. Geneen, Mr. McCone, Mr. Helms, the brothers Bundy, Mr. Rockefeller, and even Mr. Vance . . . [which is] designed to be self-serving, self-perpetuating, and self-protective . . .[and which] gave us Vietnam in the 1960's, assasination plots and the dark legacies of all manner of cover operations."

It is wrong, however, to assume those covert actions are a mere result of an "old boys' network." They are part and parcel of the strategy of the US foreign diplomacy aimed at saving the world for the exercise of freedom, that is the freedom of capital to accumulate at whatever cost—as in today's Chile—that freedom may require. In fact, the reading of Korry's testimony—a most informative one—shows (a) how the federal foreign affairs establishment and the multinational corporations are interlinked, and (b) how the primary purpose of the former is to optimize the interests of the latter.

CONTROL OF INTERNATIONAL AGENCIES OF LEGITIMATION AND OF CREDIT AND LENDING

The corporate-controlled foreign establishment of the US government has been dominant in the creation of most international agencies and of an international order whereby those who do not accept or submit to that order—like Cuba—are defined as outlaws, subject to repression and punishment, such as economic blockade. This exclusion and blockade is made possible by US dominance of those international institutions like the OAS, the World Bank, and the Latin American Development Bank, that are used to exercise the pressure necessary to defend the interests of the free enterprise system, in which the US is dominant. One instance, Chile, shows this situation quite clearly. The total assistance by those two institutions to Chile declined from $75 million (in loans) to $12 million in the first year of Allende's government (1971), and further to $2.1 million in the second year (1972), consistent with a policy of economic blockade that the corporate-controlled federal foreign establishment had declared against Allende's government. It is interesting to note the arguments given by these international lending institutions were presented not as political but as economic, that the policies of the Allende government, from 1971 to 1973, aimed at the nationaliza- tion of most of the monopolistic and oligopolistic industries (many of which were US-controlled), and at a profound change in the income distribution and popular consumption, were considered to be "unorthodox" for those agencies. Allende's policies, which had a substantial impact in expanding and optimizing the socio-economic rights of large sectors of the population, were considered by those international institutions to be in conflict with the sacred and ubiquitous right of private capital accumulation by US capital. And the meaning of "economic orthodoxy" appeared quite clearly when, after the coup, the Junta denationalized most of the public property and once again made Chile safe for multinational corporations, and those agencies immediately increased their loans to a most impres- sive $110 million for the first year of the Junta and $90.8 million for the second year. The Junta was following the "pattern of orthodoxy" of reinstating the dominance of the private sector with drastic reductions of government spending, with cuts in public expenditures for health services from 1,933,000 pesos in 1972 (under Allende), for example, to 850,000 pesos in 1976 (under Pinochet), with full free- dom for prices to rise, and with full prohibition for labor unions to strike and operate.[68] That freedom for capital has indeed meant a most brutal violation of not only civil and political rights, but of the socio-economic rights of the majority of Chileans. According to even

the official Junta and IMF figures, in 1976 a quarter of the population (2.5 million people) had no income at all, unemployment was
estimated to be 22 per cent (under Allende, it was 3.1 per cent), and a
phenomenon of mass hunger and starvation unknown in the history
of recent Chile emerged.[69] Actually, in that battle between property
owners and non-property owners, it is quite clear whose side the
Junta is on. In 1972, during Allende's government, employees and
workers—the nonowners—received 62.9 per cent of the national
income, while the propertied sector received 37.1 per cent. By 1974,
already the share of wage earners had been reduced to 38.2 per cent,
while that of property had increased to 61.8 per cent.[70] The consequences of those figures are enormous and impossible to present as
mere statistics. A picture of hunger, starvation, torture, harm,
desperation, and death is the result of the orthodox policies perpetuated by the centers of international economic order, and they require
a most brutal political repression to sustain and maintain them. Chile
has clearly shown what Brazil and many other countries had already
shown, that *the interests of international capital and of the international and national political institutions that sustain it are incompatible with the realization of human rights.*

In summary, I have tried to show how capitalism and its international dimension, imperialism, are incompatible with the realization
of human rights, both nationally and abroad. Let me add that this
denial of human rights is the consequence of the logic of capitalism,
not the result of the specific malevolence of individuals or groups. To
consider that the consistent denial of human rights that US foreign
policy has implied for many inhabitants of the world is a result of the
immorality of its leaders, is to have a religious but not a political and
economic understanding of the forces that move history. It is the
dynamic of the capitalist system that explains why some of the most
repressive governments in the world, like Iran, Chile, Saudi Arabia,
South Korea, South Africa, and most Latin American governments,
are also areas where US foreign capital is dominant or heavily
influential. To consider the repressive policies of those governments
as the result of the specific sadism or malevolence of their leaders, is
to have a rather limited understanding of the economic and political
determinants of human rights and denial of them. *The political
repression in those regimes is required and needed to sustain an*

economic system whereby the few (including US corporate interests)
control much, and the many (the masses of those countries) control
very little. Here, it is worth stressing a further note. While much is
being said—and, for the most part, with universal revulsion—by the
corporate-controlled media against revolutionary violence—the
force exercised by the oppressed against their oppressors—not much
is being said about the inherent violence of our institutions that
sustain and replicate a pattern of violence. As Moore has noted:

> "The way nearly all history has been written imposes an over-
> whelming bias against revolutionary violence . . . the use of force
> by the oppressed against their former masters has been the object
> of nearly universal condemnation. Meanwhile the day-to-day
> repression of 'normal' society hovers dimly in the background of
> most history books."[71]

Concluding remarks

Having explained the incompatibility between capitalism and human rights, let me now finish by postulating why the centers of the
establishment—or at least elements of it—have raised that issue.

First, indicated at the beginning of this essay, is the need to express
and demonstrate to the increasingly disenchanted American public a
new morality in the leadership of the country, and to emphasize that
repressive and regressive policies are things of the past, mistakes
maybe, but, for the most part, a mere result of the actions of specific
individuals. The denial of human rights at home and abroad is
considered to be primarily the result of individual misjudgments,
mistakes, or sins, but certainly not the result and logic of our
capitalist system. Indeed, in all those explanations, it is emphasized
that our system is morally superior to all others, and very much
superior to socialist ones whose growing attraction to other peoples
is increasingly feared. Thus, it is worth realizing that most of the
space dedicated to human rights in the text of the Carter administration's concern and in media presentations is about the rights of
dissidents in the Soviet Union. And here let me add that I count my
voice among those that protest repression in the Soviet Union, or in
any other country, for that matter. But as some people have begun to

notice, there is a clear selectivity in this concern for human rights.[72] Countries considered vital to our national interests are exempt from those criticisms or concerns. But, the question has to be raised: in whose interests are those "national interests"? Certainly, not those of the majority of the people living under repressive regimes. And not, I postulate, the interests of the American public. Rather, that concern is expressed in the interests of American capital whose value has to be saved. It is not in the interest of the average American, nor of his or her security, to have US foreign diplomacy support the most repressive regimes in today's world. As Marx indicated, it is always the custom for the bourgeoisie to define its own interests as human and universal.[73] But this essay shows that the interests of the bourgeoisie or capital—or in popular parlance, big business—are not the same as the interests of the majority of people, either at home or abroad. Actually, these interests are not only different, but are in conflict. Using Lincoln's dictum, *the liberty of the few means the tyranny for the many*, that is freedom for capital means the denial of human rights for the majority of Americans and the peoples of the capitalist underdeveloped world.

Needless to say, I am aware this viewpoint is in conflict with prevalent explanations of our realities. A minority view, perhaps, but not an Un-American one. None other than that great American, Mark Twain, said, back in 1886:

"Who are the oppressors? The few: the capitalist, and a handful of other overseers and superintendents. Who are the oppressed? The many; the nations of the earth; the workers; they that make the bread that the soft-handed and idle eat.

"Why is it right that there is not a finer division of spoil around? Because laws and constitutions have ordered otherwise . . . Then it follows that they do not have the same but contrary rights."[74]

It has been my intention in this essay to show that what Mark Twain said then is still very much applicable today as well. It is for the reader to judge.

Notes

1 Committee on Government Operations, United States Senate, *Confidence and Concern: Citizens View American Government. A Survey of*

Public Attitudes, Part I, Washington, DC: US Government Printing Office, 1973.

2 Analysis of Last Election, New York Times, November 23, 1976.

3 Pat Moynihan Declarations to the United Nations, New York Times, December 24, 1976, p. 12.

4 For a detailed presentation and discussion of that Declaration, see Appendix B in M. Cranston, What are Human Rights?, London: Bodley Head, 1973.

5 Carter's Address at the United Nations, New York Times, March 18, 1977.

6 The term "state" includes the executive and legislative branches of government as well as the state apparatus, that is the administrative bureaucracy, the judiciary, the army and the police. It is important to clarify that the state is far more than the mere aggregate of those institutions. Rather, it also includes the set of relationships between and among those institutions and with other ones that it guides and directs.

7 R. J. Lampman, The Share of Top Wealth-Holders in National Wealth, 1922–1956, Princeton, NJ: Princeton University Press, 1956.

8 P. Sweezy, The Theory of Capitalist Development, New York: Monthly Review Press, 1942, p. 20.

9 F. Engels, Origin of the Family, Private Property and the State, New York: International Publishers, 1972.

10 Smith, A. The Wealth of Nations, Totowa, NJ: Biblio Distribution Centre, 1977.

11 For a further explanation of this point, see N. Poulantzas, Classes in Contemporary Capitalism, London: New Left Review Editions, 1975.

12 There is a detailed and extensive bibliography on the class composition and dominance of the organs of the state in the USA. For a presentation and review of that bibliography, see "Social Class, Political Power and the State, Part III," in V. Navarro, Medicine under Capitalism, New York: Neale Watson, 1977.

13 R. Miliband, The State and Capitalist Society, London: Weidenfeld & Nicolson, 1969.

14 The Hart Survey. American Public Opinion and Economic Democracy, in J. Rifkin, Own Your Own Job, New York: Basic Books, 1977.

15 Miliband, op. cit.

16 Quoted in L. Huberman and P. M. Sweezy, Introduction to Socialism, New York: Monthly Review Press, 1968, p. 77.

17 D. D. Raphael (ed.), Political Theory and the Rights of Man, London: Macmillan, 1967.

18 V. Navarro, The Underdevelopment of Health of Working America: Causes, Consequences and Possible Solutions, American Journal of Public Health 66 (6) (1976): 538.

19 D. P. Discher et al., Pilot Study for Development of an Occupational Disease Surveillance Method, National Institute for Occupational

Safety and Health, US Department of Health, Education, and Welfare, Washington, DC: US Government Printing Office, 1975, pp. 75–162. Also quoted in D. Burnham, Ford Termed Cool to 3 Key Agencies, *New York Times*, January 16, 1976, pp. 1, 26.

20 J. B. Gordon, A. Ackman, and M. L. Brooks, *Industrial Safety Statistics: A Re-examination*, A Critical Report Prepared for the US Department of Labor, New York: Praeger Publishers, 1971.

21 Personal communication, Research Unit, United Mine Workers of America, Washington, DC, 1975.

22 E. B. Shoub, *Overview of Coalminers' Health Findings, Sixth Annual Institute on Coal Mining Health, Safety and Research*, Blacksburg, Virginia: Virginia Polytechnica Institute and State University, August 27, 1975.

23 D. Burnham, Nader Group Says Labor Department Lagged on Health Rules to Spur Gifts, *New York Times*, July 16, 1974.

24 A. Miller, The Wages of Neglect: Death and Disease in the American Work Place, *American Journal of Public Health* 65 (1975): 1217–220.

25 *Wall Street Journal*, August 9, 1974.

26 H. Arendt, *Eichmann in Jerusalem*, London: Faber, 1963, p. 19.

27 G. Priestland, *The Future of Violence*, London: Hamish Hamilton, 1974, pp. 19, 139.

28 *Ibid.*, p. 80.

29 *Trials of War Criminals before the Nuremberg Military Tribunals under Control Council Law 11*, Washington, DC: US Government Printing Office, 1950. Also, see A. Arblaster, What is Violence?, *The Socialist Register*, 1975.

30 S. W. Gerson, To Put a Red on the Ballot, Cross a "Legal Mine Field," *New York Times*, July 17, 1976, p. 23.

31 A. Wolfe, *The Seamy Side of Democracy: Repression in America*, New York: David McKay Co. Also, A. Davis, *If They Come in the Morning*, New York: Third Press, 1971.

32 K. Marx, The German Ideology, *Selected Works*, vol. 1, London: Lawrence & Wishart, 1962, p. 47.

33 A. Gramsci, *Prison Notebooks*, New York: International Publishers, 1971.

34 H. I. Schiller, *The Mind Managers*, Boston, Mass.: Beacon Press, 1973; H. I. Schiller, *Mass Communications and American Empire*, Boston, Mass.: Beacon Press, 1971; and J. L. Lewan-Schreiber, *The Power to Inform. Media: The Business of Information*, New York: McGraw-Hill, 1972. Also, for a review of the bibliography, see *Marxism and the Mass Media: Towards a Basic Bibliography*, International Mass Media Research Center, 1976.

35 Quoted in Huberman and Sweezy, *op. cit.*

36 Miliband, *op. cit.*, p. 238.

37 R. J. Harighurst and B. L. Neugarten, *Society and Education*, Newton, Mass.: Allyn and Bacon, 1957, p. 146.

38 A. Zelman, *Teaching "About Communism" in American Public Schools*, New York: Humanities Press, 1965, p. 43.
39 American Federation of Teachers, Commission on Educational Reconstruction, Teachers and Communism, reprinted in American Teacher, 33, 1948.
40 J. K. Galbraith, *The New Industrial State*, Boston, Mass.: Houghton-Mifflin, 1967, pp. 370–71.
41 Marx, *op. cit.*, p. 40.
42 D. N. Smith, *Who Rules the Universities?*, New York and London: Monthly Review Press, 1974.
43 For a discussion of those rights, see D. Watson, Welfare Rights and Human Rights, *Journal of Social Policy* 6, part I (1977): 31.
44 Employment Editorial, in D. Gordon (ed.), *Problems of Political Economy*, Lexington, Mass.: Lexington Books/D. C. Heath, 1977, p. 70.
45 *Estimating the Social Costs of National Economic Policy: Implications for Mental and Physical Health, and Criminal Aggression*, Joint Economic Committee, Congress of the United States, 94th Congress, October 26, 1976, Washington, DC: US Government Printing Office, 1976.
46 Cited in Huberman and Sweezy, *op. cit.*, p. 47.
47 For further discussion of this point, see G. V. Rimlinger, *Welfare Policy and Industrialization in Europe, America and Russia*, John Wiley & Sons; and H. L. Wilensky, *The Welfare State and Equality*, Berkeley, CA: University of California Press, 1975.
48 R. McKeown, Human Rights in the World Today, in *Human Rights. Comments and Interpretation*, UNESCO, 1949.
49 Interview with Carter, FMGKMN, Baltimore, March, 1976.
50 R. H. Tawney, *The Acquisitive Society*, London: Methuen, 1973.
51 Of the top one hundred multinational corporations, 65 are based in the USA, 11 in the UK, 18 in other Common Market Countries, and 5 in Japan. J. H. Sherman, *Stagflation*, New York: Harper & Row, 1976, p. 222.
52 R. Barnet and R. Muller, *Global Reach*, New York: Simon & Schuster, 1974, p. 147.
53 R. Muller, Global Corporations and National Stabilization Policy, *Journal of Economic Issues* 9 (June 1975): 183.
54 US Department of Commerce, *United States Business Investments in Foreign Countries*, Washington, DC: US Government Printing Office, 1970, p. 85.
55 Foreign Ministries of Latin America, Declaration, Vina del Mar, Chile, 1969.
56 P. Jalee, *The Pillage of the Third World*, New York: Monthly Review Press, 1968.
57 A. G. Frank, *Latin America: Underdevelopment or Revolution*, New York: Monthly Review Press, 1969, p. 21.

58 Sherman, *op. cit.*, p. 219.
59 William Simon's Declarations, *The Saturday Evening Post*, October, 1976.
60 Study of Reported Violations of Human Rights in Chile, with particular reference to torture and other cruel, inhuman, or degrading treatment or punishment, *Commission on Human Rights*, United Nations, February 10, 1977.
61 *Congressional Record, Vol. 115, Part 3, 23 June 1969*, 91st Congress, First Session, pp. 16840–6843.
62 Major-General S. D. Butler, *Common Sense*, November, 1935, as quoted by L. Huberman and P. Sweezy, *Cuba: Anatomy of a Revolution*, New York: Monthly Review Press, 1960.
63 A. McEwan, Capitalist Expansion, Ideology and Intervention, in R. Edwards, M. Reich, and T. E. Weisskopf (eds), *The Capitalist System*, Englewood Cliffs, NJ: Prentice-Hall, 1972, p. 417.
64 According to Korry, the US ambassador to Chile, President Johnson ordered, as part of the successful campaign to overthrow the leftist government of Joao Goulart, to assemble a task force of naval and airborne units to intervene in Brazil's internal affairs. A few weeks afterward, Goulart was overthrown. Testimony of Edward Korry before the Congressional Committee on Foreign Relations, December, 1976.
65 Military Juntas in Latin America, *Washington Post*, April 12, 1977. Also, *The U.S. Military Apparatus* and *The Pentagon's Protégés*, Reports of the North American Congress on Latin America, January and December, 1976.
66 Quoted in J. Stork, World Cop, *Hard Times 85*, August, 1970.
67 Stork, *op. cit.*
68 *Chile. International Policy Report*, Center for International Policy, vol. II, no. 2, September, 1976, Washington, DC.
69 A. G. Frank, *Economic Genocide in Chile*, New York: Spokesman Books, 1976.
70 O. Letelier, *Chile: Economic "Freedom" and Political Repression*, New York: Spokesman Books, 1976, p. 14.
71 B. Moore, *Social Origins of Dictatorship and Democracy: Lord and Peasant in the Making of the Modern World*, Boston, Mass.: Beacon Press, 1966.
72 T. Ajami, Human Rights: Sermons or Substance, *The Nation* April 2, 1977, p. 389.
73 Marx, *op. cit.*
74 T. Twain, *Sayings of Famous Americans*, Boston, Mass.: Beacon Press, 1976.

PART III
CRISIS, WORK, AND HEALTH

"The materialist conception of history starts from the proposition that the production, and, next to production the exchange of things produced, is the basis of all social structure; that in every society that has appeared in history, the manner in which wealth is distributed and society divided into classes or orders is dependent upon what is produced, how it is produced, and how the products are exchanged."

(F. Engels, *Anti-Dühring* 1877–78)

The labor process and health: A historical materialist interpretation*

Introduction: Work and health

A very important development in the Western capitalist world during the past decade has been the rediscovery of the relationship between work and health. The theoretization of that relationship has varied quite considerably, depending, to a large degree, on how work is conceived. For the largest number of references, work is conceived as an environmental problem. It exposes individual workers to physical, chemical, and psychological agents that may make them sick or have accidents. The strategy of intervention derived from that understanding of work is to reduce the frequency of workers' exposures to pathological agents. Without minimizing the enormous importance of that task, the theory and practice derived from that understanding of work reproduces the dichotomy, individual–environment, which seriously hinders the understanding of the social relations that determine both the individual worker and the environment.[1]

Another conceptualization of work has been that of regarding work as a source of resources—e.g. income—that may enable the worker to meet his needs and his expectations. This understanding of work has been the most prevalent one within the Weberian tradition, the dominant tradition within Anglo-Saxon sociology. In this tradition, the worker is seen primarily as a wage earner or consumer with

* Written in 1982.

specific attributes, such as income, education, status, etc. all of them defined in the spheres of exchange, distribution, and consumption rather than in the world of production. Work as an activity and as a social relation does not appear in that theoretical scenario. Citizens are primarily perceived and defined as consumers rather than workers. This explains the overabundance of studies aimed at understanding the health of the people by looking at their diet, consumption, levels of expectations, life-styles, utilization of health services, residential patterns, etc. An example is the supposedly comprehensive survey of preventive interventions on mental health published by a leading expert on mental hygiene in the USA.[2] From this and other types of studies, it would almost seem that the US people do not work, since work as a determinant of health and disease is not even mentioned. Similarly, the Health Hazard Appraisal Questionnaire, a widely used questionnaire distributed by the US Center for Disease Control, aimed at collecting data on individual risks and hazards, collects very detailed information on the individual characterization of US citizens. All types of questions about diet, smoking habits, driving behavior, etc. are asked from each individual respondent. However, no questions are asked about the individual's occupation or type of work.

This ideological bias of the consumer society is also reflected in the curricula of most medical and health professional schools. Of the more than 100 medical schools, only 12 include occupational health in their curricula, and even in those 12, the overall time dedicated to the subject is extremely low.[3]

A consequence of the perception of individuals as wage earners or consumers rather than as workers is that the strategy of social intervention is primarily aimed at monetary compensation for the damage created. Health is sold and disease and death are compensated.

Breaking with these two traditions, there are the very interesting works of Eyer and Sterling in which health and disease are seen as being determined by the social organization of society which, through stress, determines death and disease.[4] Work appears within that social totality as one more stressor in a stressful complex defined as "advanced capitalism." The great merit of Eyer's and Sterling's work has been to break with past Weberian traditions and to deal with totalities. True to the Hegelian tradition, the truth is defined as the whole. At that level of totality, however, advanced capitalism could become equivalent to "industrialization" or "progress." The undifferentiated nature of the pathogenic totality, advanced capitalism, without an explanation of how the different elements of that totality are reproduced, relate among themselves, and affect the health and disease of different groups in society limits the value of their otherwise excellent work. The merit of Eyer and Sterling is that they recognize a real trend. The weakness is that they do not identify its structural sources. By not touching on how advanced capitalism is structured and reproduced, they are also limited in their suggestions for change, for instance "individual relaxation" and "communal living."

Society is not an aggregate of stressors where the different moments of everyday life—working, consumption, and exchange—are added to form a whole. Within the social totality there are activities that shape how the other moments relate among themselves. According to the Marxist tradition, production determines the nature of the other moments. Within this tradition, Laurell, for example, sees work as both the primary organizer of social life and as a concrete expression of social contradictions. As she says,

> "At least in capitalist society, where the productive part of the productive-reproductive process of social life predominates, it seems possible to argue that the requirements of the work process organize all social life. In certain situations this becomes quite clear, and the ideologically imposed separation between the world of work and the world of consumption disappears. For example, the working-class neighborhood built around the factory in some places shows how the social space is organized based on the needs of the workplace; at the school, named after the boss, children are educated to become workers; on the playground children learn what kind of leisure is good leisure; and the shrill whistle which signals the start of each work shift imposes the rhythm of the factory on the surroundings."[5]

Production occupies a key place in the reproduction of society and its social phenomenon, including health. The awareness of that reality leads to specific strategic interventions. As Palloix has written,

"To transform the world, that is, to transform the mode of production, through the process of class struggle is to change, among other moments, the mode of organization of production and the process of work. Otherwise, all process of change can be in vain, because it is the mode of organization of production and of the process of work where we find the roots of the division of social classes, the class struggle, and where capitalism is reproduced and reborn."[6]

Contrary to the claim of Foucault and "the new philosophers" that Marx "considered power in a position of exteriority *vis-à-vis* other types of relations; namely economic processes,"[7] the reverse is true. Marx and the traditions that follow him consider production —what Foucault calls the economic space—as the most important area of reproduction of power.

To say this, however, is not to say that all power is reproduced at the moment of production, that all relations are class relations, or that everything in society is explained by what happens at work. Far from it. What happens in other moments—exchange and consumption—and what happens on other levels—ideological and political —has an autonomy of its own. Those moments and levels influence production and are influenced by it, but they are created and articulated within a whole—a social formation or society—where production is the determinant moment that characterizes the social formation. For this reason, Marx did not speak of the "capitalist mode of production, exchange, consumption and distribution" but rather the "capitalist mode of production."

Because of this understanding, I believe that to comprehend the relationship between health and society we have to start by understanding the relationship between the forces and relations of production and health. Within this latter topic, a key area is the relationship between work, relations at the work-place, and health.

A note about style of discourse

The dramatic under-representation of Marxist positions in the USA, the result of an overwhelming ideological discrimination, explains why little theoretical work in the area proposed to be studied here has yet been done using both the Marxist method of analysis and terms of discourse. A note in passing needs to be made regarding this point. It is very difficult in the form of sociology dominant in the USA to use the concepts and terms of Marxist discourse. Concepts and terms such as class struggle, capitalism, and imperialism are very frequently considered to be rhetorical and dismissed by the dominant functionalist and positivist schools. They are usually written between quotation marks as if to alert the reader that they are subject to suspicion. Marxists contributing to social science journals are very frequently encouraged to rewrite their articles using a more "understandable" style and "less value loaded terms" more attuned to prevalent sociological thought. Language and discourse are not neutral, however. An ideological position has its own terms of discourse (dismissed as rhetorical by its adversaries) that give meaning to its positions. A change of terms is far more than a semantic shift. It is an imposition of one position over another. It is because of this that I have not followed traditional advice. The terms and approach presented in this essay are placed within a Marxist tradition. Moreover, I will frequently refer to Marx and Engels texts, not following a Talmudic vocation, looking for sacred texts, but rather to establish the roots of my understanding of the relationship between work and health in their writings. As Althusser has eloquently indicated,[8] the reading of Marx is the reader's specific reading of Marx—in this case my own reading. It is important, therefore, that I state the sources of that reading and understanding.

A final comment that one needs to make in the empirical culture of the USA is that the "facts" presented in this article are not presented as "proofs" of my positions but, rather, as illustrations of my case. It is not new "facts" that I am presenting. Rather, I am trying to articulate those facts within a theoretical whole that may better enable us to understand our reality. Needless to say, I am aware that this is a first step that will undoubtedly require further elaboration and correction.

The elements of the labor process and health

In this article I will conceptualize and theorize the relation between work and health by using historical materialism as the method of analysis. By historical materialism, I mean the analysis of a social whole (composed of several moments—production, consumption, and exchange—and several levels—economic, politico-juridical, and ideological) taking production as the starting point in that analysis.[9]

As Engels indicated,

"The materialist conception of history starts from the proposition that the production and, next to production, the exchange of things produced, is the basis of all social structure; that in every society that has appeared in history, the manner in which wealth is distributed and society divided into classes or orders is dependent upon what is produced, how it is produced, and how the products are exchanged. From this point of view the final causes of all social changes and political revolutions are to be sought, not in men's brains, not in man's better insight into eternal truth and justice, but in changes in the modes of production and exchange. They are to be sought, not in the *philosophy*, but in the *economics* of each particular epoch."[10]

In other words, the basis of any society is what is produced, how it is produced and how it is distributed. All production is characterized by two inseparable elements: the *labor process*, which is any process of transformation of a definitive object either natural or already worked upon, into a definite product, a transformation effected by a definite human activity, using definite instruments of labor; and the *relations of production*, which are the concrete historical forms in which the labor process is realized.

In each labor process (presented graphically in *Figure 1*) we find the following different elements:

Figure 1

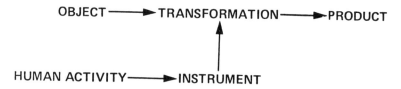

OBJECTS OF LABOR

These are the objects on which labor is done.

In the production of material goods there can be two types of objects: (1) raw materials, and (2) primary materials.[11] Raw material is a substance which comes directly from nature, and the primary task of labor is to extract it or take it away from its natural form. Examples are minerals extracted from the mines, trees from the forests, etc. Primary material is a substance that has already undergone some modification as a result of labor. An example is refined ore.

Primary materials can be the principal element of a product or they can intervene as auxiliary primary materials. They can (a) be absorbed by the instruments of labor themselves, e.g. oil for the wheels; (b) be incorporated in the principal primary material to produce in it a transformation, e.g. dye in leather or wool; or (c) simply serve the performance of labor, as is the case of materials destined to illuminate or heat the places where work goes on.

In modern industries, such as chemical industries, the distinction between principal and auxiliary primary materials is blurred since, in the final product, none of the primary materials appear. On many occasions, it is impossible to separate and distinguish the different primary materials.

The study of the work object should take into account its physical, chemical, and biological properties since they might constitute serious health risks. Raw materials such as ore, or primary ones such as the thousands of chemicals used in industry can affect the health of the producers.

THE MEANS OF LABOR

According to Marx, there are the means of labor in a *strict sense* and in a *broad sense*. Means of labor in the strict sense are the instruments or tools that the worker directly uses for his work and that he interposes directly between himself and the object of labor. They serve as intermediaries between the laborer and the object of labor. Examples are the mechanized shovel for the miner, the sewing machine for the tailor, the typewriter for the typist, etc. Means of labor in the broad sense include, in addition to the means of labor in the strict sense, all the material conditions that, without intervening directly in the process of transformation, are indispensable for its realization. Without them work cannot be done. Examples are factories, land, etc.

The means of labor can be analyzed in terms of their technical sophistication or as an expression of specific social relations. From the first perspective, areas to look at include the physical effort needed to execute the work, the interaction between the workers, between them, the objects of work, and the means of labor, and the degree of control that the workers have over the means of work and over the process of work. Each one of these different components of the labor process are expressions of the social relations that have created them. For example, the instruments of work created under machine capitalism characteristically impose on the worker a specific manner of working. The instruments of work, such as machines, dictate the rhythm of work and limit the decision-making of the workers. Both increase, under certain conditions, the accident proneness not of the worker but of the instrument of labor.[12]

No production of material goods can be realized without the participation in it of the objects of work and means of work. This is the reason why Marx calls these elements the means of production. The means of production are constituted by the objects of labor and the means of labor in the broadest sense (see *Figure 2*).

LABOR POWER

The human activity involved in the process of production is commonly called labor or work. This work, which is expressed in a certain quantity of products, implies the expenditure of a certain quantity of human energy. Marx called the human energy expended in the process of work *labor power*. Labor power and work are two different concepts, however, and it is of great importance to differentiate them. Each one refers to different realities. For example, a machine does a definite amount of work in a certain number of hours (canning a definite amount of vegetables) and to achieve this end uses a certain quantity of electricity. Similarly, a worker in a noodle factory in eight hours of work a day packs a definite quantity of pounds of noodles and to do this expends a certain quantity of

Figure 2   Elements of the labor process

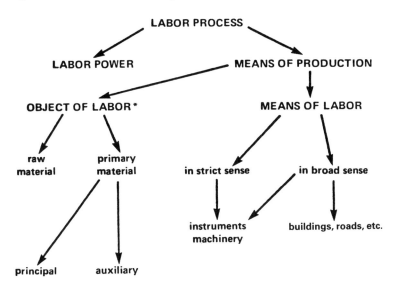

* in production of material goods

human energy. Therefore, the human energy or labor power is radically different from the realized work, which is only the expression or expenditure of that labor power.

By confusing the two concepts, classical economy was and is incapable of discovering the origin of capitalist exploitation, that is the creation of value. It presents the view that wages are the price of the work realized by the worker. In popular parlance, it is said that "a day's wage for a day's work." If that would be the case, however, then the way to estimate how much each worker should be paid would be by calculating the price of the work he does (price of shoes multiplied by the number of shoes made, for example) and pay the worker that amount, since that would be the price for the worker's work. Capitalists, of course, do not pay workers in that way. Capitalism would disappear if that were the way of paying workers.

Nor do the classical economists really calculate the price of labor in that way. They calculate the price of the objects and services which the worker has to consume to restore his labor power. The costs to reproduce that labor power are historically and politically determined. They depend on the strength of the working class in the process of class struggle. The point that needs to be repeated is that workers always produce more than they consume. In other words, capitalists need the cost of reproducing labor power—individual and social wages—to be lower than the price of the products produced by the workers. *Surplus value* is the value that the worker produces over and above the value of his labor power. *The degree of exploitation is measured by this surplus value or unpaid labor.* For example, in 1977, 197,000 production workers produced bituminous coal and lignite. These workers added $10.9 billion value to the coal in the process of mining it, but they were paid only $3.2 billion. That means that the average worker earned $16,200 but the coal operator, the operator's parent company, and its banks received $39,000. The worker was permitted to keep (before federal and state taxes took more out of his/her income) only 29 cents out of each dollar he produced.[13]

There are two different modes of increasing the surplus value which correspond to two different forms of appropriation of labor power. Each form, in turn, implies different forms of wearing out the worker and expropriating his health. One is by increasing the overall time of work. If a worker who produces in four hours the value equivalent of the value of his labor power, works another four hours, he produces a surplus value of 100 per cent. But, if the capitalist is able to lengthen the hours of work to twelve hours, then the worker doubles the value produced and the rate of exploitation increases to 200 per cent. Marx calls this increased value added due to the lengthening of working time, *absolute surplus value.*[14] That lengthening of working time has, however, biological limits, since the worker under this work regime wears out quickly. As Marx wrote, "when capitalist production lengthens the hours of work, it shortens the lives of workers."[15] The other limit on how much that working day may be lengthened is a political one, determined by the working class' achievements in limiting the length of that working day.

The extraction of absolute surplus value usually occurs in labor processes with little development of the forces of production (such as processes with low technology, elementary organization of labor, or low specialization of labor). In those instances, there is heavy physical effort, insufficient resting time and high caloric costs. An example of this labor process is the production of agricultural products in some underdeveloped capitalist countries. In these instances, with low levels of development of the forces of production, wages are the most important determinants of the amount of profit. Consequently, the capitalist aims at combining the lengthening of the working day with the lowering of wages, with subsequent low consumption by the worker and his family. This situation leads to the "over work/under consumption" pattern that typifies the conditions of the workers in a labor process with a low level of development of the forces of production.[16]

The strength of the working population increasingly limits, however, the ability of capitalists to lengthen the time of work. Consequently, capital is forced to increase the extraction of surplus value by either increasing the intensity of work (e.g. forcing the worker to work faster) or by introducing changes in the means of work (instruments), in the organization of work, or in the specialization of the worker or in all of them. In all these cases there is an extraction of surplus value that Marx called *relative surplus value* and that is the predominant form of appropriated value under advanced capitalism. This has many consequences for the health of the workers. Just to mention a few, the intensification of work and the introduction of new forms of organization lead to problems of fatigue and stress, while the introduction of new means of production (objects and means of work) may lead to new exposures to risks from accidents and toxic materials.

In summary, we can speak of the *absolute rate of expropriation of health* related to the absolute rate of exploitation of labor in underdeveloped capitalist countries, and of the *relative rate of expropriation of health* related to the relative rate of exploitation of labor in developed capitalist countries. These two forms of exploitation of labor and of expropriation of health result in different types of mortality and morbidity. Figure 3 summarizes the relationship between the elements of the labor process and health.

Figure 3 Study of the labor process and health

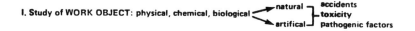

I. Study of WORK OBJECT: physical, chemical, biological
→ natural
→ artifical
— accidents
— toxicity
— pathogenic factors

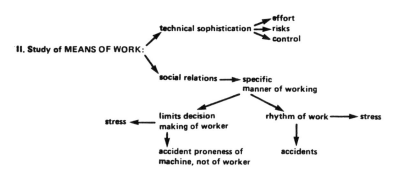

II. Study of MEANS OF WORK:

technical sophistication
→ effort
→ risks
→ control

social relations → specific manner of working

stress ← limits decision making of worker

rhythm of work → stress

accident proneness of machine, not of worker

accidents

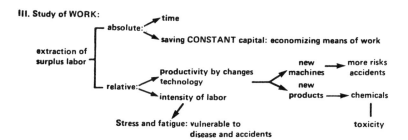

III. Study of WORK:

extraction of surplus labor

absolute:
→ time
→ saving CONSTANT capital: economizing means of work

relative:
→ productivity by changes technology
→ intensity of labor

new machines → more risks accidents

new products → chemicals

toxicity

Stress and fatigue: vulnerable to disease and accidents

The changes in the labor process

In the previous section, I discussed the elements of the labor process—the object, means of labor, labor power, and product—and their analytical value in explaining the relation between work and the worker's health. In this section, I will deal with the historical evolution of that labor process and its consequences for health.

In petty commodity production, the worker owned the object of work and the means of work and had control over the labor process. The artisan or small peasant produced work in isolation. He decided when and how and where to work. There was a unity between the worker and the means of labor. Later, several artisans sold their labor power to a capitalist who owned the objects of work and some of the means of work, such as buildings in which to work. This is how *manufacture* was born. Each laborer performed the same work that he had previously done as an artisan, but now he did it in cooperation with other laborers. At this stage, the worker still controlled his instruments of work and had his own skills. He lost control over where to work (he worked in factories with other workers) and when to work (he had to follow the working time defined for all workers by the capitalist). But he still had control over how to do his work. Soon, however, this type of *simple cooperation* under which all laborers realized the same or very similar tasks was substituted by a *complex form of cooperation* established on the basis of a *technical division of labor*. For example, in the process of sowing, some laborers made the furrows, some planted the seeds, etc. Thus the technical division of labor was born within manufacturing. Laborers specialized in various tasks, tasks that took on each time a more partial and more limited character. Work or labor was characterized in this type of production by (a) *manual labor* which depended to a large degree on the ability with which the worker managed his tools of labor, and (b) *detail labor* which was labor in which each worker was specialized in a very specific task and only the sum of all these labors came to constitute the total product. The technical division of labor in which each worker performs a specialized task requires the existence of a coordination, organization, and direction carried out by the *indirect workers*. These indirect workers plus the *direct workers* or workers who are in direct contact with the objects of work and the instruments of work are constitutive of the *collective worker*. The technical division of labor is determined by the need to increase surplus value, which requires control over the labor power. Thus, indirect workers have not only a coordinating and directing function but also a controlling function over the direct workers. This function is what Marx called the *global function of capital*. Coordination, supervision, and direction are the avenues by which to exercise that control over workers. An enormous handicap for the capitalist in maintaining complete control over the worker is that in manufacture, the worker still has control over his skills and instruments of work. There is still a unity between the detail laborer and the instruments of labor.

The introduction of machinery with *large scale industry* broke with that unity of the tools of work and the worker and established a new unity of tools (machines) with the capitalist. From then on, in large scale industry it was not the worker that directed the tool but the tool that directed the worker. This situation completely transformed the relation of the worker with the means of labor. It completely separated the laborer from the means of labor. The introduction of the machine also enabled the capitalist to increase the intensity of labor (Taylorism) and replace manual labor with machine or dead labor. From then on, the capitalist in large scale industry had not only the ownership or property (a juridical category) of the means of production but also the real power and control (defined by Balibar as possession)[17] over the labor process. He can put the worker to work as he sees fit. He controls both the means of production and the labor process.

At the beginning of large scale industry, the capitalist divided the labor process and simplified its tasks, enabling the carrying out of tasks by unskilled labor like women and children who were the majority of direct workers in the industrial revolution. As Marx said, "the work of women and children was the first cry of the capitalist application of machinery."[18] Also, the capitalist class enlisted to its service science and technology, enabling that class to produce increasingly sophisticated machines whereby the intellectual demands on the worker and his ability to control the machine were continually diminished. Skills and control were shifted from the worker to the machine, permitting the hiring of very cheap and unskilled labor. Consequently, the capitalists at the beginning of large scale industry hired unskilled women, children, and unskilled peasant migrant workers in the place of adult male skilled artisans. Moreover, since the productivity of labor increased substantially, fewer workers were needed than before, generating masses of unemployed: that ever present reserve army whose impact in diluting labor militancy and disciplining labor was (and still is) enormous. Under those conditions the rate of exploitation of labor increased, not only the relative, but also the absolute rate of exploitation. Marx and Engels wrote vividly of the terrible conditions that the industrial revolution brought to bear in workers' lives, and described crowded factories with laborers (many of them women and children) working seventeen and more hours a day. In France, for example, the length of the daily work continuously increased after 1815, reaching the level of seventeen hours in 1828–29. Class struggle later forced limits to the hours of work for women and children. In 1848, the French government, for example, established a limit of eleven hours for children. This limit on working time for women and children had the impact of capitalists' hiring back adult men, since there were not yet limits for adult men's working hours.[19] In brief, the industrial revolution meant a change in the labor process that had, as a consequence, its social costs for the working population.

The changes in the labor process in large scale industry were not a mere result of the capitalists' wants but, rather, an outcome of the class struggle carried out under the dominance of the capitalist class. In that struggle, the capitalist class aimed at deskilling the laborer and dividing the working class. Due to the importance of this subject, let us now focus on the deskilling process and its impact on health.

THE DESKILLING OF THE LABOR POWER AND THE DEVALUATION OF THE HEALTH OF THE LABORER

The fragmentation of tasks allows for a devaluation of the labor power of the worker through the reduction of the level of skill required for the job. That fragmentation also lessens the degree of control which the worker has over (a) his own work; and (b) the entire labor process. He is increasingly directed to the execution of tasks which are conceptualized and decided by the capitalist and his indirect workers. That fragmentation occurs not only among direct workers but also indirect workers, the workers that carry a double function of coordination and direction of the labor process, and supervision and control of the direct workers.

In order to expropriate as much labor power as possible and increase the level of control, there is, in the labor process, a tendency towards the centralization of the direction and control function carried by indirect workers. That centralization is facilitated by the fragmentation of the indirect workers' tasks, which reduces their responsibility and tends to loosen their control and surveillance over other workers. The task of the foreman, for example, became less one of control and more one of coordination. The controlling and direction function is increasingly centralized in the capitalists' agents at the center of management of the labor process. Thus, the process of fragmentation of the labor process affects not only the direct workers but also the indirect workers, with the consequence of devaluating their labor power and reducing their capacity of control over others, as that control is increasingly centralized.

This, for example, is what has happened in the field of engineering during the last thirty years. What was formerly the job of a professional with a university degree is today the job of a technician with only a high school diploma. This lowering of job qualifications has been done by introducing in the labor process new instruments which can be handled by a technician and by a new technical division of labor that requires less span of control over the process by that technician. In this way there has occurred a devaluation of labor power through a dequalification of the job. It should be added that this technical dequalification of the job is also a social dequalification of the worker who does that job. The worker has less skills and also has less control over his work and over the work of others. It has lessened his control functions. The social position of the individual doing that job has been dramatically devalued. This change is referred to by many as "the proletarianization of the new middle class or new petit bourgeoisie,"[20] which is explained not only by the increasing devaluation of labor power (deskilling) but also by its parallel process, the disappearance of the global function of capital through a technical and social dequalification of work positions.[21,22]

This tendency towards losing control over one's own work is thus the characteristic of the labor process under capitalism. Needless to say, this situation creates enormous dissatisfaction as expressed in high turnover rates, absenteeism, resistance to the prescribed work pace, indifference, neglect, and overt hostility to management. The capitalist class responds to that situation in many ways. An important one is to make workers accept that situation as "a given", the inevitable outcome of "progress" or "industrialization", or whatever. The social relations of work are considered as unavoidably determined by the technical requirements of the labor process. A whole ideological mystification appears, and even in its radical version (e.g. I. Illich), the problem is seen as being generated by the technical requirements of industrialization.[23]

Another response by capital appears in the areas of industrial sociology and psychology where, in the study of work and the labor process, the focus is not on the degradation of the worker but, rather, on the difficulties raised by reactions, conscious and unconscious, to that degradation. In these studies, the analysis of "subjective" phenomena, how workers feel, gathered by the ubiquitous questionnaires, takes priority over the study of the work *per se.*

Yet another response by capital to that degradation of work is to divide the workers both in the labor process and in the social realm outside the work-place. An important element in the fragmentation of tasks is the fragmentation of workers into different categories separated by (a) their situation in a hierarchical structure; (b) their conditions of work; and (c) their different levels of compensation (individual and social wages). That fragmentation and separation of workers among themselves is further stimulated by increasing differentials among categories of work. There are, for example, 2,572 different categories in the listings of personnel in the Bethlehem Steel Company. This fragmentation goes side by side with a strong competition that stimulates the worker to view his fellow worker as a competitor for the system of rewards established within the hierarchy of labor. In brief, an extremely important mechanism of control needed by capital to increase the appropriation of surplus labor is the isolation of the worker from other workers. This isolation reaches its extreme form in home piece-work where individuals are contracted to work in their own homes.

ALIENATION AND THE LABOR PROCESS

In analyzing the evolution of the labor process, we have seen how in this process of appropriation of surplus labor power by the capitalist the *worker is separated from the object of work, from the means of work, from the control over the process of work, from his own skills and knowledge and from his fellow workers.* This separation is what Marx called *alienation.* He developed a typology of alienation in his *Economic and Philosophical Manuscripts of 1844.*[24] He referred to workers' alienation from the work product, from the work process, from himself or self-alienation and from others. Alienation for Marx was not an existential and subjective category, intrinsic in the human condition, but, rather, an objective condition due to the separation of the worker from his labor power. Because of this, Marx defined wage labor as alienated labor. Thus, alienation is not part of the human condition, as many existentialists would have it, but, rather, the outcome of social relations that would need to be broken to overcome alienation of the worker. From that perspective, socialism can be defined as the struggle against alienation, the struggle towards the establishment of the unalienated and unalienating society or communism.

The objective condition of that separation or alienation of the worker from his work may appear in many different forms. The consequences of alienation for the health of the worker are many. For example, several studies have concluded that workers consider work as a major determinant of life satisfaction and self-esteem, far more important than non-work activities such as education and leisure pursuits. To have an interesting rewarding job is reported in these studies as being one of life's most important goals.[25] Work contributes substantially to the construction of one's personality. As Bertel Gardell, a well known Swedish social psychologist has concluded, "unless these needs are satisfied at the workplace, the individual experiences a basic frustration that manifests itself in different efforts to achieve adjustment."[26] Equally important is Gardell's conclusion that the most important conditions that have negative effects on workers are [27]

(a) machine pacing of work rhythm and machine control of work methods;

(b) monotonous, repetitive work, activating only a limited part of total human capabilities;

(c) lack of possibilities for contact with other people as part of the ongoing work;

(d) piece rates and related payment systems (in addition to contributing to employee wear and tear, such systems are often detrimental to the observance of safety requirements);

(e) authoritarian and detailed control of the individual, be it through foremen or impersonal systems (computer-based planning).

All of these conditions are related to different forms of worker alienation that can determine different modes of pathology, including death, disease, disability, dissatisfaction, anxiety, stress, and unease. For example, several studies have shown that certain types of morbidity are higher among those workers who have less control over the process of work than those who have retained some form of control. Frankenhausen and Gardell[28] in a recent study comparing machine with self-paced workers in Swedish sawmill operations found more feelings of monotony, general mental strain and exhaustion at the end of the work day, as well as frequent sick leave requests and greater morbidity, among workers in machine-paced jobs than those in self-paced work. Medical examinations also revealed a higher incidence of psychosomatic, cardiovascular, and stress diseases among machine-paced workers than among those who control their own pace. Frankenhausen and Gardell concluded that the lack of control over working conditions was probably the key continuing factor explaining the increased wear and tear on machine-paced workers.

Similarly, several studies have shown that for certain types of conditions, morbidity and mortality are higher among individuals doing routine types of work requiring low levels of skills than among individuals working in jobs that demand a large number of skills and which allow for some type of control over one's own work. A recent study[29] found, for example, that university professors, scientists, physicians, and some craft workers, though having a heavy work load, scored very low on the psychological and somatic stress measures indicated as stress related. This type of work allows for creative experimentation and individual expression, unlike the large majority of blue-collar and even larger number of white-collar workers. Machine-paced workers reported the highest levels of anxiety, depression and irritation, in addition to difficulty in sleeping, loss of appetite, accelerated heart rates, and other symptoms of physiological strain.[30]

Within the same type of occupation, there is a worsening of the health condition of the workers to the degree that the skills required for the job and the social standing of the job worsens. For example, Kornhauser, in his classic study of automobile workers found that "the mental health of factory workers declined as we moved from skilled, responsible, varied type of work to jobs lower in these respects."[31]

It is important to stress that the ill effects of psychologically unrewarding work conditions spread to life outside work and, hence, color the individual's total life situation. As Gardell has shown, this is particularly true of work characterized by automation and mechanization. The view that the worker would be able to compensate for a monotonous, boring job by stimulating and enriching activities in his free time is being replaced by an understanding of the strong links between a job that is circumscribed and repetitious and a leisure which is passive and psychologically unrewarding. In other words, those persons whose jobs are restricted and monotonous are less likely to engage in leisure activities that require participation and effort.[32]

The labor process and the division of social production

Earlier in this essay, I spoke about the technical division of labor within a given process of production, a division determined by the social relations of production.[33] This technical division of labor is especially developed in modern industry. Each worker or group of workers does a specific task within the labor process. In the automobile industry, for example, groups of workers work in producing different components of the automobile, complementing each other's tasks. The final product—the car—is the combined effort of all the workers.

In addition to this technical division of labor, there are two other divisions of labor, the *division of social production* and the *social division of labor*. The division of social production refers to the division of labor according to different branches of economic activities, e.g. agricultural labor, industrial labor, commercial labor, services labor, etc. Also, within each branch we can find several sub-branches. For example, within industrial labor, there is metallurgy, chemicals, textiles, etc.

An important point is that the technical division of labor can lead to the division of social production. For example, the chemical industry started as a component of the textile industry. Within the technical division of labor to produce textiles, chemical activity was a specialized task. The work of the chemical worker contributed to the final product, textiles. Eventually, however, the chemical activity became autonomous and constituted itself as a separate industry. The capitalists in textiles must now buy the chemicals from the chemical industry to include them in their own process of production. In this case, the product of the chemical industry goes to the market—as a commodity—and not directly to a definite process of production, in this case textiles.

In summary, what characterizes the technical division of labor is that the specialized, isolated workers do not produce commodities. What each specialized worker produces is only a part of the final product. This final product or commodity is the result of the collective worker. When some components of that specialized task separate from the initial technical division of labor and sell their product, we have a new branch of economic activity. This is how the division of social production takes place.

THE DIVISION OF SOCIAL PRODUCTION

All economic activities can be grouped in different categories.

1. Extractive industries such as agriculture, fishing, forestry and mining. As their names indicate, their labor process aims at extracting an object from nature.

2. Transformative industry such as construction, food, textile, metal, chemical, machinery, miscellaneous manufacturing, and utilities. Their labor process aims at transforming an object into a worked product.

3. Distributive services such as transportation and storage, wholesale trade, and retail trade (except eating and drinking places). Their labor process aims at distributing objects, means of labor, commodities, and labor.

4. Producer services such as communications, banking, credit, and other financial services, insurance, real estate, engineering and architectural services, accounting and bookkeeping, miscellaneous business services, and legal services. Their labor process aims at providing services to producers and individuals who control property in its various forms. Many of these services were formerly components of the labor process within transformative industries. For example, accounting and advertising were once performed by each individual firm, but when they became more important and made up a greater share of a firm's expenses, a demand appeared for independent accounting and advertising agencies that could take over this assignment.

5. Social services such as medical and health care services, education, welfare and religious services, government, miscellaneous professional and social services. Their labor power aims at the reproduction of the labor power (basically medical, health, education, and welfare services) and at the reproduction of the existing social relations among classes (state administration and services). Needless to say, each service can perform both functions. Moreover, although many social services cater to the individual, their growth responds more to a collective-social than individual demand.

6. Personal services, probably the most heterogeneous group which includes domestic services, hotel and lodging places, eating and drinking places, repair services, laundry and dry cleaning, barber and beauty shops, entertainment and recreational services, and miscellaneous personal services. Their labor process aims at providing personal services to individual consumers and they respond primarily to individual rather than collective social demand.

The typology presented in this division of social production is somewhat arbitrary with criteria for inclusion being on occasion a matter of emphasis.[34]

The social relations of production are the determinant of not only the technical division of labor but also the division of social production. What is being produced and exchanged in society depends primarily on (a) which class owns and possesses the means of production; and (b) the class struggle within that society in which a specific mode of production is dominant. For example, the reasons for the USA having a relatively smaller share of employment in the transformative sector, compared to most western European countries, is partially due to the large amount of capital invested by the US capitalist class outside the USA, particularly after World War II when the price of labor power (wages) increased substantially due to the class struggle in the USA. Also, the high cost of occupational and environmental health programs imposed on the US capitalist class in the process of class struggle has stimulated the mobility of capital to other countries with lower wages and less protection of workers and the environment. Yet another example of the determinant effect of class struggle is the enormous growth of the social services in the USA and other Western capitalist countries which is due not only to the needs of capital accumulation but also to the demands by the working class and popular masses for larger collective-social services such as medical and social services.[35]

Conversely, the larger share of employment in producer services (e.g. banking, insurance, and communications) in the USA compared to most European countries is partially due to the central role that the US capitalist class plays within the Western capitalist economic system. To a large degree, the administration of the Western system of power takes place in the USA.

THE DIVISION OF SOCIAL PRODUCTION AND HEALTH

The division of social production influences greatly the level of health of the working population. This influence may take place in different forms:

The creation of new industries

These new industries employ new products and substances that may be toxic. For example, the separation of the chemical process from the textile industry allowed an enormous growth of the highly toxic chemical industry. In the 1950s and 1960s, there was a boom in rubber, pesticides, and plastic industries, considered by some to be responsible for the increase in cancer rates in the USA.[36] Actually, for the first time in twenty-five years, the rate of cancer in the USA is increasing. From 1973 to 1976, cancer increased by 9 per cent among white males and by 14 per cent among white females in the surveyed population.[37] After considering all existing evidence, the US White House Council on Environmental Quality in 1980 concluded that "(1) the incidence of cancer is increasing; (2) this trend suggests new or intensifying factors; (3) only a small portion of chemical carcinogens have been regulated to date; and (4) exposures to unregulated carcinogens will probably cause the incidence of cancer to continue to rise."[38]

There are currently 60,000/70,000 chemicals in production and the list is expanding at a rate of about 700 per year. While only 20 chemicals have been recognized and regulated by OSHA as human carcinogens, the International Agency for Research of Cancer (IARC) lists 221 chemicals and NIOSH over 2,000 chemicals as suspected carcinogens. Altogether, NIOSH and NIEHS have estimated that 20–38 per cent of all cancers may be due to occupational exposure. The evidence being generated by several studies is alarming. The following are examples of findings:[39]

"Of four million workers who have had heavy exposure to asbestos, 20–25 percent can be expected to die of lung cancer, 7–10 percent of mesothelioma (cancer of the lining of the lung), and 8–9 percent of gastro-intestinal cancer. Coke oven workers face two-and-a-half times as great a chance of dying from lung cancer and are seven times as likely to die from kidney cancer as the general population. Smelter workers heavily exposed to arsenic trioxide for more than 15 years had an eightfold excess of respiratory cancer. Other well-known occupational carcinogens include vinyl chloride, bis-chloromethylether, benzene, and benzopyrene. In a retrospective study of a coal tar plant where benzidine was used, 44 percent of the workers exposed to benzidine developed bladder tumors. Another study showed that 94 percent of workers exposed to benzidine and betanapthalene for over five years developed bladder tumors."

In summary, the majority of carcinogens have been introduced into the labor process since 1950 with a continuous growth in the 1960s and 1970s. Thus, it is reasonable to believe that the recent increase of cancer incidence resulting from the boom in chemical production may be only the beginning.

Introduction of new technologies in old and new economic sectors

The introduction of a new industry or economic sector is usually accompanied by the introduction of new skills that may require new professionals. The tendency in the labor process towards devaluating labor power, however, determines the need to introduce new technology and new organization of work that allows that rapid deskilling. For example, the establishment and expansion of the producer services employed large amounts of new professionals in banking, insurance, communications, etc., with a highly labor intensive labor process. The introduction of the computer and microprocessors —the most recent technological revolution—has had, however, an enormous impact in the deskilling of the labor force in those sectors, making them capital intensive. This massive deskilling of the labor force has gone side by side with the superspecialization of a few who carry out the tasks of conceptualization. In that respect, the impact of the introduction of this new technology is similar to the impact of the machine in the labor process of manufacturing.[40]

This new technology—computers and microprocessors—has also spread to other economic sectors such as the extractive and transformative sectors, enabling capital to enormously expand the span of control over the labor process. It is important to stress that this enlargement of that span of control over the labor process enables the capitalist to keep the process of production as its optimum design, including the continuous matching of labor power to the labor process, without interruption of production. *Shift work* thus became a large percentage of the whole work: 25 per cent of the labor force in the USA and 21 per cent in France work in shifts.[41] This type of work, in addition to physical and psychological wear, destroys all possibilities for the workers to enjoy normal daily life relations.

This new technology also enables capital to centralize the control and conceptualization of the labor process and to decentralize its execution with an easy exchange of labor and tasks within the same labor process, allowing for bypassing elements of disruption (such as strikes) within the process. This new situation has been defined as a most important "strike breaker." When one sector of labor is on strike, management can shift whole sectors of the labor process, bypassing the striking workers. For example, during the well-known strike of 1975 in the aerospace industry, McDonnell-Douglas's management was able to maintain production at 60 per cent with the use of microprocessors and automation. Also, in another well-known strike in 1973, GM's management was able to easily shift production from one sector of the industry to another by the use of microprocessors that have predesigned all the different changes required in the labor process.[42]

Another consequence of the introduction of that new technology is, of course, unemployment. New robots used in Good Year and Luckey, Ohio can do the work of several workers at considerably less cost. According to *Business Week*, the average life of a robot is eight years with a daily cost of $4.50, while the cost for a worker is $14.50 per hour.[43]

THE LABOR PROCESS IN SOCIAL SERVICES

The introduction of new technologies and new organization of work occurs *in all areas of social production*. There are no areas or sectors that are instrinsically labor intensive. This point needs emphasis in view of the widely held belief that social and personal services are intrinsically labor intensive. It is assumed that the personal nature of those services, such as medical care, require the personal involvement of large numbers of personnel. This position should be questioned both on theoretical and empirical grounds. The overall trend of the labor process under capitalism is the deskilling of labor and the substitution of living labor (workers) by dead labor (machines). This trend applies to the social services as well. These services have had a most impressive growth in employment rising from 12.4 per cent in 1950 to 21.9 per cent in 1970. Interestingly enough, public administration did not contribute greatly to this gain. Most of the changes were due to medical service and education. Specifically, the three sub-industries of medical services, hospitals, and education more than doubled and together they accounted for over four-fifths of the total increase.[44] This dramatic growth, however, is relatively recent. It took place primarily in the 1970s. The empirical evidence shows that all new industries become, with time, capital intensive and become deskilled. This is already happening in hospital services: witness, for example, the great proliferation of technical nurses doing the work that nurses used to do before. The deskilling of nursing has gone a long way. Another example of that incipient trend is the automation of laboratory services. There is nothing intrinsic in the labor process in the health sector that prevents the fragmentation of tasks and the deskilling of labor power. The speed with which the changes in the labor process in the services sector will occur will depend on the one hand on the pressure by the capitalist class to extract as much work as possible from the service worker by increasing the rate of exploitation of that labor and, on the other, on the resistance by the service workers to the increase of their exploitation. This tendency also occurs, of course, in public service, since it is to the advantage of the capitalist class if public workers consume as little of the overall surplus value as possible, so that more value is appropriated by the capitalist class.[45]

CRISIS, INTERNATIONAL MOBILITY OF CAPITAL, AND ITS IMPACT IN THE LABOR PROCESS AND ON HEALTH

The international mobility of capital has broken to some degree the dichotomy referred to before whereby capital exploits labor in the developed industrialized capitalist countries by increasing the relative rate of exploitation, and in the underdeveloped capitalist countries by increasing the absolute rate of exploitation. For example, in the current conjuncture, we are witnessing the attempt, for the most part successful, of increasing the absolute rate of exploitation of labor in both developed and underdeveloped capitalist countries. This increase takes place by:

1. *Lengthening the overall working day.* Indeed, we find that side by side with large unemployment, there is an overworked labor force. For example, while in theory the majority of workers at Ford work only 35 hours per week, in practice they are forced to make

extra time (mandatory overtime) to a weekly total of 52 hours. This mandatory overtime is compulsory and written into the work contract.[46] Similarly, in the Toyota factories in Japan, each worker has to add a minimum of two hours extra to the eight formal hours and frequently must work an extra 3–3½ hours.[47] When these industries operate in underdeveloped countries, this lengthening of the working time is even larger. For example, while the "formal" working week (without counting extra time) in most developed countries is 40–44 hours a week, in South Korea it is 50–58, the Philippines 45–50, Singapore 49, and in Thailand 47–51. In Hongkong, the working week is 60 hours with 58 per cent of the labor force working seven days a week. According to the census of 1971, that year 174,439 workers worked 75 hours a week with 13,792 working 105 hours a week! (The labor force in Hongkong is 1,900,000 with those workers in manufacturing being 700,000 in 1975.)[48] The overall increase of labor time also occurs with the involvement of the worker in several jobs (multiemployment). This is particularly accentuated among women who also do household work. For example, in 1978, working women in the USA spent 69 hours of labor a week and men spent 53 or, altogether, 122 for a family of two, the equivalent of three full-time jobs. According to a recent report prepared by the National Commission on Working Women, 55 per cent of the women surveyed reported having no leisure time at all, with only 14 per cent indicating that job and family did not seriously interfere with each other.[49]

2. *Reducing the costs of reproduction of labor power.* The largely successful intent of cutting the individual and social wages of labor in both developed and underdeveloped capitalist countries is having a significant impact in increasing the rate of exploitation of labor. This situation is facilitated by:

(a) The mobility of labor across nation/state boundaries with the establishment in developed capitalist countries of large sectors of the working class—the immigrants—who do not have voting or civil rights and whose position *vis-à-vis* capital is very weak. The wages paid to immigrants are often less than the cost of reproducing their labor power. This "superexploitation" or what Marx called *primitive accumulation* is made possible by (i) the subsidy of those costs by the unpaid labor of the spouse; and by (ii) the payment of those costs by the community where those immigrants came from and later retire to.

(b) The mobility of capital across nation/state boundaries permitting the lowering of labor costs by moving to countries with very low wages. Andre Gunder Frank and Michel Chossudovsky have shown, for example, the enormous country wage differentials in the textile industry which explains the enormous mobility of US capital towards Taiwan, South Korea, Brazil, and other countries. This exploitation requires an enormous political repression frequently carried out by brutal military regimes.[50,51]

3. *Increasing children's and women's labor whose reproduction costs tend to be very low.* For example, it has been estimated that nearly 90 per cent of newly employed labor in new industries established in underdeveloped countries in electronics and textiles are women (with 20–50 per cent lower wages than the already very low male wages) and children.[52] The number of children under fourteen years of age in today's world who are "economically active" has been estimated at 54 million.[53]

In addition to increases in the absolute rate of exploitation, the capitalist class also *increases the relative rate of exploitation* by increasing the intensity of labor and by adding new substances and new technologies to the labor process. As a result, we find an increase in the number of fatalities and accidents at the work-place and further increases in fatigue and stress-related disease. In South Korea, for example, major disabilities at the work-place rose 2.7 times between 1970 and 1976. In São Paulo, Brazil, there were 712,000 accidents in 1973 and 780,000 in 1974. Almost 24 per cent of the labor force had had major accidents, three times higher than those in France.[54] Also, the use of new toxic substances in the labor process in underdeveloped countries reproduces the same type of toxic related morbidity as in developed capitalist ones.[55]

In summary, as a consequence of that international mobility of capital in underdeveloped countries, the two types of labor processes create two types of mortality and morbidity. One is the labor process characteristic of a low level of development of the forces of production. In that labor process, the exploitation of labor and the expropriation of health takes place primarily through increases in the absolute rate of exploitation. The other, superimposed over the previous mode of exploitation is the process characterized by the predominance of large scale industry where the expropriation of labor power and of health takes place through increases both in the absolute and relative rates of exploitation. The overlapping of death due to cancer with death due to famine is becoming the trademark of capitalist development in underdeveloped countries.

Conversely, in developed capitalist countries, we find a brutal attack by the capitalist class against the working class aimed at increasing not only the relative but also the absolute rate of exploitation of labor. To the degree that labor is defeated, both the appropriation of absolute and relative surplus value and the expropriation of health increase.

CLASS STRUGGLE AND THE LABOR PROCESS

In the process of class struggle, the capitalist class creates the conditions that enable the expropriation from labor of their labor power and their health. At the economic level, for example, the capitalist class creates under and unemployment that stimulates labor discipline. Also, as capital moves from state to state it continuously recreates the conditions of exploitation (e.g. low unionization).

Another important condition for the reproduction of exploitation is the ideological one. It is important for the capitalist class that labor accept the "industrialization" ideology in which damage at the work-place is seen as an unavoidable outcome of industrialization or progress. Other ideological positions advanced by the capitalist class include the individualization of the responsibility for disease, seeing damage created at the work-place as the worker's fault or worker's parents' fault. The development of cancer among workers is presented, for example, as a result, not of exposure to carcinogens, but, rather of the existence of genes in the workers that make them specially sensitive to those substances. Consequently, the strategy for the resolution of the cancer problem at the work-place increasingly involves the genetic screening of workers. As Anthony Mazzocchi, Director of Health and Safety for the Oil, Chemical and Atomic Workers International Union said recently, "I think that in the 1980s we are going to see a lot of victim blaming. The emphasis will be not so much what you work with, it will have to do with who your mother and father were."[56]

The ideological position of considering cancer at the work-place as an outcome of unavoidable progress has led some health leaders in the USA, such as the American Health Foundation—a most prestigious forum for the US medical establishment—to recommend placing aged workers in those job positions exposed to carcinogens with the assumption that they will die of age prior to development of cancer![57]

Needless to say, the working class has not remained passive. In a process of continuous struggle, the working class has fought for changes in the labor process from shortening the working time to changing the intensity, technology, and organization of work. Almost every change in the labor process has occurred because of the desire by the capitalist class to break down or control working-class resistance to conditions of oppression. Interventions such as humanizing of work and workers' participation are also intents by capital of minimizing that resistance. It is worth stressing that such measures may or may not be "co-opting" depending on the political correlations of forces existing at the work-place.

In this struggle there are some recent developments that merit discussion. One is the questioning of the concept of "productivity" as defined by the capitalist class. The enormous social costs that production imposes on the worker, expropriating his health, do not appear in the calculation of that productivity. The Chicago Committee on Occupational Safety and Health (COSH), however, has estimated the health "costs" in producing a car in Detroit. *Table 1* summarizes the components of the labor process and the damage created by each element in that process. Segments of labor are demanding that those "hidden" costs be recognized.

Another development is the questioning of bourgeois ideology that damage at the work-place is unavoidable. Earlier acceptance of that ideology had led labor to focus on struggles over *compensation*. From the late 1960s, however, sectors of the European and North American labor have expanded that concern to the *control* of the labor process.[58] That concern appears in different forms which include the demand by sectors of the Oil, Chemical and Atomic

Table 1

components of labor process	expropriation of health (related diseases and injuries)
FOUNDRY: engine block	silicosis, cancer, burns
SCRAMPING PLANT: Sheet steel body	deafness, amputations
MACHINE SHOP: gears	dermatitis and lung disease
RUBBER PLANT: tires	leukemia
ASBESTOS PLANT: brakes and clutches	lung cancer, asbestosis
BATTERY PLANT: batteries	lead poisoning
CHROME: trim and bumpers	nasal and sinus cancer
GLASS FACTORY: windows	lung disease, cataracts
PLASTIC PLANT: vinyl tops and seats	angiocarcinoma (liver cancer)
SMELTER: copper wire	lung and skin cancer
PIGMENT AND SOLVENT PLANT: paint	lead poisoning, liver diseases
SYNTHETIC FIBER PLANT: seat cushions	emphysema and bronchitis
ASSEMBLY:	stress, mental disturbances
REFINERY: gasoline	leukemia and skin cancer

Workers Union in the USA to control occupational health services, to the demand of Fiat workers in Italy of the power to veto any changes in the labor process suggested by capital.

The experience of the labor movement seems to indicate that there is a need to develop forms of direct democracy at the work-place, where assembled workers try to regain control over all elements of the labor process, control that the capitalist class will oppose by all means. Still, meaningful forms of direct control can be developed even under capitalism, as is shown by the splendid example of the Italian workers in the early 1970s with the development of the Consiglios de Fabrica.[59]

This form of direct participation needs to be complemented by forms of indirect or delegated democracy where assembly types of bodies elect their representatives in the instruments of labor such as unions. The working class needs to carry its struggle both in the work-place and outside. In these struggles, and especially in areas outside the work-place, the working class, through its own instruments and movements, needs to establish alliances with other classes and groups and movements with whom they share interests. The expropriation of health that takes place at the work-place is further reproduced by the expropriation of health that occurs in the communities, in the environment, in the family, in all sides and components of everyday life. The articulation of the work-place related struggles with the non-work related ones, and the articulation of forms of direct with indirect democracy, are key issues for the resolution of the exploitation and expropriation of health of the majority of our peoples.[60]

Notes

1　See V. Navarro, Work, Ideology and Science, *International Journal of Health Services* 10 (4) (1980): 533.

2　L. Eisenberg, A Research Framework for Evaluating the Promotion of Mental Health and Prevention of Mental Illness, *Pubic Health Report* 96 (1) (January–February, 1981): 3–19.

3　A. Mazzocchi, Training Occupational Physicians, *Health Policy Advisory Center Bulletin* (Health/PAC), No. 75 (March/April, 1977): 7.

4　J. Eyer and T. Sterling, Stress Related Mortality and Social Organization, *Review of Radical Political Economics* 9 (1) (Spring, 1977): 1.

5　C. Laurell, Work and Health in Mexico, *International Journal of Health Services* 9 (4) (1979): 545.

6　C. Palloix, *Proceso de Producción y Crisis del Capitalismo*, Barcelona: Blume Ediciones, 1980, p. 15.

7　M. Foucault, *La volonté de savoir*, Paris: Gallimard, 1977.

8　L. Althusser and E. Balibar, *Reading Capital*, New York: Pantheon Books, 1970, p. 73.

9　The labor process is discussed by K. Marx primarily in volume 1 of *Capital*. In this article, I borrow heavily from that volume as well as from M. Harnecker's *Los conceptos elementales del materialismo historico* Siglo XXI, 1977 edn. An English version is being currently translated by *Theoretical Review*. The concepts presented by M. Harnecker have on occasion been modified and even changed on those points that needed correction.

10　F. Engels, *Anti-Dühring*, Mexico: Grijalbo, 1964, p. 264.

11　In the production of services, the object upon which labor is done can also be the consumer of the product or services. For example, the student or patient, the object of teachers' or physicians' labor, is also the consumer of their services. For an interesting discussion of the differences between production of material goods and production of human services, see G. Stevenson, Social Relations of Production and Consumption in the Human Services Occupations, *International Journal of Health Services* 8 (3) (1978): 453.

12 R. Sass and G. Crook, Accident Proneness. Science or Non-Science, *International Journal of Health Services* 11 (2) (1981): 175.

13 Miners Create Huge Surplus Value, *Economic Notes*, Labor Research Associates, Inc. 49 (1–2) (1981): 2.

14 K. Marx, *Capital*, vol. 1, pp. 252–53.

15 Ibid., vol. 1, p. 207 (25; 152). Also, for an interesting discussion of absolute and relative surplus value see Labor Mobility and Production of Value, in J.P. de Gaudemar's *Movilidad del trabajo y acumulación de capital*, Mexico: Ediciones Era, 1979, p. 147.

16 Laurell, *op. cit.*

17 E. Balibar, The Basic Concepts of Historical Materialism, in Althusser and Balibar, *op. cit.*

18 Marx, *op. cit.*, p. 323 (25; 167–68).

19 Cited in Gaudemar, *op. cit.*, p. 154 (25; 154).

20 G. Carchedi, *On the Economic Identification of Social Classes*, London: Routledge & Kegan Paul, 1977, p. 173.

21 N. Poulantzas, *Political Power and Social Classes*, New York: NLB, Schocken Books, 1975, pp. 271–82. Also, see Carchedi, *op. cit.*, p. 208.

22 The unawareness of this dual function of the petit bourgeoisie is the main error of radical analysis of the new petit bourgeoisie. To see this new petit bourgeoisie only or primarily as an agent of social control misses the other function, that of assisting the actual labor process. This unawareness also explains the overabundance of references among radical analysts of medicine, education, etc. in seeing those institutions primarily as agencies of control. See as examples B. and J. Ehrenreich, Medicine and Social Control, *Social Policy*, May–June, 1974, and I. Illich, *Medical Nemesis*, London: Calder & Boyars, 1975.

23 Ivan Illich, *Tools for Conviviality*, London: Calder & Boyars, 1973.

24 K. Marx, Economic and Philosophical Manuscripts, in Eric Fromm's *Marx's Concept of Man*, New York: Ungar, Frederick, Publishing Co., 1963, pp. 85–196. For Marx's concept of alienation, see Adam Schaff, *Alienacion como fenomeno social*, Barcelona: Critica Grijalbo, 1979; and B. Ollman *Alienation*, Cambridge: Cambridge University Press, 1971.

25 B. Gardell, Alienation and Mental Health in the Modern Industrial Environment, in L. Leads (ed.), *Society Stress and Disease*, Oxford: Oxford University Press, 1972; and F. Friedlander, Importance of Work versus Non-Work During Socially and Occupationally Stratified Groups, *Journal of Applied Psychology* 50 (4, 1) (1967).

26 Gardell, *op. cit.*

27 B. Gardell and B. Gustavsen, Work Environment Research and Social Change: Current Developments in Scandinavia, *Journal of Occupational Behavior* 1 (1980).

28 M. Frankenhausen and B. Gardell, Underload and Overload in Working Life: Outline of a Multidisciplinary Approach, *Journal of Human Stress* 2: 35–46.

29 R. Caplan, *Job Demands and Worker Health*, NIOSH, 1975, US Government Printing Office, p. 191.

30 For a comprehensive review of current literature on detailed labor and occupational stress, see Jeffrey V. Johnson, *Work Fragmentation, Human Degradation and Occupational Stress*, 1980, unpublished mimeograph.

31 A. Kornhauser, *Mental Health of the Industrial Workers*, New York: John Wiley & Sons, 1965, p. 76.

32 B. Gardell, Technology, Alienation and Mental Health. Summary of a Social Psychological Research Programme on Technology and the Worker, *Acta Sociologica* 19 (2; 2) (1976): 83–94.

33 Social Relations of Production are those relationships which are established between the owners of the means of production and the direct producers in a definite process of production, relationships which depend on the type of ownership relation, possession, dispossession or usufruct which they establish with the means of production. Social Division of Labor is the distribution of the different tasks which individuals perform in society (economic, ideological, and political tasks) and which are carried out as a function of the place which they occupy in the social relations of production.

34 The typology of economic activities presented in this article follow the typology presented in H. L. Browning and J. Singelmann, The Transformation of the US Labor Force. The Interaction of Industry and Occupation, *Politics and Society* 8 (3–4) (1978): 481–509.

35 For an interesting discussion of the impact of the class struggle on the US division of social production, see M. Castells, *The Economic Crisis and American Society*, Princeton, NJ: Princeton University Press, 1980.

36 From 1950 to 1974, production of synthetic rubber, pesticides, and plastics increased from (all in billions of pounds per year) 0.8 to 6, 2.5 to 12.5, and 1.3 to 3.2, respectively, *Science* 204 (1979): 587.

37 E. Pollack and J. Horn, Trends in Cancer Incidence and Mortality in the United States, 1969–1976, *Journal of National Cancer Institute* 64 (1980): 1091.

38 Toxic Substances Strategy Committee, White House Council on Environmental Quality, A Report to the President. Office, Washington, DC, May, 1980.

39 E. Loechler, Cancer and the Work Place, *Science for the People* 12 (3) (1980): 14.

40 M. Goldhaber, Politics and Technology. Microprocessors and the

Prospect of a New Industrial Revolution, *Socialist Review* No. 52 (1980): 9.

41 P. Jardillier, Evolution recente et devenir des conditions de travail, *Revue de l'enterprise*, num. 13 (1978): 11–21, and D. Baker, The Use and Health Consequences of Shift Work, *International Journal of Health Services* 10 (3) (1980): 405.

42 Both examples are cited in M. Debouzy, Los sindicatos americanos responden a la invasion tecnologica, *Transicion*, Febrero, 1981: 37.

43 *Business Week*, 26 March, 1979.

44 Browning and Singelmann, *op. cit.*, table 2, p. 493.

45 Carchedi, *op. cit.*, p. 10.

46 Debouzy, *op. cit.*, p. 38.

47 Report on the Japanese Miracle. The Working Conditions of the Toyota Factory, *International Journal of Health Services* (in process).

48 Frank, *La crisis mundial*, Barcelona: Bruguera, 1980, p. 248.

49 All these figures are cited in E. Currie, R. Dunn, and D. Fogarty, The New Immiseration. Stagflation, Inequality and the Working Class, *Socialist Review* No. 54 (1980): 15.

50 *Ibid.*, p. 267.

51 M. Chossudovsky, Human Rights, Health and Capital Accumulation, in V. Navarro (ed.), *Imperialism, Health and Medicine*, Farmingdale, NY: Baywood Publishing, 1981.

52 T. Fröbel, J. Heinrichs, and O. Kreye, Tendency Towards a New International Division of Labor. World Wide Utilization of Labor Force for World Market Oriented Manufacturing, *Economic and Political Weekly*, February, 1977.

53 Frank, *op. cit.*, p. 240.

54 *Ibid.*, pp. 256, 257.

55 B. Castleman, The Export of Hazardous Substances, *International Journal of Health Services* 9 (4) (1979).

56 Genetic Screening by Industry, *New York Times*, February 3, 1980, p. 36.

57 Quoted in R. Severo, The Genetic Barrier; Job Benefit or Job Bias?, *The New York Times*, Wednesday, February 6, 1980, p. A. 17.

58 C. Crouch and A. Pizzorno, *The Resurgence of Class Conflict in Western Europe since 1968*, vol. 2, New York: Macmillan 1978.

59 G. Assennato and V. Navarro, Workers' Participation and Control in Italy: The Case of Occupational Medicine, *International Journal of Health Services* (2) (1980): 217.

60 For an expansion of this point, see V. Navarro, The Nature of Democracy in the Core Capitalist Countries: Meanings and Implications for Class Struggle, *The Insurgent Sociologist* 10 (2) (Summer, 1980): 3.

PART IV
CRISIS AND IDEOLOGY

"The docs keep telling me there's nothing wrong with the place where I work. I guess they're supposed to know it all because they've had a lot of education and everything. I'm no expert like they are, but I sure as hell know there's something wrong in that mill and the other guys are saying the same thing. One thing I know for sure—that place is killing us."

(Cancer patient and steelworker
from the Bethlehem Steel
Corporation mills,
Baltimore, Maryland, 1978,
Personal communication)

Work, ideology, and science: The case of medicine*

Introduction: Class struggle and health

There is a concern among the centers of power in the Western capitalist world that something is going wrong with the nature of work in that world. Editorials in the daily press, articles in scholarly papers, reports of powerful foundations, exposé programs on television, and, even more recently, some commercial films have focused on different dimensions and components of what has been called the "crisis at the work-place" in contemporary society. Part of this crisis is the rebellion of the working populations against their conditions of work, rebellions which appear in different forms such as absenteeism, turnover, or just plain sabotage. These have reached such proportions as to become a cause for major alarm by the establishments of those societies. An example of this concern and alarm is one of the reports of the powerful Trilateral Commission. A major recommendation of that commission, which includes representatives of the power structure of the top capitalist developed societies,[1] is that "a major intervention is required in the area of work in our societies" to attack workers' discontent and alienation at its roots since, otherwise, those rebellions can threaten the whole survival of the Western economic system—a euphemistic term used to define Western capitalism. The representatives of the bourgeoisie

* Written in 1980.

or capitalist class, or, to use a more American term, the corporate class, as the most class conscious of all classes, tend to perceive quite clearly from where they sit where trouble may come from, that is from the working-class rebellion against the main column on which the entire capitalist system is built: *the nature and the conditions on which basis work is extracted from the workers.*[2]

On the other side of the ideological fence, progressive forces in the USA have only recently begun seeing signs of that potential storm. Many, however, still seem to be stuck in that scenario so widely emphasized by ideologists of capitalism and radicals alike that the working class has practically disappeared as agents of change, and, instead, has been absorbed into society, becoming part of the larger consuming and undifferentiated masses. According to some radical theorists, other groups are supposed to have taken over that task of carrying on the much-needed struggle for change. The working class, however, has been "lost," and has become part of that one-dimensional society.[3] Witness, for example, a recent publication edited by a leading radical in this country who, in covering the changes in the cultural meaning of medicine, refers in his introduction to the impact of black's and women's struggles in the redefinition of health and medicine, but not once does he refer to the struggles which are taking place at the sites of work in the Western capitalist societies,[4] struggles which I believe are among the most important ones in changing the nature of our society, including the definition of health and medicine. Just in the USA alone, millions of workers were involved in strikes in the 1970s having to do primarily with work conditions and health. From the wildcat strikes among steelworkers in Ohio, who asked to change conditions of work and medical regulations which applied in their working places, to the coal-miners who struck for three months—threatening, as President Carter indicated, the stability of the economy, that is US capitalism —for the right to strike for health and safety conditions and for the right to retain some form of control over their health plans, many instances show that major struggles are taking place at the workplace questioning the meaning of work under capitalism and its effects on the health and well-being of our working populations. Health-related issues have been triggering points in many of those struggles, and health-related movements have had an important impact on changing the nature of political and social institutions, including labor's own institutions. An example is the key role played by the Black Lung movement in creating Miners for Democracy. That movement rallied the majority of coal-miners around the issue of democratizing their union, the United Mine Workers, and over-throwing the corrupt leadership of Boyle.[5] A very important issue —a key one—in that fight was a health-related issue: the need to recognize and compensate black lung as an occupation-related condition, and the right to strike for safety conditions. The miners fought a tough battle to redefine health and medicine, showing —against the verdict of coal companies, state and federal legislative bodies and agencies, and even large sectors of the academic commu-nity—that coal-mining was indeed a very unhealthy occupation in our society.

It would be erroneous to consider those struggles new or just limited to the USA. The long struggle the working class carried out in the nineteenth and twentieth centuries in the USA, and many other countries as well, to limit the daily working hours to eight, already had as its goal a redefining of the meaning of work and health. As an Italian folksong of the nineteenth century put it,

> We want to change the social order,
> We are fed up with work without meaning,
> We want to enjoy life and health, sun, and flowers;
> We want eight hours for work, eight hours to rest, and
>   eight hours to live, to have joy, and to dream.[6]

The history of the working class in the USA, and other countries as well, is punctuated by a continuous struggle to redefine the nature of work and health. And these struggles have heightened to such an extent that, as the Trilateral Commission indicates, they are threatening the current international capitalist order. Most of the strikes in the Western developed capitalist world in the last two decades have had to do with working conditions and how those working conditions affect the well-being and health of the laboring populations.[7] Actually, a key characteristic of the current interna-tional capitalist crisis is the conflict which appears between the demand by the representatives of capital for higher productivity at the work-place (extracting as much work as possible from each worker) and the resistance by the workers (although not always by their unions) to that demand for higher productivity. The workers know quite well the meaning and impact which higher productivity —with higher speeds of work, longer number of working hours, night shifts of workers, and the like—has on their health and lives. Economic successes that have been presented as "miracles," highly applauded in established centers of power, have concealed enormous sacrifices which they have implied for the working populations. Just one example among many is the economic "miracle" in the 1960s in Italy. Even in the land of the Vatican, that economic "miracle" did not have much of a spiritual intervention. The spiritual had a bloody, earthy touch. Just in cost of major occupational injuries at the work-place, the figures speak for themselves: 440,000 in 1946; 950,000 in 1956; and 1,400,000 in 1970.[8] There was a clear relationship between higher productivity and higher damage at the work-place in the 1950s and 1960s (the period of the "miracles"), not to speak of the immense suffering in disease, stress, malaise, and ruined personal and family lives. Actually, the social unrest and final explosion which took place in Italy in the late 1960s, and in particular in the "hot autumn" of 1969, when workers and communities took over factories and other economic and social institutions, represented a rebellion against those working and living conditions. In those rebellions, the control of work, the meaning and purpose of that work, and its consequences in workers' lives, were the focus of the struggle. As a group of workers indicated in the slogan they hung on the door of the factory they had taken over, "We want a society where workers will sing while working."[9]

Needless to say, these struggles against the nature of work under capitalism occur, not only because of the actual damage imposed on the worker at the work-place, but also because of the harm done to the workers both within and outside the working place and in all dimensions of their lives. Two recent examples show how work under capitalism affects the most profound and intimate aspects of workers' lives, including their sexuality, and how workers rebel against that damage. One occurred at the British Leyland factory in the UK when management wanted to establish a night shift. The workers rebelled and struck because they perceived that that change would affect their sexual relations with their partners. Their slogan,

"Make love, not night work," put it quite clearly. Similarly, the workers of Pesaro in Italy noticed that when using machines which produce high-frequency vibrations, their sexual appetite was affected. When they approached the occupational doctors of the factory about it, they were told that something must be wrong with them or their lovers. Consequently, they were advised to change lovers. But the workers felt that their change in sexuality did not have anything to do with their lovers but with the bosses' machines, and in what has been called the "first strike for love" in Italy, they struck and forced management to change those machines.[10]

In summary, the fight for the realization of health is very much at the center of the conflict between capital and labor which takes place at the work-place and heightens in moments of crisis like the current one. The struggle which occurs at the places of work in our Western societies is a most important one, since it questions the very basic social power relations of capitalism.[11]

The nature of work under capitalism

Let us analyze the conditions of work of the working class, that class by whose sweat and pain the goods and services in our society are produced. A primary characteristic of work is that its controllers increasingly shape the nature of work to optimize their pattern of control over (1) the productive process; (2) the individual producers; and (3) the collectivity of producers—the working class.[12] By means of this process, the workers are: (a) compartmentalized into increasingly narrower tasks; (b) hierarchicalized by a division of labor which reproduces the class relations in society; and (c) expropriated from all possibility of controlling, influencing or having a say in the design or development of the work process or of the products they create.

The outcome of this process is a set of relations which cannot be defined as less than totalitarian. Democracy, the capacity of individuals to control their own lives, stops at the gates of the working places. This set of authoritarian relations where one class—the bourgeoisie—controls that process of production and work, and the other—the working class—does not, is what Marx called the *dictatorship of the bourgeoisie*, understanding as such not a specific

148 · Crisis, Health, and Medicine

political form of government but rather an overwhelming dominance and control which the bourgeoisie has over the means and process of production. Nowhere for the millions of workers does that dictatorship appear more clearly than at the place of work. Michael Bosquet, in his usual vivid way, puts this quite clearly when he invites the reader to,

> "Try putting 13 little pins in 13 little holes 60 times an hour, eight hours a day. Spot-weld 67 steel plates an hour, then find yourself one day facing a new assembly-line needing 110 an hour. Fit 100 coils to 100 cars every hour; tighten seven bolts three times a minute. Do your work in noise 'at the safety limit,' in a fine mist of oil, solvent and metal dust. Negotiate for the right to take a piss—or relieve yourself furtively behind a big press so that you don't break the rhythm and lose your bonus. Speed up to gain the time to blow your nose or get a bit of grit out of your eye. Bolt your sandwich sitting in a pool of grease because the canteen is 10 minutes away and you've only got 40 for your lunch-break. As you cross the factory threshold, lose the freedom of opinion, the freedom of speech, the right to meet and associate supposedly guaranteed under the constitution. Obey without arguing, suffer punishment without the right of appeal, get the worst jobs if the manager doesn't like your face. Try being an assembly-line worker."[13]

A popular movie in the USA—*Blue Collar*—shows how people work, a theme very rarely treated by the media in the USA. And in spite of its many serious political and ideological flaws, it shows the reality of life inside a factory. It shows in essence the Gulags of capitalism. Actually, this movie understates the conditions of work, since it was filmed in a small car factory, rather than in a more typical large one where the speed of work is much higher. The managers of those more typical car manufacturing industries did not want to show the inside of their factories.[14]

But these characteristics of assembly line work are not unique to workers in the automobile industry or workers in manufacturing alone. Many other studies have been done showing how assembly line work, where the individual worker is carrying out *predetermined tasks* over which he or she does not have much control, is also the most frequent type of work among sales, clerical, and large sectors of public service workers. Indeed, that expansion of the atomized hierarchical and authoritarian division of labor is growing rather than diminishing in most areas of work in society, and is being presented as needed to increase the efficiency and productivity of the worker, to extract as much work as possible from the worker. But that demand by representatives of the capitalist class is not made without misgivings about how long the working class will tolerate those conditions of work. As a leading exponent of the establishment put it, "How long can our political system stand the seventy million who live the majority of their working hours in an atmosphere which is totalitarian?"[15]

In the following pages of this essay, I will explain how *bourgeois ideology reproduces these dominant/dominated relations* in the sphere of production (first section); in the area of politics (second section); and in the area of science (including medicine) (third section). (By ideology, I mean, with Gramsci, the ethical, juridical, political, esthetic, and philosophical ideas about social reality as well as the set of customs, practices and behaviors which consciously or unconsciously reflect that vision of reality.) Needless to say, dominance does not mean complete control.[16] The working class does not remain passive against that domination. *A continuous process of class struggle* takes place where the working class also wins significant victories and determines changes in the boundaries, means, and instruments of that dominance.[17] How this class struggle affects that dominance in the world of production, of politics, and of science is also covered in these three sections. In all three sections, *I have chosen medicine and medical knowledge as the primary points of reference.*

Work, market ideology, and the reproduction of power relations

How is class dominance being reproduced? By different means. For example, the division of labor within the working class, by dividing the labor force into different categories, erodes a sense of class solidarity. As a leading trade unionist of the health sector in Great Britain has noted, "By dividing workers into a multiplicity of sections and grades, management tries to lead them to believe that they have no common interests and that their interests are opposite."[18] Also, tending to reproduce those dominant/dominated relations are the conditions of work, highly hierarchical and authoritarian, which tend to create a habit of submission and subordination, further accentuated by a fear of unemployment or dismissal which tends to produce an obedient body of workers and citizens.

But besides these reasons, there are two others which explain the reproduction of these relations. One, very important ideologically, is that this type of work is presented, not as a result of specific power relations in society, but rather as a *logical, rational, and natural* outcome of the unavoidable and unchangeable industrialization and technologization of the work process. Thus it is the unchangeable industrialization and technology of work that causes the workers' pains rather than the social power relations which determine this specific type of oppressive industrialization and technology. Needless to say, the absence in the current historical period of models of alternative processes of production and work strengthens the ideology that ours is the only logical, rational, and natural way of organizing production. Furthermore the dominant ideology tries to impress on the worker that those relations are not only *natural* but also *fair*, particularly in the labor market, where those dominant/dominated exploitative relations are veiled and mystified and made to appear as a matter of free, unfettered, and equal exchange between the laborer who sells his labor and the capitalist who pays a wage for it. Needless to say, bourgeois ideology may even be willing to admit and accept that much work today is oppressive and does not offer the possibility for self-fulfillment to the worker. But this same ideology will quickly add that the worker is compensated with a fair wage that will allow him or her to obtain the key to the door to self-fulfillment in the house of consumption. The worker, denied the possibility for creativity and self-fulfillment in the world of production, is said to be given that possibility in the world of consumption. Although he has no control over the work process, he is being told that he has control over the product of that process where, not as a worker but as a consumer, he can, through the free expression of his wants in the market, allocate the resources in that society. Thus the sovereignty denied to the worker in the world of production appears as the sovereignty of the consumer in the world of consumption. In this scenario, the criteria and discussion of fairness is not over the control of the process of work but rather on the price to pay and compensate the worker for his work so that he may reach a sense of fulfillment, control, and pursuit of happiness in the world of consumption.

Suffice it to say, it is of paramount importance for the reproduction of the capitalist system that all struggles at the point of production be shifted to the area of consumption, *with the focus of the struggle being the cost of labor—personal and social wages—rather than the control of the process of production*. The acceptance of this shift in the struggle from the world of production to the world of consumption by the trade unions and their consequent focus on the price of labor has been a primary reason for the reproduction of capitalist relations. As Gramsci indicated, "trade unionism by organizing workers not as producers but as wage earners had accepted and submitted to the rationale of the capitalist system where workers are merely sellers of their labor power."[19] The shift from workers to wage earners is a key mechanism of reproduction of capitalist relations and responds to the intrinsic need of capitalism to separate the world of consumption from the world of production, focusing all areas of conflict on the former and not on the latter. Capital, in its position within the class struggle, clearly perceives the correctness of Marx's position as presented in the *Grundisse* that, "the important point to be emphasized here is that whether production and consumption are considered as activities of one or separate individuals, they appear as aspects of one process in which production forms the starting point and therefore the predominant factor."[20] A predominant factor whose control capital cannot allow to be questioned.

A consequence of that bourgeois ideological dominance and acceptance of the *unalterability* of the process of work (and shift of the struggle from the world of production to the area of consumption) has been the acceptance by the unions of damage created at the work-place as being unavoidable, and thus the *champ de bataille* has been on the compensation for that damage. Consequently, occupational medicine, a branch of forensic medicine in its beginnings, had, as its initial task, to define for management the nature and size of the damage which needed to be compensated. Occupational doctors, still called company doctors in many countries today, had as a primary function, to defend management interests and obfuscate or veil the actual damage created at the work-place. The struggle was, and still continues to be, between labor, which demanded a higher compensation, and capital (helped by occupational doctors), who wanted to minimize that compensation, denying for as long as they could that there was any relationship between work, disease, and death. Let me add here that not only occupational physicians directly employed by management, but many in academe, medical schools, and schools of public health, supported directly and indirectly by grants or funds from industry or industry-financed foundations, contributed to the veiling and mystifying of that relationship between work and disease.[21]

A further consequence of the separation between the worlds of production and of consumption was that the damage created at the work-place, when and if recognized, was perceived to be unrelated to the damage produced outside the work context. Thus, a dichotomy was established between the branches of medicine responsible for the definition and administration of disease at the work-place (occupational medicine) and at the non-work-place, in the world of consumption (medical care). That dichotomy, production/consumption, is still present today and is being reproduced in the structure of health services, with different administrations responsible for those two separated branches of medicine.

In summary, that shift of the struggle around the work-place from (a) control of work to compensation for damage; and (b) from the world of production to the world of consumption, has led to the establishment of occupational medicine as a separate branch of medicine historically controlled by management and with management in charge of defining damage and compensation. Needless to say, the priorities within the social system were higher for the medicine of consumption than for the medicine of production, particularly considering that a primary function for the latter—the one of policing the labor force—was achieved under capitalism by other more effective means than occupational medicine.

All these struggles on compensation were, for the most part, carried out under the supervision of the state institutions where capital was far more influential than labor, which leads me to discuss the second area where those dominant/dominated relations are being reproduced, in the realm of the political institutions.

Work, political ideology, and the reproduction of power relations

In the same way that it is of paramount importance for the reproduction of the dominant/dominated relations at work to shift all struggles around the control over the process of production to the world of consumption, it is equally important to shift those same struggles from the world of work to the world of representative politics. Indeed, just as the worker/subservient relationship is concealed at the economic level of our society under the ideology of consumer sovereignty, the worker/subservient situation is concealed at the political level with the dominated worker being presented as citizen/sovereign. According to bourgeois ideology, people decide through the market what they consume and through the political process what they want. A clear representative of this position is Eli Ginzberg, Professor in the Business School at Columbia University, who begins a book entitled *The Limits of Health Reform: The Search for Realism*, with the following sentence, "In our society, it is still the citizens who, through their voice in the market place and in the legislature, ultimately determine how their resources will be allocated."[22] According to this ideology, workers become citizens, and as such, have the same rights as the controllers of their work. The assembly line workers are supposed to have the same political and juridical weight, according to legislative discourse, as the Henry Fords of America. Both categories—bosses and workers—are abstracted into a new category, the citizens who decide, with equal weight, the major political decisions. In the political-juridical realm, they are both equal. But is it really true that they both have the same power to choose, decide, and develop different political alternatives? Many studies have been written showing that the Henry Fords of America, or of any other Western capitalist country, have far more power—an overwhelming power to shape the nature of what is discussed, voted upon and presented in the political debate—than the assembly line or other type of workers.[23]

In order to consider them with equal political power, Ginzberg and others with him, have had to consider workers as individual citizens, an abstract category which levels off everyone independent of his or her position in the world of production, where goods and services are being produced. But men and women under capitalism are not equal. That assumed equality in the realm of politics is continually shown as inequality in the realm of production. Under capitalism, the relations of production allocate men and women into different social classes, defined by their differential access to and possession of the means of production.[24] Agents within those classes have, indeed, different political and thus juridical power. The class which owns, controls, and possesses the means of work has a dominant hegemony in the political-juridical apparatuses of the state and in the ideological-cultural apparatus of society.[25] It goes without saying that the intellectual representatives of that class deny this, dismissing it as a simplification, tolerable for "ideologues" but not for reasonable people. They present it as a matter of fact that the political-juridical institutions are an outcome of the people's will, who, via the electoral process in representative democracy, periodically elect those on whom authority is being bestowed. Consequently, bourgeois dominance in the apparatus of representation is denied by bourgeois ideology in which bourgeois domination is veiled and mystified as representing the popular sovereignty and the *vox populi*. According to this ideology, the workers, regardless of how exploited in the economic arena they may be, are still supposed to be free and equal citizens who, by their will, have chosen, and continue to choose, a system which reproduces that system of exploitation. This is the most important ideological legitimation of the bourgeois rule, that is people want it and choose it.

It is worth stressing that in this scheme of things, democracy is not—as Lincoln said—government by the people—but one occasionally *approved* by the people. Democracy is thus defined differently from self-governance. In such a democracy, governments come and go at the approval of the people. In this respect, the government is assumed to represent *we, the people*, and what happens in our societies is what we, the citizens, want. As Etzione indicated in *The Washington Post*, "We, in the United States, have decided that we value production more than risk or damage at the work place."[26] And that *we* is supposed to mean, of course, the American people who have expressed their political will through their political institutions. We, the citizens, have chosen to maximize production rather than safety at work. It speaks of the overwhelming dominance the bourgeois position has in official and academic discourse, that those authors such as Ginzberg, Etzione, and many others can consider these expressions as merely factual and absent of ideological meaning. They would strongly deny, of course, that they are bourgeois ideologists who reproduce the scheme convenient and favorable to dominance of our lives by the bourgeoisie. It is easy to predict that the bourgeois theorists would dismiss as "rhetorical" the interpretation that it is not we, the American people, but the capitalist class which primarily—although not exclusively—dominates the state functions; and that it is not we, but the controllers of work, who decide on the nature of production and consumption in society. They would, indeed, dismiss that as Marxist "rhetoric." But they do not realize, or want to realize, that theirs is also a rhetoric and one which reproduces a pattern of class power relations where the minority and not the majority makes the major decisions. In summary, each ideological position has its own discourse dismissed as "rhetoric" by its adversary. The untenability and incredibility of bourgeois rhetoric which assumes that we, the American people, decide on major issues in society, is increasingly clear for all to see. The majority of American citizens who belong to the working class and lower middle class know reality far better than the bourgeois theorists. In many polls, they have expressed their belief that the two major parties are controlled by corporate America and that the government institutions work principally for the benefit of Big Business—that folksy term used to refer to the capitalist class.[27]

In summary, then, the dominant/dominated relations at the workplace are being reproduced by shifting struggles from the world of production to the world of representative politics where the bourgeoisie is the dominant force. It is of paramount importance for the bourgeois order that a clear separation be established between the *economic* class struggle confined within trade union battles (primarily concerned with the price of labor and compensation of work and damage), and the *political* struggles carried out primarily by the political parties in the realm of representative democracy. As many points in history, from the General Strike in Britain in 1926 to the May events of France in 1968, show quite clearly, the shift of the locus and focus of struggles from the place of work to the arena of representative politics has had a most important effect in diluting threats to the bourgeois order. But why this dilution—this weakening of that threat when the area of struggle shifts from the floor of the factory to the parliament? One reason is that representative democracy converts the process of participation *from active to passive*, delegating popular power to elected and/or selected representatives. These representatives, however well they may represent the interests of the working class and popular masses, have to conform to a set of rules and operate within a set of *state institutions where the bourgeoisie is, by definition, dominant*—a bourgeois dominance which gives its character to those institutions, including the institutions of representation and mediation.[28] Thus, it has always been in the interests of the bourgeoisie to demobilize the mass struggles occurring in the places of production by shifting those struggles to the parliament or its equivalent.

The previous paragraphs should not be understood as shying away from or slowing down the struggles which need to be carried out within the state and organs of representative democracy. *The class struggle carried out within the apparatuses of the state can lead to substantial victories for the working class.* The NHS in the UK, for example, was, no doubt, a remarkable achievement for the British working class. But it would be wrong to consider the NHS as a socialist apparatus within a bourgeois state.[29] I have shown elsewhere how the NHS is under hegemony of the bourgeoisie, a hegemony which appears in the ideology, composition, and distribution of medicine in the UK.[30] Similarly, the occupational health legislation which has appeared in the USA from the late 1960s and early 1970s has to be seen also as a great achievement for the US labor movement. But the fact that these achievements have occurred within a state that is under bourgeois dominance explains the limitations and the nature of that progressive legislation. The consequences of bourgeois dominance are many. One is that programs established by legislative mandates tend—*in the absence of continuous pressure from the working class*—to be manipulated by the components and strata of the bourgeoisie affected by that legislation. Lobbies of those groups are "always there, close to the corridors of power" to limit and change the progressive impact and nature of those programs. But, more importantly, those programs have to operate within parameters defined by the overall power relations in that society and which cannot be touched upon by those programs. For example, great stress is made by all governments that occupational health programs cannot interfere with the overall pattern of capital accumulation. Capital formation and the subsequent class power relations it sustains cannot be affected by that type of legislation. And when it is, enormous pressures are brought to bear on governments to assure that that situation be reversed.

Last but certainly not least, another consequence of bourgeois dominance in the apparatuses of the state, including those progressive programs, is that the implementation of those programs is carried out within the ideological framework convenient to the reproduction of the bourgeois order. For example, the prevalent approach of state regulatory agencies in occupational medicine is to protect the worker against an environmental agent, such as the toxic substance which can harm the worker. Consequently, a struggle takes place around the allowable exposure of the worker to that toxic substance.[31] That struggle *is a very important and needed one.* But it is still carried out within that ideological dichotomy of worker versus environment that assumes an independence and autonomy where the worker is on one side of the working scene and the environment is on the other. The dichotomy of patient or potential patient versus environment characterizes, as I will discuss later on, the conception of risk and disease in bourgeois science. In the same degree that bacteria was perceived to be the external cause of disease, the toxic substance is now perceived to be the cause of that disease. In either case, however, such a dichotomy is a faulty one. The social power relations which determine the environment of exposures also determine the nature of the work process and of the agents of that process, the workers. The social power relations which determine the working environment also determine how the worker fits within that environment, relates to that environment, and perceives himself or herself in relation to fellow workers and to the controllers and managers of that environment. In other words, by focusing only on a specific item of that environment (the toxic substance), and by not touching on the power relations which shape both the environment and the worker, the bourgeois order is reproduced.

Bourgeois dominance, ideology, and knowledge in medicine

I have discussed how bourgeois dominance appears in the world of production and in the political-juridical level of society, and how that dominance has many implications in medicine as well. In this section, I will focus on how that class dominance appears also in the production of knowledge in medicine. Many studies have been written showing how bourgeois dominance of our research institutions, including medical research institutions, has determined a set of priorities that, while presented as apolitical, are, in fact, clear political statements which reflect the class dominance of those institutions. Elsewhere, I have discussed how that overwhelming class dominance of our research institutions explains, for example, why most of cancer research in Western capitalist countries has focused on biological and individual behavior, but not on other factors such as carcinogens that exist in people's work-places, which could be threatening to the sections of the bourgeoisie that have a major influence in the funding institutions for cancer research.[32]

It would be erroneous, however, to believe that those cancer research priorities are merely a result of the influence of powerful interest groups in the top corridors of power in funding agencies. There is more to it than that. These groups belong to a class—the bourgeoisie—which has an ideology or vision of reality with an internal logic and consistency which, in turn, leads to the support of some positions, conclusions, and priorities, and to the exclusion of others. This bourgeois ideology is the dominant one under capitalism. That it is dominant, however, does not mean that that bourgeois ideology is the only ideology. In this regard, it has to be stressed that each social class has its own vision of reality and ideology. In other words, there is not, under capitalism, just a single ideology that is upheld by all classes, races, and sexes. I stress this, because on both sides of the ideological spectrum, there are ideological currents which postulate that there is in any society *just one ideology*—the dominant or ruling ideology—which has resulted from that society's choice, wills, and wants (as the bourgeois theorists believe), or from an overwhelming dominance, tantamount to control, the bourgeoisie has in that society.[33] Agreeing with Marx, I believe that classes have different ideologies which also appear in different forms of culture. "Upon the different forms of property, upon the social conditions of existence, rises an entire superstructure of distinct and peculiarly formed sentiments, illusions, modes of thought and views of life. The entire class creates and forms them through tradition and upbringing."[34] But one of them, the ideology of the dominant class, is the dominant ideology. As Marx and Engels indicated, "*the ideas of the ruling class* are in every epoch the ruling ideas, i.e., the class which is the ruling *material* force of society, is at the same time its ruling intellectual force."[35] But this "ruling" does not imply that the working-class ideology is either non-existent or absorbed in the bourgeois one. Nor does it imply that a clear-cut division exists between the two ideologies, with a well-delineated boundary between them. Class struggle is continuously taking place, with victories and defeats that influence both ideologies. For example, I have already indicated how bourgeois values appear in the working class. An example is when the working class accepts the belief that the nature of work is determined by industrialization. And vice versa, the rhetorical (although not actual) acceptance by the bourgeoisie of democracy as a part of dominant ideology was forced by the working class on the bourgeoisie, when the latter social class needed an alliance with the former in its struggle against the aristocracy, then hindering the rise to power of the bourgeoisie.[36] In other words, democracy was not a set of values and practices spontaneously created by the bourgeoisie, but, rather, an ideology forced on the bourgeois ideology by the working class. The bourgeoisie has always fought by all means the expansion of democracy, including the expansion of universal suffrage, freedom of association, freedom of the press, and many other freedoms the working class has had to win with great sacrifice and not without heroic struggle.

In summary, there is, under capitalism, a dominant ideology which appears in all institutions, including the institutions of science and medicine.

CLASS DOMINANCE IN SCIENTIFIC MEDICINE

How does the bourgeois vision of reality appear in science and medicine? In many ways. Let us outline some of them.

Dichotomy science versus ideology

An extremely important view within bourgeois ideology is that there is a clear-cut dichotomy between science and ideology. Actually, science was the creation of the nascent bourgeoisie and was contraposed to religion (seen as the ideological expression of aristocratic dominance) which it was considered to transcend and supersede. Science was supposed to be a new global vision of reality which would rationalize and legitimize the new bourgeois social system. Galileo, one of the founders of the scientific revolution—and who, incidentally, was working as an advisor to coal-owners on how to increase the rate of exploitation of coal-miners[37]—established the basis for the creation of new knowledge based on what was called objective observation and not on theology. And that dichotomy, objectivity versus subjectivity, science versus ideology, has lasted throughout the history of science. Science was thus perceived as a body of neutral and value free knowledge built in a painstaking and linear process in which each new scientific discovery was built upon a previous one. Science and technology became part of the forces of production and, as such, their development was considered to be intrinsically positive. According to bourgeois ideology, science and technology (and the process of industrialization they determine) were forces of progress, determining, almost in a fatalistic way, the nature and shape of society. Recent versions of those positions are the ones taken by Daniel Bell[38] and others, who indicate that power has shifted from the owners of the means of production to the managers of the process of that production and, more recently, to the producers—the scientists—of what is perceived as the most important ingredient of production, science and technology.

It is worth stressing here that the bourgeois interpretation of the value free character of science has also appeared within the labor movement, particularly since Stalin.[39] As Sweezy and Bettelheim,[40] as well as Lecourt,[41] have eloquently indicated, the forces of production, including science and technology, under Stalinism were perceived as neutral. Their development was perceived to be a primary condition for the achievement of a change in the relations of production at a later stage. That change in the relations of production was perceived as needed, because they were retarding and hindering the full development of the forces of production.[42] In this dichotomy—forces versus relations of production—the forces of production were primarily understood as the instruments of production, and their development was considered to be the primary motor of history. The point that has to be stressed here, and Lecourt ignores it, is that that instrumentalist understanding of forces of production already appeared in Lenin. It was Lenin who believed that the Western forces of production (including Taylorism) should be imported and put to proper and better use by the Soviet revolution. Lenin was an enthusiast of Taylorism. As Claudin-Urondo has indicated, Lenin conceived science and technology as neutral entities, rather like tools, the function of which can be changed depending on the use being made of them.[43] It should be pointed out that immediately after the October Revolution, a massive democratization in scientific institutions, such as in the medical ones, took place, with changes in the pattern of class control of medical schools and other scientific institutions, and with changes in the class origins of the medical profession and other scientists. These changes had quite an impact in redefining the nature of those institutions, and in redefining the process of creating scientific knowledge. That democratization had a very significant impact in redefining the nature of both scientific institutions and science itself. The priorities within medicine, for example, changed quite substantially, and initial changes in the understanding of medical knowledge started taking place. This process of democratization, however, was strongly reversed later on, in particular under the Stalin regime. Class control of scientific institutions and class origin of the scientists were reversed most dramatically under Stalin, giving strong political weight to the experts (scientists and technocrats), who became the controllers and administrators of scientific knowledge, closely supervised by the party apparatus. In this scheme of things, the development of the USSR meant primarily the fantastic growth of the forces of production (including science and technology) and the better redistribution of the product of that process. But it did not change the process of production and work, nor those forces of production. The nature of science and technology (and, as I have shown elsewhere, medicine) did not change under Stalinism.[44]

Forces of production are not neutral, however. They carry with them the social relations of production which determine them. In other words, factories or hospitals are not neutral institutions. They are bearers of power relations which determine how work in those institutions is done, by whom, and with what type of instruments. How the work process takes place in those and other institutions in society is determined by the power relations existent in that society. It is not the process and forces of production which determine the social division of labor (as the theorists of industrialism postulate), but, rather, it is the social division of labor, its concomitant power relations, and the ideological relations those power relations carry, which determine the forces of production including science and technology. The power relations in society appear also *within* scientific knowledge, and the bourgeois ideological dominance appears and is being reproduced in the production of knowledge itself. The dominant ideology reproduces itself in scientific knowledge. And this reproduction takes place, not only by selecting the subjects of inquiry, but also by choosing the method of inquiry, and the relations the researcher or inquirer has within the overall process of production. Needless to say, this position—that bourgeois ideology reproduces itself in science and thus science is value loaded and not value free—is continuously denied by scientists and other bourgeois theoreticians. Science appears as the epitome of objectivity. And all series of ideologies rush to be called sciences to gain legitimacy and credibility in bourgeois society. Not only natural sciences, but a long list of ideological positions appear with the sanction of sciences, for example business sciences, management sciences, social sciences, political sciences, economic sciences. Sciences become the newly accepted vision of reality that would enable the citizenry to cope with the world in a better fashion. All types of ideologies are thus made compulsory subjects in our scholarly institutions, from schools to academe, provided they are presented as sciences (i.e. "value free and neutral"). In this way, while the parents of a ten-year-old child would strongly object to having him/her subjected to compulsory classes of a certain religion or certain ideology, they would not object, or would not be given the right to object, if that subject were, or is, presented as a science, like for example economic science. Science becomes that magic word which allows the transformation of value loaded knowledge into a value free one. Thus, the dichotomy of

science/ideology constitutes a most powerful ideology for the reproduction of bourgeois relations.

The Division between Experts and Laymen

Once this dichotomy of science/ideology is established, then we have
to ask what is science? And the bourgeois response is that science is
an objective body of value free, classless and universal knowledge,
based on testable observations of reality. As such, the production
and reproduction of scientific knowledge takes place in scientific
institutions and is carried out by individuals who—in the overall
social division of labor—have been assigned the task of producing
and reproducing that knowledge, that is the scientists. *Science then
becomes what scientists—a small group of individuals in society
—do. And scientific medicine is what medical scientists and practitioners do.* Needless to say, all systematic knowledge produced
outside those institutions, and by individuals other than scientists, is
not considered science. According to this criterion, the documents
produced by research groups in occupational medicine that concluded in the 1930s, 1940s, 1950s, and even 1960s in the USA, that
there was not a relationship between black lung and coal-mining
were supposed to be "scientific documents and conclusions" and
thus trustworthy. On the other hand, the knowledge accumulated by
generations of coal-miners—knowledge which appeared in their
culture as folksongs, popular writings, etc.—that the work in coal-
mines was destroying coal-miners' lungs was dismissed as cultural,
folksy, ideological, and, in summary, untrustworthy. Thus, knowledge is legitimized only and exclusively when it comes from the
scientists. This dichotomy of science/ideology then appears oper-
ationally as the dichotomy of expert/non-expert in which the control
of the definition of science and expertise is delegated by the dominant
bourgeoisie to another class, the petit bourgeoisie or professionals
who carry on that task, namely, the production of knowledge under
the hegemony of bourgeois ideology.

This last point of delegation raises the question of the autonomy of
science. Can science become autonomous from the dominant ideology? My answer is yes and no.[45] Yes, *in the limited sense* that once
established it has an internal logic of its own, the logic of that

discipline or branch of science. No, *in the major sense* that scientific knowledge is continuously growing under the dominance of bourgeois ideology. In other words, scientific knowledge and scientific institutions are under bourgeois dominance, and that reality shapes the nature of that knowledge. For example, and as I will explain in the next section, bourgeois dominance in medicine established a vision and an understanding of disease in which that disease was seen as the lack of equilibrium within the different parts—organs and humors—of the body. This specific understanding of disease generated a medical knowledge which developed autonomously. But the division of labor within medicine—specialization—developed according to the bourgeois understanding of disease. Consequently, this internal logic of scientific medicine led to the creation of specialities which follow organistic bases: cardiologists, nephrologists, etc. Thus, medical knowledge developed according to its internal logic given by that bourgeois conception of disease. In other words, *bourgeois dominance always determines in the ultimate instance what occurs in the realm of scientific knowledge.*[46]

HOW BOURGEOIS IDEOLOGY APPEARS IN MEDICAL KNOWLEDGE

In the previous section, I indicated how the bourgeoisie's definition of science—knowledge produced by an elite, the scientists—appears and is reproduced in our society. In this section, I will discuss how that bourgeois ideological dominance over science appears in the production of knowledge. But, first, let us clarify what we mean by production of knowledge. It is the process whereby a perception of reality is transformed into a specific product, knowledge, a transformation which in science takes place by intellectuals whose primary instruments of work are the theories and methods of science. Scientific theories in each science consist of a group of concepts which belong to that specific branch of science (e.g. the law of gravity in physics). Scientific method is the way in which those concepts are used. Both theory and method allow that intellectual—the scientist —to transform this perception into knowledge.[47] Needless to say, this knowledge is being reproduced, not in abstract but in specific institutions, subjected to class hegemony, and by scientists whose very specific visions of reality are molded by the ideology of the dominant class (the bourgeoisie); their own social class (the petit bourgeoisie); their race; their sex; their discipline; their political position, among others. The scientist does not leave all those ideologies outside the walls of the scientific institutions. The scientists carry those visions of reality in the production of knowledge as well. That production is submerged into and is part and parcel of those ideologies, of which the most important one is the ideology of the dominant class or bourgeoisie.

How does this bourgeois dominant ideology appear in medicine? By the submersion of that medical knowledge into the positivist and mechanistic ideology which typifies science created under the hegemony of the bourgeoisie, and which I would call bourgeois science. Actually, positivism and mechanicism appeared as the main ideologies of the bourgeoisie in the nineteenth and twentieth centuries in Europe with the works of Hume, Comte, and, later on, Durkheim. According to positivism, science must focus on specifics to build up the general, looking at social phenomena as if those phenomena were natural, ruled by natural and thus harmonious rules. As Durkheim indicated, positivism reduces social phenomena to natural phenomena.[48] And within that interpretation, causality was supposed to be explained by association of immediately observable phenomena.

Positivism appears in medicine in its definition of disease as a biological phenomenon caused by one or several factors that are always associated and observed in the existence of that disease. For example, in one of the most widely used textbooks on epidemiology in the Western world, MacMahon describes epidemiology—the science of studying the distribution of health and disease—as an extension of demography, and he defines that distribution according to age, sex, race, geography, etc., giving major importance to those individual characteristics that are either biological or physical. Moreover, in explaining causality, MacMahon quotes Hume and indicates that that causality can only be seen but not explained, since we can only focus on the degree of associations between several subsequent events.[49]

A legitimate question at this point is to ask how that positivist conception of medicine came about. To answer that question, we have to go to the origins of scientific medicine as we understand it today. And these origins appeared primarily in the nineteenth and twentieth centuries during the same time that science appeared as a recognized and legitimized area of endeavor. Those were times of large social upheavals and unrest in Europe. Capitalism was being established, changing from a mercantile system to an industrial one. Those changes had an overwhelming importance in defining the nature of medicine as well as that of health and disease. One version advanced by the working class and by the revolutionary elements of the bourgeoisie, such as Virchow, saw disease as a result of the oppressive nature of existent power relations of society, and thus saw the intervention in smashing (the revolutionary) or modifying (the reformist) those power relations. Epitomized by the dictum that medicine is a social science and politics is medicine in a large scale (Virchow), its best representative was Engels whose work on the conditions of the working class in England was a dramatic document showing the political nature of the definition and distribution of disease. His solution was written, with Marx, in the *Communist Manifesto*, with his call for revolutionary change, where the first steps included the actual democratization of political, economical, and ideological spheres in society.

This version of medicine, however, did not prevail. The bourgeoisie, once it won its hegemony, supported another version of medicine that would not threaten the power relations in which it was dominant. The bourgeois social order was considered from then on as the natural order where its class rules would be veiled and presented as rules of nature. Accordingly, disease was not an outcome of specific power relations but rather a biological individual phenomenon where the cause of disease was the immediately observable factor, the bacteria. In this redefinition, clinical medicine became the branch of scientific medicine to study the biological-individual phenomena and social medicine became that other branch of medicine which would study the distribution of disease as the aggregate of individual phenomena. Both branches shared the vision of disease as an alteration, a pathological change in the human body (perceived as a machine), caused by an outside agent (unicausality) or several agents (multicausality). This mechanistic vision of health and disease is still the prevalent and dominant interpretation of medicine. Witness the definitions of health and disease in Dorland's *Medical Dictionary* in which health is defined as "a normal condition of body and mind, i.e., with all the parts functioning normally"; and disease is defined as "a definite morbid process having a characteristic strain of symptoms—it may affect the whole body or any of its parts, and its etiology, pathology, and prognosis may be known or unknown."[50] From this mechanistic understanding of health and disease, it follows that the division of labor (specialization) in medical knowledge and practice has evolved around component parts of that body machine, for example cardiology, neurology, etc.

A related point is that the mechanistic interpretation of medicine was built upon knowledge which had been generated previously (blood circulation by Harvey in 1628, microscope by Van Leeuwencheck in 1683, and others). But it would be erroneous to consider scientific medicine as a mere linear evolution starting with those previous discoveries. *These discoveries did not lead to or create scientific medicine.* Rather, it was the victory of the industrial bourgeoisie which established that positivist conception of science and of medicine. The fact that those previous discoveries were used and presented as the origins of scientific medicine was due to the change in the correlations of forces and subsequent victory of the bourgeoisie as the dominant class under industrial capitalism. In this respect, scientific medicine was not the linear growth of previous knowledge. Rather, and to use a Kuhnian term,[51] a shift of paradigm took place, establishing a new paradigm that carried a new, a positivist, vision of disease which added to what had already been built. This point has to be repeated, because it is part of the bourgeois understanding of scientific knowledge that this knowledge evolves linearly with "new" discoveries based on previous ones, as if these discoveries were the bricks on which the scientific building was constructed.[52] According to this understanding, science and technology grow and determine the nature of power relations in our societies; and the history of humanity becomes divided into stages determined by the discovery of new technologies which shape the nature of that historical stage, for example industrial revolution, nuclear age, etc. Science and technology thus appear as the "motor" of history. But, as Braverman,[53] among others, has shown, the so-called "technological breakthroughs" were not the ones which established new social orders—rather, the reverse was the case, that is a new correlation of forces used those *already known* technological breakthroughs which were, later on, presented as the actual cause of that change in the social order. But those breakthroughs or scientific and technological discoveries were used and put forward by new correlations of forces. The victory and subsequent hegemony of the bourgeoisie, for example, was the one which stimulated science, including scientific medicine. It was this political reality which determined the advancement of the positivist and mechanistic conception of medicine, health, and disease.

In other words, the power relations which existed under the bourgeois order were the ones which determined the form and nature of medicine. It led to a scientific inquiry where the aim of that inquiry was the discovery of the cause or microorganism, and the instrument of that inquiry was the microscope. By focusing on the microcausality of disease, however, science ignored the analysis of the macro-causality, the power relations in that society. Scientific inquiry in medicine developed into a search for the cause: bacteria, parasite, virus, or, later on, the toxic substance. Consequently, the strategy of intervention was the eradication of what was supposed to be the cause of disease. Needless to say, that interpretation of disease and of medical intervention was supposed to be presented and perceived only and exclusively as scientific and certainly not political. The dichotomy of science versus ideology was made quite clear and explicit. The alternative explanation, that the assumed "cause" was a mere intervening factor and the actual cause of disease resided in the power relations of that society, was dismissed as political, anti-scientific, and, in some circles, perceived also as needing "eradication." In a report of the Rockefeller Foundation on Health in Latin America, it was stressed that there was a great need "to eradicate disease in vast areas of rural South America, otherwise the virus of the tropics will soon attack the metropolis, a virus that can be biological or, even worse, *political*."[54] A clear call for scientific eradication of undesirable ideological explanations! The limitations of this strategy of eradication based on the unicausal interpretation of disease led to the later strategy of control instead of eradication. But, most importantly, that unicausal explanation was, and is, increasingly abandoned by the multicausal explanation of disease.

Disease was later on supposed to be determined by several causes, some of which included socio-economic causes. But these socio-economic variables were added to other causes as if they were independent variables, independent of each other. Social class thus appears as one more variable which may be indirectly associated with the direct and most important explanatory variables.

This limitation of the concept of causality to the immediately observable association between disease (e.g. cancer) and other specific events, such as smoking, occupation, and others is intrinsically limited since it leaves the key question unexplained, that is how those different events are related. As a report on cancer research published by the US government in 1978 indicates, "a major defect in most cancer research in the western world [and I would add other worlds as well] is that most cancer research has been based on looking for a single or multiple cause, ignoring the interrelations among those assumed causes."[55] What this report touches on is that the primary cause for our ignorance of the causality of cancer has been a limited understanding of causality, a limitation that comes from the positivist understanding of knowledge which I have indicated. By focusing on statistical association, positivists are touching on the appearance but not on the reality of the phenomena. In other words, what are presented as "causes" are not the actual causes.[56] The epistemological problem thus created cannot be solved either by indicating that those assumed causes are intermediate causes, part of a network of causalities whose linkage among the knots (intermediate variables) can be measured by statistical associations. The actual way of studying disease in any society is by analyzing its historical presence within the political, economic and ideological power relations in that specific social formation. And by this, I do not mean the analysis of the natural history of disease but rather the political, economic, and ideological determinants of that disease, determinants resulting from the overall power relations which are primarily based on the social relations of production. These power relations are the ones which determine the nature and definition of disease, medical knowledge, and medical practice. The understanding of the evolution and causality of black lung in the USA, for example, cannot come from an analysis of the natural history of black lung. It has to come from an understanding of the class power relations in the USA and how the class struggle shaped both the scientific definition, recognition, and knowledge of black lung in the USA and the actual production and distribution of that disease.

What I have said so far should not lead, however, to the opposite conclusion that the inquiry should be limited to the discovery of associations between specific power relations and disease. In other words, it is not enough to establish an association between specific forms of capital accumulation or, say, economic cycles and certain diseases. It is not enough to say that capitalism, for example, determines a certain disease profile. It is necessary to research how those power relations appear, how they are being reproduced, and how they determine the nature of death and disease in society. The different categories of analysis such as world of production, consumption, and legitimation need to be understood in detail and related to the specific mediating mechanisms that those sets of relations have with the apparent "causes" of disease. In other words, what is needed is not the incorporation of the social as mere additions to "environmental" variables which act on the individual; but, rather, what is needed is an understanding of how diseases mediate social relations, how the social power relations determine both the social and physical environment and the individual's experiences within that environment, including disease. Actually, there is an urgent need to break with that new dichotomy of individual/environment which is as false as the old dichotomy of mind/body.

Consequently, the terms of the discourse have to be changed. Instead of using the dichotomy, individual/environment, we should analyze how social power relations determine disease. Taking black lung as an example, we have to understand how the social power relations defined and determined the working and living environment of the coal-miners; how the workers struggled against them; and how, in that context, medical knowledge and medical practice came into being to obfuscate or clarify the nature of the damage inflicted on the coal-miners. Needless to say, in the process of this struggle, individuals and classes have different knowledge, perceptions, and ideologies regarding their own experiences, which leads me to the last point I want to stress, namely, the existence of bourgeois science and working-class science.

BOURGEOIS SCIENCE OR WORKING-CLASS SCIENCE: UTOPIA OR REALITY?

Knowledge is accumulated, stored, produced, and reproduced in the daily practice of people's lives. And the nature of that knowledge varies considerably, depending on the social class practices. Each social class has its own practice which appears in its own ideology and culture, that is a vision of reality; and vice versa, that ideology and culture also appear as class practices. Thus, there is a bourgeois ideology, culture, and knowledge given and reflected in bourgeois practice. And there is a working-class ideology, culture, and knowledge given and reflected in working-class practice. There is a bourgeois knowledge and a working-class knowledge. Both classes have different practices which generate different types of knowledge. The knowledge (legitimized under the name of science) produced by the bourgeoisie and reproduced in scientific institutions, which denied, for example, that there was any relationship between work and cancer, was bourgeois knowledge aimed at reproducing bourgeois power and practices. The knowledge (perceived in scientific discourse as "hot air," "folklore," or populist culture) produced by the working class and reproduced in its cultural forms, affirming that work was killing them, was, and is, working-class knowledge based on experience. From this, I conclude that there can be two types of sciences: a bourgeois science and a working-class science, each one based on different sets of knowledge and practice. To deny the above dichotomy is to assume a classless nature of knowledge, and thus a knowledge absent of practice. These two different and even conflicting visions of reality, the bourgeois and the working-class visions, are not separated by clear-cut boundaries without one influencing the other. Through the process of class struggle, the working class develops and imposes its own vision of reality on bourgeois science: witness current interest in researching the relationship between work and cancer. This new development is due to a large degree to working-class and the general population's outcry on the damage being created at the work-place. But, still, the hegemony which the bourgeoisie has in all scientific institutions explains the nature and bias of that response, a bias reflected both in the choice of areas to be researched and the means and ways of researching it. The scientist does his/her job in institutions *with* the bourgeoisie. In this respect, the scientist is, to use a Gramscian term, an organic intellectual of the bourgeoisie who explains the reality with and for the bourgeoisie. This relationship of scientist/bourgeoisie is overwhelmingly clear in the USA where most research is sponsored either by private foundations or by the state where capital's representatives are extremely powerful and influential.

The alternative, the socialist alternative, would be to carry on scientific inquiry *with* the working class, analyzing reality based on the extremely powerful knowledge given by the daily practice of the working class, and *under* the direction of the working class. In this area I see a great area of struggle: to democratize the institutions and to change the patterns of accountability of intellectual workers; and to work together with manual workers until eventually that dichotomy of intellectual/manual will be questioned and diluted. No doubt, this change of accountability requires a tough struggle: the one of democratizing our institutions. In this respect, it was a great victory for the Italian working class when it won the right to control occupational health services at the factory level and also when it won the right to undertake research at the factory with the researchers chosen by the workers. This is a clear example of how the struggle for democracy and for knowledge are one and the same.

Let me finish by saying that I am aware that many eyebrows will be raised when reading this section of my article. The nightmare of the Stalinist distinction between bourgeois science and proletarian science will undoubtedly be remembered. And the case of Lysenko will be immediately raised as a warning against those dichotomies. My answer to that legitimate concern is that the Stalinist version of proletarian science was not the science developed by the working class (which was not in power), but rather the version given by the Stalinist leadership of the party which identified proletarian science with dialectical materialism as defined and controlled by them. The fact that that agency of control was mislabeled proletarian science did not make that science proletarian, nor does it make the whole concept of class-bound knowledge meaningless. That is the mistake of Lecourt.[57] It throws the baby out with the bathwater. There is proletarian knowledge and mass knowledge which will fully appear and will flourish unhindered when there will be mass democratization in the process of the creation of knowledge with the deprofessionalization of science, changing not only the class composition of scientists, but, most importantly, the method and creation of knowledge, knowledge created not by the few—the scientists—but by the many—the working class and popular masses. As Gramsci once indicated, while all human beings are capable of being intellectuals, only a few are assigned that task. Similarly, while all human beings are capable of creating knowledge, only a few are given that task. Mass democratization would imply a redefinition and redirection of that process of the creation of knowledge. *This process would not mean, of course, the absence of a division of labor.* But it would mean a change in the power relations in the creation of knowledge with a dramatic expansion of the capability of creation of knowledge, with the working class and popular masses being the agents and not the objects of that knowledge.

In other words, science is a *social relation* and, as such, the key operational issue is not only *for* what class that knowledge is being produced (the uses of science) but, most importantly, *by* what class and its related question, *with* what class (the class character of science) that knowledge is being produced. The failure to understand the importance of these points explains the overabundance of references in which authors continue to search for the perfect socialist scientific method that would enable them to find the socialist truth. That search is not only a theoretical but a practical task as well. *And it requires a political and professional commitment to the working class.* In other words, it requires the scientist to break with the role to which he or she is assigned under bourgeois order and to ally himself/herself with the working class, not to lead that class but to assist it in its potential for human liberation and creation of knowledge. Let me try to be very specific and advance an example of the proposed relationship with which I have experience, namely, two different ways and approaches to find reality at the work-place.

One would be the bourgeois or positivist approach to find the nature of a specific health problem (e.g. toxic exposures) in a factory and a way of solving it. The "expert" (epidemiologist or any other social scientist) usually called by management would, first, establish a hypothesis *de travaille* based on his previous knowledge of that problem. Needless to say, it is part of the scientific ideology that he should be "objective" and unemotional about the issue under study.

His only aim is to find the truth. As such, he would have a "healthy skepticism" about any subjective statements or situations, relying more comfortably on facts, and very much in particular on quantifiable facts. Second, he would try to obtain as much information as possible from each individual worker in order to ascertain the facts. Through questionnaires, interviews, medical records, etc. he would try to obtain from each worker as much "objective" and quantifiable information as he could get and find relevant. He would also try to locate the collective dimensions of the problem by adding up the individual problems. Third, last but not least, he would try to test the hypothesis by statistical manipulation of quantifiable (objective) information. He would finally submit a report for management's implementation.

In that *modus operandi* of research, workers appear as passive subjects of research, remaining in the background and not in the forefront in the analysis and solution of the problem. This method of inquiry and data gathering is the most frequent tool used in social science research. The citizens, workers, blacks, women, etc. are studied individually, providing information through key instruments of inquiry, questionnaires or interviews. In all these approaches, three ideological positions—presented as scientific conditions—are reflected: (1) theory and fact are two separate entities, in which the former is supposed to be built upon the analysis of the latter; (2) the expert, the holder of proper methods of inquiry, is the active agent while the studied object, the worker or citizen, is a passive one, the mere provider of information; and (3) collective information is the aggregate of individual information. The process and findings of this scientific inquiry are, of course, presented as objective and value free (universal and classless).[58]

It is not surprising that in the late 1960s, when many anti-authoritarian movements appeared in the Western capitalist world, many of those analyzed passive objects—workers, blacks, women—rebelled against that science and against those scientists. At that time, alternative relations of production of knowledge were established. In many Italian and Spanish factories, for example, workers' committees and assemblies were established which rebelled against the type of science that was carried out in those factories. From then on, they did not allow any scientists to come inside the factory and ask them questions.[59] Instead, they developed another approach in which the process of inquiry was carried out under their direction. Consequently, a new production of knowledge took place in which, first, all information regarding the specific health problem was (and is) produced and discussed collectively with the correct understanding that a collective problematic is far more than the mere aggregate of individual problematics. Moreover, workers' assemblies have a collective memory and experience that puts their perception of reality in a collective and historical perspective. They know what is going on and what has been going on in that factory process and environment for a long time. And they have first-hand experience with what that problem has meant for their collective and individual health and well-being. Out of their collective discussion, they develop a hypothesis of what is happening in the factory regarding the specific health problem. In that process of generating and collecting data, subjective feelings, anxieties, and uneasiness are the propelling forces which guide all processes of gathering both objective and subjective data. Second, the workers call in scientists of their own choosing to assist them in the collection and analysis of whatever data the workers feel need study. In this process, the workers keep a healthy skepticism about the meaning of science, expertise, and objective information. They scrutinize all objective data, and through the process of mutual validation, they accept the value of the data depending on how it fits within their own perception of reality. It is worth stressing here that many years of exposure to occupational medicine has taught workers the lesson that science is not value free knowledge but very value loaded knowledge, reflecting the values of institutions where science is created and the values of scientists who create that science. Third, once agreed collectively on the nature of the problem, the workers demand to participate collectively in the solution of that problem.

This collective production of knowledge based on collective practice is an alternate form of production of knowledge to the individual production of knowledge, characteristic of the bourgeois model. Needless to say, it puts the scientist in a *different social relation with the subject of study*. It puts him/her in an assistant role with his/her information and knowledge being just a part of a broader and more important knowledge created by the practice of the working class.

Needless to say, the majority of scientists would oppose that diminution of their protagonism, since it would diminish their power. Many arguments are likely to be used against that change of power relations—ideological arguments presented as scientific arguments to defend specific class interests. The bourgeoisie and the majority of professionals will oppose that change by every means possible, including sabotage. To believe, as Julian Tudor Hart does,[60] that the majority of doctors are willing to join the working class in that change is dangerously to ignore history. From the October Revolution[61] to Allende's Unidad Popular[62] the medical profession has always fought by all means the process of change led by the working class. Still, that the majority of professionals would oppose change does not mean, of course, that a *minority within those professions cannot play a very important role in taking sides with the forces for change.* But in that process of changing class alliances, they will have to change, not only their roles (from leaders to assistants) but also their methods of work and the social and political context in which they use them. And it will be in that new realm of practice that new social relations and a new science will be created.

Conclusion: The struggle for democracy

I have shown in parts of this essay how bourgeois ideological dominance reproduces dominant/dominated relations in the spheres of production, politics, and science, including medicine. Also, I have shown how the working class rebels against this bourgeois domination in a continuous process of class struggle, which leaves its mark on all those spheres. The class struggle takes many different forms, but aims at changing and/or breaking with those patterns of domination which oppress the working class and popular masses. It follows, from what has been said that their liberation requires the breaking of that pattern of control where the few and not the many decide on the nature of our societies. And, by democratization, I do not mean the mere existence of a plurality of parties and existence of civil rights. I mean far more than that. I mean a profound change in the pattern of control of the spheres of production, consumption, representation, ideological discourse, and scientific endeavor where the many and not just the few control. Specifically, democracy cannot be seen as limited to the passive and indirect realm of representative politics. It has to be seen, as Marx and Engels said, as the massive, active, and direct involvement by the collectivity of workers and citizens in the governance of societal institutions where they work, reside, study, enjoy themselves, and are being taken care of. As Hal Draper has indicated, the greatest contribution of Marx and Engels to the history of humanity was to reveal the clear symbiosis between socialism and democracy. As he put it, "Marx's socialism (communism) as a political program may be most quickly defined, from the Marxist standpoint, as the complete democratization of society, not merely of political forms."[63] The struggle for democracy needs to combine struggles in the institutions of representative democracy, where power is delegated to full-time representatives—the "experts" in politics—with, most importantly, struggles to achieve forms of direct and mass democracy where power is retained by the users and workers in all societal institutions. For example, in order to change not only the priorities but also the nature of medical and scientific institutions, there is a need to win control of those institutions, not only indirectly through elected officials in the realm of representative democracy, but most importantly, through direct and assembly type of democracy where workers, employees, users, and communities control those institutions. In other words, a socialist transformation will not occur without a massive and direct participation by the majority of the population in that process of transformation. As Marx once said, voting in representative democracy gives an individual the right but not the power to change society. Eugene Debs put it in a more folksy manner, "voting for socialism is not socialism any more than a menu is a meal." This right—the right to decide—has to be accompanied by the power which comes from actual direct participation and control by the majority of the population of their institutions.

To sum up, there is a need for the working class, through its different instruments and forms of struggle, to aim at a massive democratization of our societies, understanding democracy, not only as an exercise in voting every so many years, but, most importantly, as a direct form of participation on a daily basis by the working class and popular masses in all economic, political, and social institutions (including the medical and scientific institutions).

It is only in this way that the democratization of our institutions will imply a massive transformation of the majority of our working populations from being passive subjects to active agents in the redefinition of those societies, a transformation that takes place as part and parcel of their becoming the agents and not the objects of history.

Notes

1 The Trilateral Task Force on the Governability of Democracies, *The Governability of Democracies*, New York: Trilateral Commission, May, 1975.

2 By "capitalism," I mean a mode of production in which a class, the capitalist class, extracts as much labor power from each worker as possible; labor power that is needed to (a) put the means of production (owned, controlled and possessed by the capitalist class) to work; and (b) produce value, including profit. Labor power is the human energy and competence that the worker provides to enable the means of production to work. It is usually referred to as work.

3 A most representative view of this position is H. Marcuse, See his *One Dimensional Man*, Boston, Mass.: Beacon Press, 1975.

4 J. Ehrenreich, *Introduction*, in J. Ehrenreich (ed.) *The Cultural Crisis of Modern Medicine*, New York: Monthly Review Press, 1979. After having been criticized for his deafening silence about the working-class struggles around health and its consequences on the redefinition of medicine, the author added "coal miners' struggle" as a mere perfunctory note to that introduction of his volume without actually referring to it. As with many other US radicals, Ehrenreich ignores the dramatic and continuous struggles around health-related issues that are being carried out by the US working class.

5 See D. Marshall, The Miners and the UMW: Crisis in the Reform Process, *Socialist Review*, no. 40/41 (1978): 65–115, for a detailed account of those struggles.

6 Quoted by G. Berlinguer, *Malaria Urbana*, Barcelona: Editorial Villalar, 1978, p. 428.

7 For an interesting account of the resurgence of class struggles around work, see C. Crough and A. Pizzorno (eds), *The Resurgence of Class Conflict in Western Europe since 1968*, vols 1 and 2, New York: Macmillan, 1978. Also, see F. Basaglia *et al.*, *La Salud de Los Trabajadores*, Mejico: Editorial Nueva Imagen, 1978.

8 Giorgio Assennato and Vicente Navarro, Workers' Participation and Control in Italy: The Case of Occupational Medicine, *International Journal of Health Services* 10 (2) (1980): 217–31.

9 Personal observation, Autumn, 1979.

10   Mentioned by G. Berlinguer, XVth International Congress on Sexuality, Rome, Italy, 1978.

11   The struggles against the nature of work under capitalism occur, not only because of the actual damage imposed on the worker at the work place, but also because of the harm created to the workers and their dependents in all spheres of their lives.

12   See H. Braverman, Labor and Monopoly Capital, *The Degradation of Work in the Twentieth Century*, New York: Monthly Review Press, 1974. Also, for an analysis of how the process of class struggle has shaped the form of bourgeois dominance in the process of work, see A. L. Friedman, *Industry and Labour, Class Struggle at Work and Monopoly Capitalism*, New York: Macmillan, 1977.

13   M. Bosquet, The Prison Factory, *New Left Review* 73 (1972): 23. Also, see R. Linhart, *L'établi*, Paris: Editions Minuit, 1978.

14   See The Working Class Goes to Hollywood, *Cineaste* 9 (1) (1978). Also Review of *Blue Collar*, *Cineaste* 10 (3) (1978).

15   Quoted from R. J. Doye, *Management Accounting*, 1970.

16   Class dominance is a process of continuous endeavor on the part of the capitalist class or bourgeoisie to maintain, regain, strengthen, and extend their interests in all economic, political, ideological, and cultural spheres of society over the ones of the dominated class or working class. In this article, dominance and hegemony are used interchangeably.

17   Class struggle is the conflict among classes that appears in all economic, political, ideological and cultural spheres of society and that takes place in the pursuit of their interests. Under capitalism, the main conflict is between the capitalist class and the working class.

18   M. Taylor, Creating a Health Workers' Democracy, in M. Barret Brown and K. Coates (eds), *Trade Union Register*, 3, London: Spokesman Books, 1973.

19   A. Gramsci, *Quaderni del carcere*, Rome: Einaudi, 1978, p. 30. It is worth stressing that the unions are, of course, very important instruments of struggle by the working class. But the focus of those struggles in economic issues transforms them into limited and limiting instruments for revolutionary change, i.e. change from one to another mode of production.

20   K. Marx, *Grundisse*, Harmondsworth: Penguin Books, 1973.

21   See D. Kotelchuck, Asbestos Research: Winning the Battle but Losing the War, Health PAC Bulletin, 61, 1974, pp. 1–32. Also S. Epstein, *The Politics of Cancer*, San Francisco: Sierra Club Books, 1978, pp. 86–7.

22   Eli Ginzberg, *The Limits of Health Reform: The Search for Realism*, New York: Basic Books, 1977, p. 3.

23   See E. Greenberg, *The American Political System. A Radical Approach*, Cambridge, Mass.: Winthrop Publishers, 1977.

24   By means of production, I mean not only the means that the workers use for their work but also the infrastructure of production and

distribution that enables the produced goods and services to be used and consumed.

25 For an expansion of this position, see Vicente Navarro, *Dictatorship and Democracy. Meanings and Implications for Class Struggle*, Johns Hopkins University (mimeograph), 1979.

26 A. Etzione, Risk at the Work Place, *Washington Post*, December 28, 1978.

27 Hart Poll, *Common Sense*, vol. 3, 1975. That lack of trust for American people in the US political institutions represents a major crisis of legitimacy of bourgeois ideology in today's USA.

28 Contrary to bourgeois ideology that postulates that the state apparatuses are neutral and can be used undistinctively by any class or group, I believe that the state's apparatuses reflect the power relations of the whole of society and thus are under the dominant influence of the capitalist class. That dominance explains its composition (the class position of the top echelons of the state personnel), its structure and its function (i.e. to reproduce the capitalist relations). For a further expansion of this position, see V. Navarro, Part III, State, Power, and Medicine, *Medicine under Capitalism*, Neale Watson, 1978.

29 Two examples of that perception are J. Tudor Hart, The Point Is to Change It, *Medicine in Society* 4 (4) (1979), and Karl Figlio, Sinister Medicine, *Radical Science Journal* 9 (1979): 47. Although different in their political position, they both share that vision of the NHS as a socialist island in the capitalist state. Hart reduces socialism to a juridical-political category, i.e. the nationalization of the health sector. Figlio reduces socialism to the absence of market relations and to the mechanism of societal allocations done by the state for the "benefit of society." In that vision, socialism is defined by the relations of exchange, not by the relations of production. Socialism, however, is a social formation in which the working class and its allies are the dominant class. Thus, socialist control is working-class control.

30 V. Navarro, *Class Struggle, the State, and Medicine*, New York: Neale Watson, 1978.

31 D. Kirschten, Risk Assessment. How Much is a Life Worth, *National Journal* no. 7 (1979): 252. Also, for an excellent account of struggles in the USA to protect the workers against the risky environment, see D. Berman, *Death on the Job*, New York: Monthly Review Press, 1978.

32 V. Navarro, The Crisis of the Western System of Medicine in Contemporary Capitalism, *International Journal of Health Services* 8 (2) (1978): 205.

33 Representatives of this position are H. Marcuse and most of the theorists at the Frankfurt School. A more recent example of this single society's ideology is D. Kellner, Ideology, Marxism, and Advanced Capitalism, *Socialist Review* no. 42: 37. It is worth mentioning that the first major works of Althusser (*Pour Marx* and *Lire le Capital*) also carried that position of a single society ideology. Since 1968, however,

Althusser has broken with that position. For an excellent and detailed critique of Althusser's position on this subject, see A. Sanchez Vasquez. *Cienca y Revolucion*, Mejico Alianza Editorial, 1978.

34 K. Marx, *The Eighteenth Brumaire of Louis Bonaparte*, in K. Marx, and F. Engels, *Selected Works*, London: Lawrence & Wishart, 1968, pp. 117–18.

35 K. Marx, and F. Engels, *The German Ideology*, London: Lawrence & Wishart, 1974, p. 64.

36 G. Therborn, *What Does the Ruling Class Do When It Rules*, New York: NLB, Schocken Books, 1978.

37 Quoted in Interview con Suclovico Geymont. El mito del progreso y de la neutralidad de la ciencia, *El Viejo Topo* no. 24 (1978): 13.

38 D. Bell, *The Post Industrial Society*, New York: Basic Books, 1977.

39 See J. Stalin, Dialectical and Historical Materialism. A good critique of the work appears in D. Lecourt, *Proletarian Science. The Case of Lysenko*, London: New Left Books, 1976, pp. 110–11.

40 P. M. Sweezy and C. Bettelheim, *On the Transition to Socialism*, New York: Monthly Review Press, 1971.

41 Lecourt, *op. cit.*

42 Social relations of production are the relations which exist in a given process of production between the owners of the means of production and the producers, a relation which depends on the type of ownership, possession, capacity for allocating and designing those means of production, and the use of the products of that process of production. Forces of production are the forces, instruments, labor, and knowledge which are organized to produce goods and services in any society. How the forces of production are organized, designed and related among themselves is determined by the social relations of production.

43 C. Claudin-Urondo, *Lenin and the Cultural Revolution*, Atlantic Highlands, NJ: Humanities Press, 1977.

44 V. Navarro, *Social Security and Medicine in the USSR. A Marxist Critique*, Lexington, Mass: Lexington Books, 1977.

45 I am not using the categories of Yes or No in an either/or type of relationship. Rather, I am using them in a dialectical way, that is that the autonomy of science takes place within a set of class relations that both influence science and are influenced by science.

46 The meaning of "ultimate instance" is that although conflicts may appear between scientific developments and capitalist relations, those capitalist relations tend to eventually impose themselves on those developments.

47 Marta Harnecker, *Los conceptos elementales del materialismo historico*, Siglo XXI, 1977, pp. 3–5.

48 E. Durkheim, *Las Reglas del Metodo Sociologico*, Buenos Aires: La Pleyade, 1974, p. 50.

49 B. McMahon, *Principles and Methods of Epidemiology* (in Spanish: *La Prensa Medica Mexicana*), Boston, Mass.: Little, Brown and Co. 1975,

p. 2. For an excellent critique of ideology within epidemiology, see J. Breilh, *Critica de la Interpretacion Ecologica Funcionalista de la Epidemiologia*, Universidad Autonoma de Mexico, 1977 (mimeograph).

50 F. J. Ingelfinger (ed.) *Dorland Medical Dictionary*, New York: Holt, Rinehart and Winston, 1982.

51 T. Kuhn, *The Structure of Scientific Revolutions*, Chicago: University of Chicago Press, 1962.

52 For a critique of the concept of linearity in scientific knowledge, see *ibid*. Also for an alive but not always rigorous discussion on this subject, see P. Feyerabend, *Science in a Free Society*, London: New Left Books, 1978.

53 Quoted in Braverman, *op. cit.*

54 Quoted in Breilh, *op. cit.*

55 K. Bridford, *et al.*, *Estimates of the Fraction of Cancer in the United States Related to Occupational Factors*, Prepared by the National Cancer Institute, National Institute of Environmental Health Sciences and National Institute for Occupational Safety and Health, September 15, 1978.

56 The fact that those assumed causes are only apparent but not the real ones does not make them irrelevant. They may allow for a description but not for an explanation of reality. The vast array of empirical phenomena immediately observable in social life can only be explained if one analyzes the social reality behind those appearances.

57 Lecourt, *op. cit.*

58 For a critique of similar positivist approaches used in social science see Scientific Method in Sociology, in H. J. Sherman and J. L. Wood, *Sociology. Traditional and Radical Perspectives*, New York: Harper & Row, 1979, pp. 275–324.

59 For an analysis of the political and economic forces that determined the Italian experience and for a more detailed account of the process outlined here, see E. Assennato and V. Navarro, Workers' Participation and Control in Italy. The Case of Occupational Medicine, *International Journal of Health Services* 10 (2) (1980).

60 Julian Tudor Hart, The Point, However, Is to Change It, *Medicine in Society* 4 (4) (1979): 13.

61 Navarro, *Social Security and Medicine in the USSR.*

62 See V. Navarro, What Does Chile Mean, *Health and Society*, Spring, 1974: 93.

63 Hal Draper, Marx on Democratic Forms of Government, *Socialist Register*, 1974: 101.

PART V
CLASS, POLITICAL POWER, AND SOCIAL CHANGE

"The history of all hitherto existing society is the history of class struggles."

(K. Marx and F. Engels, *Communist Manifesto* 1848)

Medical history as justification rather than explanation: A critique of Paul Starr's "The social transformation of American medicine"*

Starr's major position: Americans' beliefs as the motor of history

Very few books on medical history have received so much acclaim as Starr's *The Social Transformation of American Medicine*. Not only professional journals but also the lay press have defined this publication—which received the Pulitzer Prize in 1984—as an indispensable reference to understanding the evolution of the institutions of medicine in the USA, referred to as the institutions of "American medicine."[1] Starr, in no less than 154 pages, explains why American medicine has evolved the way that it has. His explanation covers many subjects, including why American medicine was born at the time that it was, why there is no national health insurance in this country, why there is a large involvement of corporate interests in the field of medicine, why we are witnessing a retrenchment of the expansion of government intervention in American medicine, and many other important questions.[2] We all should agree that the answers to these questions have enormous importance for the resolution of many health policy issues that the USA faces today. History is, after all, a much-needed element in the explanation of today's realities.

Before answering these questions, Starr criticizes and dismisses previous explanations which have emerged from different ideological

* Written in 1984.

poles. One, defined by him as the "most influential explanation of the structure of American medicine," traces the evolution of medicine to forces within medicine, and very much in particular to the scientific and technological advances that have acted as the primary motors in the evolution of medicine.[3] While Starr agrees that these forces are important, he maintains that they cannot by themselves explain the evolution of American medicine. Scientists need to be reminded of the need for humility, after all.

The other explanation of American medicine is the instrumentalist interpretation that Starr attributes to Marxist authors. According to him, Marxists view the development of American medicine as an "outcome of the objective interests of the capitalist class or the capitalist system."[4] According to this theoretical scenario, American medicine is what the capitalist class wants it to be. That class uses and shapes medicine in the way that best serves its class interests. Starr dismisses this interpretation, which he defines as *the* Marxist interpretation, as erroneous, that is it does not actually explain the evolution of American medicine. A proof that Marxists are wrong is that the capitalist class has attempted to rationalize medicine many times and has failed miserably. For example, Starr observes, "The [capitalist] foundations have made repeated efforts to rationalize medical care [and] it is impressive how little these efforts have succeeded."[5] Marxists and the Marxist historical method are thus plain wrong.

Starr's book represents in large degree an intent of offering an alternative explanation of American medicine to the ones recently presented by radicals and Marxist scholars. Thus, after dismissing these types of explanations of American medicine, he provides his own answer to the key question of why American medicine has evolved in the way that it has. His explanation is remarkably simple: *American medicine has evolved as it has because Americans have wanted it that way.* American beliefs, concerns and wants have been the determinants of what has taken place in America's medicine, from its birth to the present. Needless to say, an interaction exists between forces within medicine (such as the power of physicians and other interest groups) and forces outside of medicine (such as Americans' beliefs). But of these forces, Starr maintains, the ones that determine the parameters of what happens or does not happen within medicine are the forces outside of medicine, of which the most important ones are the values and beliefs of Americans, by which it must be assumed Starr means the values and beliefs of the majority of Americans.

For example, the birth of what became known as scientific medicine is presented as an outcome of the power of persuasion of the physicians who convinced a responsive American public of the value of their tools and skills. Starr writes that "professional medicine drew its authority in part from the changing beliefs people held about their own abilities and understanding."[6] At the time when medicine started, "there were profound changes in Americans' way of life and forms of consciousness that made them more dependent upon professional authority and more willing to accept it as legitimate."[7] Also,

"towards the end of the nineteenth century . . . Americans became more accustomed to relying on the specialized skills of strangers. . . . Bolstered by genuine advances in science and technology, the claims of the professions to competent authority became more plausible, even when they were not yet objectively true; for science worked even greater changes on the imagination than it worked on the processes of disease."[8]

Consequently, Americans were convinced and persuaded that they needed the medical profession to solve their health problems:

"Rather than trusting one's own skills and knowledge or those of competing sects or groups, Americans were persuaded to rely on the skills of the nascent medical profession; the less one could believe 'one's own eyes' . . . the more receptive one became to seeing the world through the eyes of those who claimed specialized, technical knowledge validated by a community of their peers."[9]

In summary, Starr sees the rise of the medical profession as an outcome of Americans' beliefs, a result of their being persuaded by the medical profession's claims of the value of their skills. Once again, he castigates Marxists for believing that the monopolization of medical practice by regular physicians was accompanied by the repression of competing systems of medicine. He indicates that "to see the rise of the [medical] profession as coercive is to underestimate how deeply its authority penetrated the beliefs of ordinary people and how firmly it had seized the imagination even of its rivals."[10]

Thus, Starr sees persuasion of the majority of Americans by a minority as the primary intellectual force behind social change in America. Several pages after having explained the birth of medicine as the result of the medical profession's powers of persuasion, Starr goes on to interpret the failure to establish a national health insurance, on the eve of World War I, as a result of the failure of social reformers to persuade Americans of the merits of that program. To the same degree that Americans have been "persuaded to adopt compulsory insurance against industrial accident, Americans could have been persuaded to adopt compulsory insurance against sickness."[11] Social reformers, however, failed to do so. In conclusion, America did not get national health insurance at that time because Americans did not want it.

American beliefs, wants, and values appear again as the primary explanation of the events that took place in American medicine after World War II. This period is presented by Starr as characterized by the efforts of different interest groups to win the hearts and minds of the American people. Thus, one of the most conflictive periods in the history of the USA—which included the nightmare of McCarthyism, with brutal repression against radical and Marxist forces in the USA—is presented by Starr (in a chapter meaningfully entitled the "Triumph of Accommodation") as merely an outcome of US labor's decision to change its image, style, and strategy. Labor decided to change from radical to moderate in order to accommodate its interests to business interests and, in doing so, avoid antagonizing the majority of Americans, now redefined as the middle-class public.[12] Indeed, Starr writes,

> "the unions' struggle for influence in welfare programs was one of their few political successes during the post war period. Strikes during and immediately after the war antagonized much of the middle class public, and in the backlash against the unions, employers took the opportunity to get back some of the control they had lost."[13]

According to Starr, moderation as a tactic for persuasion was successful. Americans, via Senator Taft and the Supreme Court, included the right to bargain health care benefits in the Taft–Hartley Act. In this way, "unions have won the right to a say in health care."[14]

American beliefs, values, and wants are also perceived to be responsible for what happened in American medicine in the 1960s, with the establishment of new programs such as Medicare and Medicaid that were not allowed to interfere with the power relationships in existence in the institutions of medicine. According to Starr, Americans

"in the early 60's wanted to change, but did not want *to be changed*. This was very much the case with regard to medical care. Americans wanted medicine to bring them change (new advances, more services), but they were not yet prepared for the sake of health to make changes in their way of life or their institutions."[15]

Needless to say, the final shape of those government programs also depended on the interplay of the different interest groups that operated within the institutions of medicine. Starr quickly adds, however, that American beliefs and public concern were the main forces responsible for the establishment and development of these programs.[16]

Rolling along with time and moving on to the next historical period, American beliefs appear once again as the main force behind changes in American medicine in the 1970s and 1980s. Thus, the expansion of government health interventions (expenditures and regulations) at the beginning and middle of the 1970s and their reduction in the early 1980s is explained as an outcome of a particular change in American beliefs. At the beginning of this period, Americans believed in government; at the end of the period, they did not. Starr summarizes this development as follows:

"Like American politics more generally, the politics of health care passed through three phases in the 1970's: (1) a period of agitation and reform in the first half of the decade when broader entitlements in social welfare and stricter regulation of industry gained ground in public opinion and law, (2) a prolonged stalemate, beginning around 1975 ... and (3) a growing reaction against liberalism and government, culminating in the election of

President Reagan in 1980 and the reversal of many earlier and regulatory programs."[17]

While at the beginning of the 1970s the majority of Americans favored government expansion, by 1980 "the majority of Americans clearly shared a general antipathy to government."[18] According to Starr, when the decade began, reformers were criticizing the inefficiency of the health care industry and they were able to persuade Americans of the need for government intervention; when the decade ended, the industry was criticizing the inefficiency of reform and was able to persuade Americans of the need to curtail government intervention.[19] As a result of this situation and effective persuasion, "the public seems to be expressing a desire to return to older and simpler ways."[20] Thus, Reagan's current drastic policies of cutting health expenditures for the elderly, poor, disabled, and children, and of weakening government interventions, are perceived as responding to a popular mandate; these policies are the ones that Americans want.

Starr's interpretation of current events is a logical extension of his historical interpretation of American medicine. In his history, the social transformation of medicine is reduced to the ideological transformation of Americans' beliefs and wants expressed either through the market or through their representative public institutions. In this theoretical scenario, the history of American medicine becomes the history of how interest groups have or have not been successful in persuading Americans of the merits of their proposals and ideas and how these groups have interacted among themselves to define the probable within the parameters of what Americans have already defined as possible. It is therefore not surprising that Starr concludes his explanations of the past and present of American medicine by predicting that the future of American medicine will depend primarily on what Americans want to happen. The last sentence of the book summarizes it well: The future of American medicine depends on "choices that Americans have still to make."[21] History is, after all, a way of reading our own future.

Starr's ideological and political assumptions

I have gone to great lengths to summarize Starr's explanation of American medicine and to quote extensively from his acclaimed work because his views are highly representative of the view towards the workings of health policy upheld by large sectors of academia, government, and the media of the USA. His view sustains the ideological position that whatever has happened and will happen in America and its institutions is very much the result of what Americans want and believe.

Starr's interpretation of America sees the past and present structure of power in the USA as reflecting the wishes of the majority of Americans. To see the structure of power in America as the outcome of what Americans want, however, is to beg the question of which Americans. If by Americans it is meant the majority of Americans, then two assumptions are being made. One is that the majority of Americans share a set of beliefs, values, and wants that provide an ideological cohesiveness to the totality of the unit called America. The other assumption is that that majority of Americans have had and continue to have the power to determine what happens both in the private sector of America (through the market forces) and in the public sector (through the representative public institutions). To these two assumptions Starr adds a third one: the dominant ideologies and positions become dominant through their powers of persuasion rather than through coercion and repression of alternative ideologies and positions.

These are the assumptions that sustain Starr's theoretical position and discourse. Needless to say, this interpretation of America is the one favored by those who benefit from current power relations in the USA. It rationalizes the power of the establishment. They are there, on the top, because people want them there. Moreover, theirs is the power of persuasion rather than the power of coercion and repression. This legitimization function, incidentally, is what explains the "popularity" of Starr's book in the establishment's media and academia. Indeed, that acclaim cannot be attributed to the book's explanatory value of our realities (which is limited) but rather to its propagandizing function within that reality (which is large).

An alternative explanation of our realities

An historical analysis of US realities in general and of American medicine in particular shows that none of Starr's assumptions is correct. The historical analysis of the USA shows that Americans have been and continue to be divided into classes, races, genders, and other power groupings, each with its own interests, set of beliefs and wants that are in continuous conflict and struggle. And these conflicts appear because, given the economic, social, and political structure of the USA, power is divided by class, race, and gender (among other power categories). Moreover, these power differentials are structural rather than conjunctural; they are built into the fabric of American society. In terms of classes, corporate America, for example, has far more power than working-class America. This power differential results from the dominant position that the capitalist class—corporate America—has over the means of production, consumption, and exchange. And the hegemony of that class in the ideological and cultural sphere is due to its overwhelming influence over the means of value formation and legitimation. Needless to say, dominance and hegemony do not mean absolute control. The working class can also win victories. Power competition does exist after all. However, this competition is consistently and unavoidably unequal, skewed, and biased in favor of the dominant class, race, and gender. As Miliband has indicated: "There is competition, and defeat for powerful capitalist interests as well as victories. After all, David did overcome Goliath. But the point of the story is that David was smaller than Goliath and that the odds were heavily against him."[22]

To believe that there is a dominant class, race, and gender does not mean that they alone determine the nature of what happens in the USA and its institutions, including the institutions of medicine. Indeed, to have a dominant class, race, and gender means that there are dominated classes, races, and a dominated gender who do not necessarily accept that domination in a passive way. Conflict and struggle continuously take place; and it is this struggle and conflict (rather than merely what one class wants) that determines changes in US society and in American medicine. Starr is unaware of this reality. He indulges in facile stereotyping of Marxist positions by defining them as instrumentalist, that is they see the evolution of government and medicine as the outcome of the wishes of the capitalist class, which in a rather omnipotent fashion, shapes government and medicine to optimize its own interests. Starr's acquaintance with

Marxist scholarship is characteristically limited. He would have benefited from a more rigorous reading and familiarity with that branch of scholarship before dismissing it so quickly. To reduce the large body of historical scholarship rooted in Marx to instrumentalism is abusive to an extreme.[23] Actually, it is neither Marx nor any of his followers, but rather President Woodrow Wilson, who said that "the masters of the government of the United States are the combined capitalists and manufacturers of the United States."[24] Although I find this instrumentalist vision of government too simplistic, I consider it equally simplistic to believe, as Starr does, that it is not the capitalist class but rather the will of the American people which defines government policies.[25]

American institutions, including the institutions of government and medicine, are the results of conflicts and struggles, of which class conflict is a key one. And by key I don't mean that class conflict is the only one. Other types of conflict do exist, of course, but class conflict is the one that explains the parameters within which all other conflicts unfold. And that conflict appears and has consequences in all societal institutions, including medicine. Moreover, that conflict emerges within a set of class (as well as race and gender) forms of dominant/dominated power relations which *are reproduced not only by persuasion (as Starr believes) but, more importantly, by coercion and repression.*

In summary, and as I have shown elsewhere, to understand the evolution of the USA and of American medicine, one has to understand the economic, social, and political structure of the USA and how it is reproduced through conflicts and tension among different groups and classes, conflicts that appear in all realms of society, including medicine.[26] What happens in medicine is not the outcome of the conflicts between the different interest groups that exist within medicine, interacting within the parameters defined by the majority of Americans whose beliefs and wants eventually define what does or does not occur in medicine. These interest groups are, in reality, segments of classes (and other power categories) which, when considered in a systemic and not just sectoral fashion, are found to possess a degree of cohesion far transcending their specific differences and tactical disagreements. Thus, to understand the behavior and dynamics of the visible, and equally important, non-visible actors in the medical sector, we have to understand their position within the overall economic and political scheme of the USA, that is their class and power position. Their position within a matrix of class, as well as sex, race, and other types of power relations, explains why certain possibilities are being reproduced and others are being inhibited and repressed.

Let me illustrate this point by referring to an example: the historical evolution of occupational and other branches of medicine.

Repression, besides persuasion: The establishment of dominance

From its inception, occupational medicine was very close to management. As indicated in 1919 by one of the founders of occupational medicine, Dr C. D. Relby, "industrial medicine is a specialty in the service of management."[27] Forty-two years later, the head of the Council for Occupational Medicine of the American Medical Association, Dr W. Shepard, put it equally well: "The physicians' place in industrial medicine . . . is auxiliary to the main purpose of the business: production and profit."[28] This closeness of industrial medicine to the corporate class explains the sharing of views and beliefs among most industrial health professionals and that class. Both social groups believe that:

(a) most work-related accidents are caused by workers' carelessness;

(b) there is a need for voluntary cooperation between management and labor and for voluntary enforcement of services and standards rather than compulsory government enforcement;

(c) occupational health and safety professionals are scientists and therefore neutral;

(d) most interventions need to be aimed at personal preventive devices; and

(e) workers need to change their behavior and life-styles.

These positions were and still are the dominant positions within industrial medicine and within the business establishment. However, this dominance was not, as Starr would have us believe, a result of the medical profession's persuasiveness. Rather, the rise of this position to dominance was based on a most brutal repression against alternate views of industrial medicine that saw most industrial accidents as caused by management's prioritization of productivity and profits over workers' lives, by faulty planning and equipment design, and by the use of toxic and hazardous materials that should either not be used or should be better controlled.[29] This alternate view remained a repressed minority view because it conflicted with the interests of the employers who did not want to accept responsibility for the workplace damage; nor were they willing to change working conditions if this implied a reduction of their rights, privileges, and benefits. The class of employers offered (a) rewards to those who favored the ideological position that reproduced their power and (b) sanctions and repression against those who offered alternate explanations and solutions that challenged their power. The overwhelming influence of the class of employers in the funding of scientific endeavors, in the employment of occupational physicians, and on the agencies of the state explains why "the individual workers' responsibility" thesis became the dominant one in industrial medicine. The dominance of this position was based not on the power of persuasion of the industrial physicians, but rather on the power of coercion and repression held by the dominant class those professions served, and whose ideology they accommodated.

The rewarding of those medical positions that reproduced the dominant ideology, and the repression and exclusion of those that conflicted with these positions, *appeared in all areas of medicine.* Dominant professional positions become dominant not because of the persuasiveness of their upholders but rather because of their articulation within the dominant/dominated power relations. Interpretations that conflict with the dominant relations are likely to be repressed while those that strengthen dominant explanations of reality are likely to be rewarded. Needless to say, and like the David–Goliath conflict, the dominated positions can occasionally win. Moreover, the dominant positions cannot just ignore the dominated ones. There is a continuous need to repress them and recycle those elements of the dominated positions that can be absorbed within the dominant ones. But here again, the point of the story is that most of the time one position becomes dominant or not depending on how it articulates itself with the overall power relations in society.

I suspect that some would argue that occupational medicine is not representative of what happened with medicine in general; that most of the institutions of medicine did not have such a close relationship with the corporate class as the occupational medical institutions did. While it is true that the other branches of medicine did not have as close a relationship with the corporate class, still, the differences involve degree rather than substance. The reality is that, from its birth, the dominant medical ideology and position became hegemonic because it complemented and reproduced the dominant class ideology. For example, American medicine as we know it—Flexnerian medicine—was established in Germany in the nineteenth century, with the active support of the German bourgeoisie whose dominant ideology was compatible and in accordance with what was later to be called scientific medicine. Positivism was the ideology of the nascent bourgeoisie, and positivism appeared in the interpretation of health and disease that became the dominant one within medicine.[30] Consequently, disease came to be perceived as a biological phenomenon caused by one or several factors which were always associated and observed in the existence of that disease.

We have to realize, however, that side by side with this interpretation was an alternate one that saw disease primarily as a result of the oppressive nature of the existent power relations of society at that time. The intervention was viewed as one modifying (Virchow) or smashing (Engels) those power relations. This version of medicine did not prevail. Rather, it was repressed by the dominant classes who, of course, felt threatened by those alternative explanations of disease and the operational proposals for its resolution. These classes preferred to support the biological and individual interpretation of disease which has since been reproduced in curative and preventive medicine. Thus, medical interventions were aimed at eliminating, eradicating and controlling the outside microagents—bacteria or viruses—that created the disease.

This interpretation of disease and of medicine was also the one that became dominant in the USA and it became dominant for the same reasons. The established centers of power favored that interpretation of disease and medicine, repressing other interpretations that represented a potential threat to their power and privileges. Starr dismisses this explanation of the birth of American medicine. He actually belittles the explanation that the dominance of Flexnerian medicine also meant the repression of its alternative. He denies, for example, that capitalist ideology favored medicine over public health. He writes,

"It is difficult to see why capitalism as a system, would have benefited by favoring medical care over public health. . . . To be sure, many companies resisted public health measures that would have increased their production costs or limited their markets. On the other hand, for equally self-interested reasons, life insurance companies actively stimulated public health measures."[31]

By posing the question the way he does, however, he already provides the answers. The question that needs to be asked, however, is not so much why the capitalist class favored curative medicine over public health, but rather, why the dominant ideology of disease was the same in both (medicine and public health), that is the positivist biological one that led to medical and public health interventions focusing for the most part on individual interventions that minimized conflict with the power relations within and outside medicine. A clear example of this is the approach that both public health spokespersons and the life insurance industry took towards prevention. C. E. A. Winslow (one of the founders of what became the established public health position) included in his report prepared for the Metropolitan Life Insurance Company (entitled *The Health of the Worker: Dangers to Health in the Factory and Shop and How to Avoid Them*), the following analysis of what was wrong at the workplace and what should be done:

"*Do you know* that a great many men and women die every year on account of the conditions under which they work? *Do you know* that if a man goes into certain trades it means he will have five, ten or fifteen years less of life than if he earned his living in some other way? It is true. The death rate among cutlery grinders in Sheffield, England, for instance, is just about twice as high as it is for other men of the same age. Half the men who die in this trade die of *industrial disease* (chiefly tuberculosis), due, largely, to breathing in sharp particles of dust.

"Most industrial diseases are preventable. The bad conditions that exist in factories and other industrial establishments are due mainly to ignorance. They keep the worker uncomfortable, they hinder his work, and they make him an easy prey to sicknesses that come along. They are likewise harmful to the employer's interests, for he is a constant loser from poor and careless work, spoiled stock, absences and the breaking in of green hands. *Dangerous conditions continue to exist because neither employer nor employee knows what is going on.* They do not understand that dust and fumes, bad air, poor lighting and dirt make sick men and a poor product. This book is written to help its readers to think of these things; for conditions will be made better as soon as people begin to think about them. You cannot keep your shop healthful unless your employer does his part. Neither can he unless you do yours."

(Emphasis in the original.)[32]

"Ignorance" was presented in that report as the primary source of the problem. Winslow's examination of the "dangerous trades," however, did not lead him to ask Metropolitan's subscribers to force their employers to clean up their factories. It is a rather hyperbolic statement to present, as Starr does, that call for information and health education as examples of "active" public health interventions. The reality is that the meaning of "active" is dramatically reduced within the parameters of non-conflictive solutions. A more updated version of this interpretation of public health is reflected in current Reagan health policies that focus on individual health education as the best measure of prevention, while weakening government regulations and other collective interventions.

It is important to understand that side by side with the dominant interpretation of public health focused on the individual, there has always been another interpretation which views public health as a set of interventions that frequently conflict with the dominant capitalist relations existent in the areas of work, consumption, environment, and residence. This latter interpretation has more often than not been repressed. The power of this alternative interpretation has primarily depended not on its power of persuasion but rather on its articulation with an alternate source of power, such as militant sectors of labor or other rebellious forces capable of facilitating its expression. Thus, the periods in which this alternate view has opened up new spaces have been those where militant sectors of the working class and related rebellious forces have been able to press for these types of interventions. As I will show later on, expansion of government public health interventions has occurred in periods when labor and allied rebellious forces have been in a relatively strong position.

An alternative explanation to legislation: Class interests as the determinant of change

Another clear example of Starr's erroneous interpretation of history appears in his rather idyllic explanations of how workers' compensation laws were passed in the USA. Not uncharacteristically, Starr explains this even as a result of the powers of persuasion of the social reformers who were able to convince Americans of the merits of their specific legislation. Reality, however, was quite different. The passage of these laws had little to do with social reformers' persuasive powers, nor with the will or wants of Americans. These laws were passed because of the interests of American corporations. The latter had enormous power and influence over the legislatures of several states that passed workers' compensation laws after 1910. At that time, there was widespread worker unrest centered around poor working conditions and the large number of workers injured at the work-place. Consequently, large sections of labor were demanding an end to management prerogatives, including management's right to control the work-place. Moreover, many workers were suing management for damages, with the courts ordering settlements that proved to be quite costly for management. Because of these pressures, the voice of the major corporations, the National Civic Federation, actively supported workers' compensation legislation. Among other consequences, that law eliminated the workers' right to sue for damages.[33] Today, we are witnessing a similar type of response to the current individual workers' litigation against Johns-Manville and other asbestos producers. Johns-Manville, one of the most offensive corporations to the health of American workers, is in the forefront of the campaign for government compensation laws for asbestos workers which will shift the social costs of the corporations' criminal behavior to the government. It requires an overgenerous reading of corporate America, indeed, to define Johns-Manville or the earlier National Civil Corporation as "social reformers" and their political muscle and influence over the state legislatures as "persuasion." The implementation of those laws had little to do with "social reforms" or with persuasion. It had to do with the threat that workers' demands posed to American corporations and the enormous political muscle they have over the state legislatures. It is Starr's unawareness of these social and political conflicts that makes his explanations so erroneous.

Similarly, to see—as Starr does—the victory of the corporativist view within labor, which occurred after World War II, as representing labor's desire to change its image in order not to antagonize the middle classes is to ignore the enormous conflicts that took place in the 1940s and 1950s, including a most brutal attack by the corporate class against the most militant section of the working class. McCarthyism represented a most brutal repression against any class threat to corporate class dominance. The Taft–Hartley Act, a result of that attack, was not a victory for labor, as Starr seems to believe, but rather a defeat. It forced labor to act as an interest group rather than as a class. Because of it, the USA is the only country in the Western developed world where labor cannot act as a class. For example, steel workers cannot strike in solidarity with a coal-miners' strike. By law, each section of labor has to act as an interest group. Consequently, this piece of legislation weakened labor most dramatically; each fraction of labor has to act on its own.[34] Thus, some sectors of labor did achieve great advances through private collective agreements; however, for the working class as a whole, their level of benefits remained far more limited than that of their counterparts in Western Europe where the working class could still operate as a class. As a consequence, the USA has an underdeveloped welfare state. In terms of health benefits the US population has less coverage (in their private and public programs) than the majority of the populations in developed countries.[35]

Starr's interpretation of recent events

The ideological and apologetic functions of Starr's interpretation comes through most clearly in his interpretation of the current Reagan policies as the outcome of a popular mandate. He uncritically reproduces prevalent conventional wisdom that Americans' opinion follows a pendular swing, oscillating from pro- to anti-government. It speaks of the overwhelming influence that corporate America has on the means of information of the USA (including academia) that this interpretation is so widespread and reproduced in spite of overwhelming evidence to the contrary. Indeed, as I have shown elsewhere, popular opinion is not as volatile as it is assumed to be. For the years that I have analyzed popular opinion polls, 1976–83, the evidence is overwhelming; by large margins, the majority of Americans are in favor of increased rather than decreased health and social expenditures, and strengthening rather than weakening government intervention to protect workers, consumers and the environment. Reagan's health policies do not follow a popular mandate.[36]

Starr is also empirically wrong when he explains Reagan's 1980 electoral victory as the "outcome of the wishes of the majority of Americans and a general antipathy to government." The opinion polls for 1980 show a similar result as previous and subsequent polls: the majority of Americans were in favor of the same government programs that Reagan soon started cutting. Moreover, the majority of Americans did not vote or voted for candidates other than Reagan. Starr should get his facts straight and be less willing to join the chorus, following the establishment's tune. Moreover, even among the minority of the electorate who did vote for Reagan, many indicated that they had voted *against* Carter because of his perceived inability to reduce unemployment rather than *for* Reagan.

To believe that Carter was defeated in 1980 because he was too progressive is to reproduce too uncritically what the establishment wants people to believe and to ignore all evidence to the contrary. Carter was elected in 1976 with a program that included an expansion of social consumption (including establishment of national health insurance) and a reduction of military expenditures—policies that he reversed in 1978, alienating large sectors of the population and, most importantly, large sectors of the grassroots element of the Democratic Party. This change of policies explains why his job rating in the opinion polls fell more precipitously from 1977 to mid-summer 1979 than had been the case for any other President since polling on the subject began in 1945.[37] In brief, there was not a popular mandate in 1980 for cutting social consumption and weakening government health regulations.

What we are witnessing in the 1980s is not the outcome of American wishes, if by Americans we mean the majority of Americans. What we are witnessing today is a most brutal class warfare, carried out by the most aggressive sector of corporate America against the advances that workers, women, blacks, and other minorities, and environmentalists achieved in the 1960s and middle 1970s. Even Lane Kirkland, the head of the AFL-CIO and a person not known for radicalism, has expressed alarm that big business in this country is involved "in an unprecedented class warfare."[38]

Why that response? Because of labor shortages in the 1960s, we witnessed the strengthening of labor's power, responsible in large degree for the passage of social and health federal legislation. In addition, other rebellious movements, such as civil rights, black liberation, women's and ecological movements, pressed for government intervention. Contrary to conventional wisdom, the 1960s and 1970s proved the effectiveness of government intervention in the social arena. By the second half of the 1970s, only 7–8 per cent of the American public remained beneath the poverty level compared with about 18 per cent in 1960. As Schwartz has shown, this reduction of poverty was accomplished primarily through government transfer programs.[39]

In the health care sector we witness a similar progress. In 1963, before the implementation of Medicare and Medicaid, fully one in five of those Americans living beneath the poverty level had never been examined by a physician. By 1970, the percentage of people living in poverty who had never been examined by a physician was reduced from 19 per cent in 1963 to 8 per cent. From 1965 to 1975, the overall infant mortality rate among the poor fell by 33 per cent. Gains among blacks were particularly evident. Between 1950 and 1965, before the great expansion in federal medical and nutritional programs, the infant mortality rate among blacks barely fell, from 44.5 per 1,000 births in 1950 to 40.3 in 1965. Following the expansion of the programs, the rate of black infant mortality declined quickly, from 40.3 in 1965 to 30.9 in 1970 and to 24.2 in 1975. There thus occurred an approximately five-fold increase in the speed of decline in the black infant mortality rate after 1965.

Other social groups also improved their living conditions because of that growth of social consumption. The growth of social expenditures was an outcome of the relative strength of labor and other social movements. At the same time, that growth also strengthened the working class *vis-à-vis* the corporate class. Working families received collective and social wages that made them less vulnerable to the cyclical fluctuations of employment and thus less receptive to employers' pressures.

Government interventions took place not only by expanding expenditures but also by regulating the protection of workers, consumers, and of the environment. Regarding the environment, the government interventions, in the Clean Air Act of 1970 and the Water Pollution Control Act in 1972, had a positive impact on improving water and air conditions in the USA. By 1979, the level of sulfur dioxide in the air had declined by about an additional 40 per cent from its level in 1970, and concentrations of suspended particulate matter in the air in 1979 had declined by an additional 17 per cent from their 1970 level. For carbon monoxide (from automobile exhaust), the decline was about 40 per cent for the same period.[40] Regarding water, the National Wildlife Federation indicates that fifty major bodies of water showed considerable improvement over the decade of the 1970s.[41]

Here again, the evidence is overwhelmingly clear that the growth of government health expenditures and of government regulations did improve the conditions of the majority of Americans and that the majority of Americans favor an expansion and strengthening of such interventions.[42] The fact that they were cut in 1978 and further cut in the 1980s was not because the majority of Americans had changed their minds. The evidence is clear that they have not. The government social and health expenditure cuts and the weakening of government occupational and environmental regulations were an outcome of a most brutal repression from the most aggressive sectors of the capitalist class in the USA who saw those advances by the working population as threats to their privileges and interests.[43] To see those policies as aimed at "getting government off people's backs" is to indulge in the realm of apologetics, not rigorous analysis. The Reagan administration is not anti-government. Actually, the percentage of public expenditures in the GNP has increased, not declined, under this administration. Primary characteristics of the Reagan administration have been (a) a dramatic transfer of federal funds from the social and health sectors to the military sectors, and (b) an enormous increase of the agencies of intervention and control, with a reduction of the trade union, civil, women's, and ecological rights for the majority of the population. These interventions respond to a specific vision of the government role in today's USA, well-defined by H. Salvatori, a key member of the Reagan transitional team. "In the history of man everyone has talked about expanding rights, having more and more freedom. But we have found that if you let people do what they want to do you have chaos . . . what we have to do is to re-structure society. Frankly, we need a *more authoritarian state*" (emphasis added).[44]

And this is what we are witnessing today. In brief, the issue is not to be pro or anti-government, but rather, whose government and for what purpose. The overwhelming influence that those corporate class interests have over the media and political and academic institutions explains that a "new conventional wisdom" has been developed in which those government policies that are creating enormous pain and suffering are presented as responding to the wishes of the majority of Americans.

It is Starr's willingness to reproduce these ideological images that explains his popularity in the corridors of power. Here again, his "success" is not due to his persuasiveness but rather to his articulation with the dominant/dominated power relations in the USA. This fact also explains his repression of alternative anti-establishment views, repression that appears in his book by stereotyping (to the point of ridiculing), or silencing all positions that clearly threaten the ideological reproduction of established class relations. This deafening silence is not without costs, however. For example, in his chapter on the increased involvement of corporations in American medicine, Starr characterizes the creation of a medical-industrial complex as an "entirely unexpected" consequence of government interventions in the 1960s.[45] A better reading of US realities would have led him to conclude that there was nothing "unexpected" in that development. Other authors (nowhere mentioned in this chapter) had predicted and explained this growth of corporate involvement in medicine. Contrary to what Starr claims, Arnold Relman, the editor of the *New*

England Journal of Medicine, was not the first author to introduce the concept of the medical-industrial complex. Kelman,[46] Salmon,[47] and myself,[48] among others, have explained how the rationale of the capitalist system and the enormous influence of corporate America in the organizations and agencies of the state determines that even when government, as a result of popular pressures, intervenes in the health and social spheres to improve the health and well-being of Americans, those interventions are limited and compromised by the need to respond to corporate interests as well, which in turn diminishes the initial intent of those interventions. All those authors predicted the establishment and enlargement of the industrial-medical complex (both in the financing and in the delivery of health services) long before Relman and Starr. The fact that Starr does not acknowledge or refer to these previous works is characteristic of the discrimination and repression against Marxist scholarship in US academia and media.[49] By ignoring these previous works, however, he remains stuck in the same trenches that other "interest group" analysts are. Indeed, this new version of the "corporatization of medicine," by ignoring the socio-economic-political context in which it takes place, and by seeing corporate America as one more interest group competing with others for government favors, is incapable of explaining why that corporatization takes place now. It is not surprising that Starr finds that corporatization as an unexpected event.[50] That event, however, is an expected and predictable one. As those authors have explained, this corporatization of medicine is the logical outcome of the dynamics of US capitalism within a process of class struggle in which the dominant capitalist class continues to have an overwhelming influence over the organs of the state. This overwhelming dominance explains that even when government responds to popular demands from working America, that response takes place within the parameters and conditions defined by the hegemonic elements within that capitalist or corporate class. The very limited power of the working class in the USA (a situation unparalleled among developed capitalist societies) explains not only the underdevelopment of the US welfare state but also the corporatization of its medicine.

In summary, government—as a branch of the state—is subjected to a matrix of influences of which some are structurally more dominant than others. Dominant influences are not tantamount to absolute control. And the majority of Americans can have a voice after all. But contrary to what Starr and the establishment would like us to believe, that voice is not the definitive one to explain our past, present, or future. Other voices exist that limit, restrain, and frequently even silence those majority voices. For example, the majority of Americans have wanted for many years that the government assure that all persons in need of health care should receive it, or that whomever needs a job should have it.[51] Neither popular wish has been fulfilled. The list of responsibilities that the majority of Americans feel their government should have and fails to have is enormous. Whether government undertakes those responsibilities or not does not depend only or even primarily on what the majority of Americans feel or want. It depends on the sets of influences and dominances that shape government interventions, of which corporate America is a major one. And the majority of Americans know it. They believe, for example, that the major political parties are in favor of big business and that American major corporations tend to dominate and determine the behavior of our public officials in Washington.[52] It would be wrong to see corporate America as the only influence, with absolute control over government. But in a matrix of influences, theirs is a very powerful one indeed. And its power appears not only in political but also in civil, social, and economic institutions. It is this overwhelming influence that compromises most significantly the meaning of democracy. Indeed, the public debate takes place within the parameters already defined by the dominant corporate class who influences, through its enormous varieties of communication agencies (academic, media, political institutions, etc.), the terms of the discourse and debate, through which that majority voice is supposed to appear. As an observer of the American scene has indicated, "the flaw in the pluralistic heaven is that the heavenly chorus sings with a very special accent. The system is askew, loaded, and unbalanced in favor of a fraction of a minority."[53]

Thus, when government has to respond due to strong popular pressure (as in the 1960s and 1970s) that response always takes place in a way that corporate class interests shape the nature of that response, continuing to be in a dominant position in those interventions. What alternatives are to be considered, and which ones are to be chosen depend not only on the majority of Americans but on many other forces as well, of which corporate class forces continue to be the dominant ones. Examples in the health sector are many. Witness the debate in the 1970s about the type of national health insurance that had to be debated in the US Congress. The power of financial capital, the commercial insurance companies, forced a change in the Kennedy–Griffith proposal—the only proposal which excluded the insurance companies—and brought about the Kennedy–Mills proposal which accepted their role.[54] As an editorial of the *New York Times* indicated, "to retain the insurance companies' role was based on recognition of that industry's power to kill any legislation it considers unacceptable. The Bill's sponsors thus had to choose between appeasing the insurance industry and obtaining no national health insurance at all."[55]

Even with those changes, the combined resistance of the dominant sectors of corporate America, side by side with the opposition of the major medical and hospital interest groups, defeated and silenced that alternative, in spite of the fact that the majority of Americans wished then, and continue to want now, a tax-based program that could assure comprehensive and universal health coverage for the whole population.[56]

Also, witness today's discussion of federal health policies; the discourse focuses on "consumer choice," "competitiveness," "rate of return," and the like, all heavily ideological terms that characterize the acceptable intellectual exchange. Anti-corporate positions are excluded by a most brutal force of repression from most of the communication agencies, including academia. Harvard University, Department of Sociology, incidentally, the academic institution in which Paul Starr teaches, has not even one token tenured Marxist professor. Repression, not persuasion, explains this reality. The presentation of alternative explanations of reality and alternate socialist solutions to the population are dramatically reduced in the institutions of ideological reproduction—like the media and academia—by unhindered repression.

In brief, the element of "choice" that Starr assumes when he writes that the past, present, and future is what the majority of Americans have and will choose, assumes that there is not a control

of information, no limitation of the agenda for change, no predeter-
mination of interest choices, and no limitations of instruments for
change, among others. Too many assumptions that the past and
present of America denies. Actually, what we are witnessing today is
the increased alienation of people towards, not the values that (at
least in theory) their government institutions should uphold (such as
responding to the health needs of all people), but rather, towards the
actual practice of those institutions that operate on their behalf.

The available evidence shows that the majority of Americans are
dissatisfied with the major political, social, and economic institutions of our country and the order of things that they sustain.[57] They
acquiesce to it because they do not see the possibility of change, or do
not see what alternatives exist or how the rules of the game can be
changed. Indeed, the future of American medicine within the corporate order will not be the one that the majority of Americans would
choose. Rather, it will be the outcome of enormous heartbreaking
struggle between the dominated and dominant classes, races, gender,
and other power categories, in which the corporate class will continue to have the major voice in defining the parameters, alternatives,
and discourses of that future. The future of the USA and its system
of medicine will depend on the resolution of that struggle.

Notes

1 It is an indicator of cultural imperialism that United States institutions
   are referred to as American institutions, disregarding the enormous
   varieties of peoples and nations that exist on the American continent,
   North and South of the Rio Grande, who are also part of America.
2 P. Starr, Preface, *The Social Transformation of American Medicine*,
   New York: Basic Books, 1983, p. ix.
3 *Ibid.*, p. 16.
4 *Ibid.*, p. 17.
5 *Ibid.*, p. 17.
6 *Ibid.*, p. 142.
7 *Ibid.*, p. 18.
8 *Ibid.*, p. 15.
9 *Ibid.*, p. 19.
10 *Ibid.*, p. 229.
11 *Ibid.*, p. 236.
12 *Ibid.*, p. 312.
13 *Ibid.*, p. 313.

14 *Ibid.*, p. 313.
15 *Ibid.*, p. 364.
16 *Ibid.*, p. 367.
17 *Ibid.*, p. 380.
18 *Ibid.*, p. 418.
19 *Ibid.*, p. 416.
20 *Ibid.*, p. 419.
21 *Ibid.*, p. 449.
22 R. Miliband, Marx and the State, in R. Miliband and J. Saville (eds), *The Socialist Register, 1965*, London: Merlin Press, 1966, p. 278.
23 For a critique of instrumentalism see V. Navarro, Marxism, Radicalism and Medicine, *International Journal of Health Services* 13 (2) (1983).
24 Quoted in E. K. Hunt and H. J. Sherman, *Economics: An Introduction to Traditional and Radical Views*, New York: Harper & Row, 1972.
25 Starr refers only once to class struggle as a possible explanation of change in medicine (p. 315). In a section in which he borrows very heavily indeed from J. Ploss' work (*A History of the Medical Care Program of the United Mine Workers of America's Welfare and Retirement Fund*. Masters Thesis, The Johns Hopkins School of Hygiene and Public Health, 1980) he explains the establishment of the United Mine Workers' health plan as an outcome of what he tactfully calls "a process of class conflict and accommodation." Otherwise, classes do not see the light of print in Starr's book. In its stead, the capitalist and the working classes are recycled as "interest groups" in which business and labor appear as two more interest groups, side by side with doctors, hospitals, drug industry and other groups, all competing for the hearts and minds of middle class Americans, assumedly the majority of Americans.
26 V. Navarro, *Medicine under Capitalism*. New York: Neale Watson, 1976.
27 Quoted in D. Berman, *Death on the Job*, New York: Monthly Review Press, 1983, p. 26.
28 *Ibid.*
29 V. Navarro, The Determinants of Occupational Health and Safety Policies in the U.S., Johns Hopkins University, 1984 (mimeograph).
30 V. Navarro, Work, Ideology and Science. The Case of Medicine, *The International Journal of Health Services* 10 (4) (1980).
31 Starr, *op. cit.*, p. 228.
32 C. E. A. Winslow, *The Health of the Worker: Dangers to Health in the Factory and Shop and How to Avoid Them*, New York: Metropolitan Life Insurance Co., 1913, p. 1.
33 Navarro, The Determinants of Occupational Health.
34 M. Davis, Labour in American Politics, *New Left Review* 123 (1980): 3–46; and M. Davis, The Legacy of the CIO, *New Left Review* 124 (1980): 43–84.

35 R. Maxwell, *Health and Wealth. An International Study of Health Care Spending*, Lexington, Mass: Lexington Books, 1981. Also see V. Navarro, An International Perspective on Health Care: Learning from Other Nations, Document prepared for the Select Committee on Aging of the US House of Representatives, May 1, 1984.

36 V. Navarro, Where Is the Popular Mandate?, *The New England Journal of Medicine*, December 9, 1982; see expanded version which appears in the *International Journal of Health Services* 13 (1) (1983): 169–74.

37 J. Faux, Lesson for Democrats: Don't Be Conservative, *New York Times*, Friday, January 6, 1984, p. A23. Also see Countdown to Election: Presidential Popularity, *National Journal* 11, October 20, 1979, p. 1729.

38 A. H. Raskin, Lane Kirkland, A New Style for Labor, *New York Times Magazine*, October 28, 1979, p. 91.

39 J. E. Schwartz, *America's Hidden Success: A Reassessment of Twenty Years of Public Policy*, New York: W. W. Norton, 1983.

40 *Ibid.*, pp. 64, 65.

41 *Ibid.*, p. 67.

42 *Ibid.*, and Navarro, Where is the Popular Mandate?

43 V. Navarro, The Crisis of the Capitalist Order and Its Implications in the Welfare State, *International Journal of Health Services* 12 (2) (1982): 169–90.

44 H. Salvatori, quoted in Reagan Policy in Crisis, *NACLA (North American Congress in Latin American) Report*, 15 (4) (1981): 10.

45 Starr, *op. cit.*, p. 428.

46 S. Kelman, Toward the Political Economy of Medical Care, *Inquiry* 8 (1971): 30–38.

47 J. W. Salmon, The Health Maintenance Organizational Strategy: A Corporate Takover of Health Services Delivery, *International Journal of Health Services* 5 (4) (1975): 609–23; J. W. Salmon, Monopoly Capital and the Reorganization of the Health Sector, *Review of Radical Political Economy* 9 (Spring, 1977): 125–33; J. W. Salmon, Corporate Attempts to Reorganize the American Health Care System, doctoral thesis, Cornell University, 1978.

48 Navarro, *Medicine under Capitalism*, ch. 4.

49 It is interesting to note that the *New York Times, Review of Books Section*, in an otherwise extremely favorable review of Starr's book, deleted the parts of the review in which the author of the review, Jack Geiger, criticized the book for its discrimination and abuse of Marxists. That part of the review was never published. (Letter from J. Geiger, author of the review. Personal communication.) For a valuable discussion of repression against Marxist positions in US academia see B. Ollman's Academic Freedom in America, *Monthly Review*, March, 1984, p. 24.

50 Starr finds this corporatization of medicine to be, besides "unex-

pected," a worrisome development. This latter position partially explains the favorable review of the book among liberals and even among some radical reviewers.

51 Cited in I. Katznelson and M. Kesselman, *The Politics of Power*, New York: Harcourt Brace Jovanovich, 1975, p. 28. Also K. M. Smith and W. Spinard, The Popular Political Mood, *Social Policy*, March–April, 1981, p. 38; and Navarro, Where is the Popular Mandate?

52 Compete Hart Polls Results, published in *Common Sense*, September 1, 1975, pp. 16–17. Also, quoted in M. Bender, Will the Bicentennial See the Death of Free Enterprise?, *New York Times*, January 4, 1976, p. 27.

53 E. E. Schattschneider, *The Semi-Sovereign People: A Realistic View of Democracy in America*, New York: Holt, Rinehart & Winston, 1960, p. 31.

54 Navarro, *Medicine under Capitalism*, ch. 3.

55 Health Plan Progress, Editorial, *New York Times*, April 7, 1974, p. E16.

56 During the 1970s and 1980s the majority or a plurality of Americans (depending on the year) have been in favor of establishing a tax-based universal and comprehensive health program. See Navarro, Where Is the Popular Mandate?, and *New York Times*, March 29, 1982, p. D11.

57 By 1982, popular confidence in the leaders of ten leading institutions had reached the lowest level ever recorded in any survey, averaging 21 per cent in the Harris Poll. S. M. Lipset and W. Schneider, *The Confidence Gap: Business, Labor and Government in the Public Mind*, Glencoe: Free Press, 1983, p. 411.

A critique of the ideological and political positions of the Willy Brandt Report and the WHO Alma Ata Declaration*

Background of the Alma Ata Declaration: world health during the 1960s and 1970s

Discussion of any social event has to take place within the historical and social context explaining that event. Thus, we cannot understand the 1978 WHO Alma Ata Declaration[1] without understanding the context and social forces that determined it. The stated aim of the Declaration, "health for all people by the year 2000," clearly establishes the intent of its intervention. A brief analysis of the current health situation of the world population shows the enormous magnitude of the proposed task. The year that the Declaration document was published (1978), the following situation existed:

1. Over 800 million people in the world lived in absolute poverty, with one-third of all deaths occurring in children under five.[2] Then and now, in the less developed countries (LDCs) approximately 11 million children under five years of age die every year of hunger, malnutrition, and infectious diseases.[3] To put the number of preventable deaths another way, the equivalent of 20 nuclear bombs explode every year in the world of underdevelopment without making a sound.

2. Approximately 80% of the population in the less developed

* Written in 1984.

capitalist countries did not have access to personal health services,[4] and the situation has since worsened for many of these and other types of services, such as environmental health services. For example, the percentage of the population covered by sanitation services in LDCs declined from 33 per cent in 1975 (three years before the Declaration's appearance) to 25 per cent in 1980.[5]

This already alarming situation has rapidly deteriorated during the current worldwide crisis, worsening some trends existent during the 1960s and 1970s. Individual and collective consumption in large numbers of capitalist underdeveloped countries, for example, declined most substantially during these decades.

The consequences of these developments for the health of the underdeveloped world's populations have not yet been studied in detail. Some studies, however, do exist. One that merits distinction is Wood's study[6] on infant mortality in São Paulo, Brazil, a study that is specifically meaningful because it analyzes the evolution of that infant mortality during the period of the so-called "Brazilian economic miracle." The period following the 1964 military coup that deposed the constitutionally elected Goulard government was characterized by a large increase in economic growth, dubbed by the World Bank, the IMF and the main academic departments of international health as the "economic miracle." The large growth of GNP per capita that took place in the late 1960s and early 1970s was put forth as the best proof of that "miracle." But what enthusiasts of the miracle did not realize or consider was that GNP per capita is not an indicator of *individual* consumption or wealth. Rather, the GNP is an indicator of the aggregate amount of goods and services provided by the economy in a specific period of time. The GNP per capita is obtained by dividing the GNP by the total population of the country, assuming that everyone gets the same amount of goods and services—an assumption that is obviously incorrect. It is assumed that producing a larger pie means that everyone gets more of the pie. Again, this assumption is incorrect. The GNP can increase in a society and the majority of the population still consumes less. Wood shows that this is precisely what happened in São Paulo, Brazil, during the so-called "miracle." As with many other assumed divine interventions, that "miracle" was based on an overwhelming rate of exploitation of the working class which determined a most substantial decline of the standard of living of the majority of the population. This exploitation took place through the following three processes:

1. An increase in the intensity of labor, lowering individual wages and lengthening the hours worked. Workers had to work longer periods of time to buy the same amount of food than before the coup. In 1975, a worker and his family needed to work 154 hours, 18 minutes for the same amount of food (6 kg of meat, 7.5 l of milk, 4.5 kg of beans, 3 kg of rice, and others for a family of four for one month) that it took only 87 hours, 20 minutes of work to buy ten years earlier. Moreover, in a situation of widespread unemployment, work—even for these low wages—was not easily available. Thus, per capita meat consumption declined and consumption of less nutritive foodstuffs increased.

2. A decline in collective consumption (i.e. state benefits and services used by individuals). The percentage of state health expenditures declined from 4.6 per cent of total state expenditures in 1969 to 2.4 per cent in 1977.[7]

3. A redistribution of income away from the working class and peasantry and towards the bourgeoisie. Analysis of income distribution between 1960 and 1970 indicates that the high annual growth rates were associated with an increase in the concentration of income. As Wood points out,[6] "Although estimates of the magnitude of the change vary according to method and data, a number of studies conclude that the Gini coefficient for Brazil, already among the highest in Latin America in the 1950's, rose substantially during this period of economic expansion."

These three developments were the outcome of political interventions that outlawed free unions and strikes and repressed most brutally the working class and peasantry. Consequently, while the GNP grew enormously (the "miracle"), the standard of living for the majority of the population declined markedly, determining an increase in infant mortality. A similar situation has occurred and is occurring in many other developing capitalist countries, although those declines in the majority's standard of living are not always reflected in an increase in the infant mortality rate.[8]

These figures encapsulate a reality that is clear for all to see: the situation for large sectors of today's world population is getting worse rather than better.

The development establishment's response

In the face of this reality, let us ask what the development establishment—that body of internationally minded individuals who are active in major Western aid agencies or who are their champions within Western political circles—has proposed.[9] In the 1960s and early 1970s, a great emphasis was placed on population control. Population growth was considered to be either the cause or a major contributing cause of world poverty. The two sides of the coin of poverty were too many people on the one hand and too few resources on the other. The theoretical framework sustaining this position was remarkably simple. Looking at the GNP rate per capita, it seemed obvious that the fewer the "capitas," the more GNP for the existing ones. The poor countries were assumed to be poor because they did not have resources or, at least, not enough resources. Thus, the answer was to control the size of their populations.

The "oil and other raw materials crisis" of the developed countries (DCs) in the early 1970s showed, however, that if those LDCs were poor, it was not because they lacked resources. Actually, a great deal of the key materials used in the rich countries came from the poor ones. Thus, it could no longer be said that poor countries were poor because they did not have resources. They did have them, and in large quantities. But the resources were consumed by the rich and not by the poor countries.

The new position that the development establishment took (not necessarily in substitution for but usually complementing the "population control" position) was that although the poor countries have material resources, they do not have the intellectual resources (i.e. the know-how or technology) to exploit them. Technological transfer from the developed to the less developed countries became the name of the game. Scientific and technological assistance became important instruments of intervention to resolve world poverty. Variants of this position soon appeared. One, represented by Schumacher,[10] among others, included a concern about the type of technological transfer. "Appropriate technology" was a term frequently used to voice the claim that not all technological transfer was positive; only the appropriate form was helpful. The meaning of "appropriate," however, varied quite considerably. For some, appropriate meant small (of the "small is beautiful" variety). For others, it meant "labor intensive." And so on.

Still another variant was the anti-technology position represented by Illich.[11] (This position appeared side by side with the anti-institutional positions, for example anti-medicine and anti-psychiatry, voiced in the DCs.) Its proponents opposed technological transfer, since they perceived such transfer as a process whereby a dependency on that technology would be created, thereby hindering the possibility for individual and collective development. The alternative offered was the development of autonomous spaces outside formal institutions, placing great emphasis on self-care and self-reliance—terms that were used almost interchangeably. Self-reliance was supposed to be for the community what self-care was for the individual.

All these ideological and political positions—population control, technological transfer, self-care and self-reliance—were elaborated by the development establishment not independently of but, rather, in response to, events occurring in the underdeveloped countries during that period. It was during those years that there appeared within the political and intellectual centers of the underdeveloped capitalist countries an increase awareness that their poverty was an outcome not of too many people, nor of the use of the right (or wrong) type of technology, but, rather, of a pattern of worldwide relations in which the few control quite a lot and the many control very little. The problem was perceived in those centers to be structural, not conjunctural. It required changes, not in the variables and factors of the developmental equation, but in the equation itself. It required and demanded a New Economic Order with a redistribution of worldwide resources. Moreover, an increased number of LDCs were breaking with that old order through confrontation and revolutionary transformation.

The development establishment's response to this new situation was to agree that some changes needed to be made in the worldwide distribution of resources, but to insist that change should be based on cooperation rather than confrontation. This cooperation would be triggered by moral calls to the worldwide community, appealing to their humanitarianism and sense of social justice, side by side with calls for the capitalist DCs to be better aware of their self-interest. Indeed, it is assumed in this new position that it is in the DCs' interests that poverty in the LDCs be eradicated. Thus, it is proposed that DCs share some of their riches with the LDCs ones. Otherwise, the world order will collapse or explode. Moreover, less poverty in LDCs will mean more capacity to consume and thus more markets for the products of the DCs.

A typical example of those positions appears in the Willy Brandt Commission Report (1980),[12] defined by Elson[13] as the brainchild of MacNamara, the President of the World Bank, and prepared by representatives of the development establishments of developed (referred to in the Commission as "Northern") and underdeveloped (referred to as "Southern") countries.[14] Characteristic of that report are the following assumptions:

1. The world is divided, not into capitalist and socialist systems and subsystems, but, rather, into the North (the "haves") and the South (the "have-nots"). The USSR and the USA are primarily defined as northern countries, while Cuba and El Salvador are southern countries. The report avoids using terms such as capitalism, socialism, imperialism, or class struggle—all dismissed, one assumes, as too "rhetorical" and "ideological." These terms are replaced by supposedly non-ideological and unrhetorical ones such as "global solidarity," "mutual interests," and the like.

2. There is not an intrinsic conflict based on capitalist and imperialist exploitation within the capitalist world order. Instead, the report is intended to provide a framework within which future conciliation and dialogue can take place.

3. Change has to occur within an unchangeable set of national and international power relations. The Willy Brandt Report refers to the development goals of the LDCs, encouraging higher growth and greater productivity, without "wishing to *suggest that changes in domestic policy must be a prior condition* for reforms in the global system"[15] (emphasis added).

4. At the international level, change is supposed to take place as a result of awareness among developed countries that it is in their own

interest to eradicate poverty in the underdeveloped ones. In a remarkable twist, the intelligent realization of one's own interest is seen as the basis for everyone's interests. "Mutual interests [are] rooted in the hard-headed self-interests of all countries and people."[16] Thus, *the task of the Commission is to make both "haves" and "have-nots" aware of the mutuality of their interests.* Once these mutual interests are recognized, "then both emotional and practical reasons will guide the powerful as well as the powerless in the direction of joint economic activity and reform."[17] Within this scenario, equity, social justice, and humanitarianism appear as abstract, moral categories; their meaning in programmatic terms is a better distribution of resources within a mutually beneficial sharing process.

In summary, in this ideological and political position, conflict, exploitation, and expropriation do not exist. Instead, cooperation, sharing, and collaboration are put forward as the solutions to today's world poverty. Needless to say, within this theoretical scenario, the concepts of class and class struggle do not appear. An alternative position, however, is that there is a basic conflict underlying the current world system, a conflict that takes place within a pattern of class power relations that explain it. It could be postulated that there is intrinsic and structural conflict in today's world, and not only between the "have" and "have-not" countries but also (and primarily) between the "haves" and "have-nots" *within* each country. These conflicts are mutually dependent and reinforceable. Indeed, a key place in that world system is the one occupied by the capitalist class of both developed and underdeveloped countries, and it is this class for whom the development establishments speak. The capitalist classes of the core capitalist countries play a key role in organizing the world capitalist system to defend their own interests. The capitalist classes of the LDCs are, for the most part, collaborator classes.

"whose function is to organize the state and economy in accordance with the core definitions of the international division of labor. The creation of an international political economic order based on the inequalities of nations is rooted in the existence of an expanding center of capitalism and a set of classes within the periphery whose own expansion and position is enhanced in the process. The insertion of particular social formations within the world capitalist market and division of labor is largely the product of classes which combine a double role—exploitation within the society and exchange outside the society. This dual process leads to the expansion of production relations and antagonistic class relations within peripheral society, growing exchange relations, and competition with the core.[18]

Thus, the *real* gap is not between North and South, but between the capitalist metropoles and the dominant classes of the capitalist periphery on the one side and the impoverished population of the capitalist periphery on the other. *It is these class relations and exploitation that are at the root of underdevelopment, poverty and the disease of the majority of the world's population.*

Some needed clarifications

Let me clarify here some points that need to be made. The proposed solutions—"population control" and "technological transfer" first, and a "cooperative and mutually beneficial new economic order" afterwards—put forward by the development establishments during the last two decades as answers to the enormous problems in today's world do not represent a conspiracy by those establishments to keep the poor poor. Nor are they lies put forward to obfuscate the truth. We have to remember that to tell a lie, one needs to know the truth. And those establishments don't know it. These positions respond to a vision of reality (or ideology) that makes sense for the class which holds it. In other words, in the 1960s when USAID and the Rockefeller Foundation put forward programs for population control in Latin America as a solution for Latin American poverty, they were bearers of a class-based vision of reality—the US capitalist class' vision of reality—that led them to believe that the cause of poverty is not capitalist and imperialist exploitation but, rather, population explosion. As Marx indicated, every class has its own ideology —vision of reality—that serves consciously or unconsciously, to reproduce its own interests.[19] It is also characteristic of every dominant class to see its own specific class interests as universal interests. This point bears repeating in view of the overabundance of references that see history as an outcome not of structures but of personalities, conspiracies, and individual motivations. Individuals may be unconscious bearers of ideologies and practices that serve quite different purposes from the ones individually and consciously desired. The international health field is crowded with such contradictions between intentions and effects.

WHO and the development establishment

All these ideologies and positions put forward by the development establishment have appeared in and are being reproduced through the WHO apparatuses. "Population control" programs, "technological transfer," "self-care and self-reliance," and "cooperative and mutually beneficial new economic order" have been sequentially presented as the solutions to the overwhelming problems of disease and poverty in the underdeveloped world. Indeed, for many years, WHO has functioned as a "transmission belt" of positions and ideologies generated for the most part in those development establishments. Here, it is important to stress several points:

There is a great need to question two dichotomies: politics/technology and ideology/science. I have previously argued that science and technology are not neutral; they carry with them a set of values and ideologies that reflect and reproduce power relations.[20] In that respect, WHO, while being a technical agency of the UN, is also a political agency which reproduces and distributes political positions through its technological discourse and practices. Thus, it is important to question the prevalent vision of WHO as merely a technical agency committed to the eradication of disease in today's world. This vision belongs to the realm of appearance rather than reality. Like any other international apparatus, WHO is the synthesis of power relations (each with its own ideology, discourse, and practice) in which one set of relations is dominant. The dominant powers are the dominant classes in capitalist DCs.

Let me stress that I am aware, of course, of the argument that the top decision-making body of WHO is the World Health Assembly, in which each country has one vote. But to believe that the Assembly is the top decision-making body would be as wrong as to believe that the British Parliament is the top decision-making body in Great Britain, or that the US Congress rules the USA. As Gramsci said, a vote gives the right but not the power.[21] The power of the dominant capitalist classes in those parliamentarian countries is exercised not only through elective bodies but, to a large degree, through the administrative, technical, and professional apparatuses as well as through their hegemony over the ideological institutions (such as universities) that feed those apparatuses. The same occurs in WHO. The power of those classes is not diminished by changing the composition of the personnel who represent their interests. In the same way that the addition of some blacks and women to the state personnel in the USA has not changed the overall pattern of class dominance in the US state apparatuses, similarly, to have individuals of LDC origin in those apparatuses does not change the existing pattern of control in the slightest. As Poulantzas has clearly shown, what counts in Western democracies is not the gender, race, class, or national origin of the state personnel but, rather, their class position.[22] The class position of state personnel appears in their technological discourse, specifically in (a) what is presented, (b) what is not presented, and (c) how it is presented. And here, again, the same occurs in WHO. Any analysis of the articles and references in PAHO publications (the Latin American branch of WHO), for example, will show (a) a consistent presentation of empirical and functionalist positions, i.e. the dominant ideologies in Western academic circles, (b) an exclusion of alternate, e.g. Marxist, positions, and (c) a presentation of the former positions as merely technological and apolitical, while the latter positions are portrayed as political and non-technological.

This situation is not unique to PAHO. It appears in most WHO branches. In all their discourse, there is a "depoliticization" of political interventions, recycling them into technological ones. Witness, for example, the great promotion ten years ago by WHO of the concept of "barefoot doctors." This profoundly political experience was stripped of its political significance (an outcome of a set of political forces that were occurring in The People's Republic of China at that time) and presented as a wise and intelligent use of paramedical personnel worthy of imitation in other political environments. It soon became clear that that experiment could not work in other settings. The WHO reports did not seem to have understood that the barefoot doctor was a political event and an outcome of specific political forces. One could not be understood without the other. The depoliticization of that event, however, was in itself political.

In summary, there is within WHO (a) a continuous presentation of political positions through its technological reports, with (b) a continuous repression of alternate positions. The extreme form of repression, of course, is the *exclusion* of alternate positions from the realm of debate. Let us now analyze how the Alma Ata Declaration fits within this interpretation of WHO.

The Alma Ata Declaration

First we have to realize that the major recommendations put forward by the Alma Ata report were not new. In 1972, the Office of Health Economics[23] (the intellectual center of the British pharmaceutical industry) and in 1975, the World Bank[24] produced reports on the state of health and medicine in the underdeveloped world that closely resemble the Alma Ata recommendations. Indeed, they are part of the "conventional wisdom" within the development establishments. These recommendations include the following: (1) a change of priorities within health care services, with more emphasis to be placed on the allocation of resources to (a) primary health care services, (b) water control and sanitation services, and (c) nutrition; (2) a transfer of medical technology, shifting from highly sophisticated to less sophisticated technology; (3) an emphasis on self-care and self-reliance; and (4) encouragement of community participation in the planning and implementation of health programs.

How are the above changes to be implemented? The Alma Ata Report stressed the message (repeated again in the Willy Brandt Report) that these changes should take place through cooperation among nations and interest groups within nations, calling on both their morality (the call for social justice) and their self-interest (the mutual interests of "haves" and "have-nots" in a better economic order).[25]

Because of the enormous importance of these points, let me further expand on what the report does say, what it does not say, and how it says it:

1. The report speaks of a world divided between "have" and "have-not" nations (and within each nation, of "have" and "have-not" individuals).[26] Nowhere do categories such as capitalism and socialism appear. Thus, capitalist development is redefined as "development," a process perceived to be so intrinsically good that it "undoubtedly brings about improvement in health."[27] Evidence exists, however, that development (of the capitalist variety) may not bring about improvements in health. I already mentioned the negative impact of the Brazilian economic miracle on infant mortality in São Paulo, Brazil. Many others have also shown how some forms and dimensions of capitalist development may indeed be more harmful than helpful for the improvement of the level of health of a population.[28]

2. The report's suggestions focus on the need to introduce organizational and technological change within the framework of current power relations. These relations are considered as given and unchangeable. For example, in speaking about "the need for women as well as men to enjoy the benefits of agricultural development," the report, after indicating that "women are engaged simultaneously in agriculture, household management, and the care of infants and children,"[29] recommends that "[women] need appropriate technology to lighten their work load and increase their work productivity. They also require knowledge about nutrition which they can apply with the resources available, in particular concerning the proper feeding of children and their own nutrition during pregnancy and lactation."[30]

In brief, the report is saying that in order to liberate women, there is a need for more technology (appropriate technology) and more education of women. The report does not mention that what is needed for the liberation of women is a redefinition of the power of women and men within the context of a profound redefinition of all power (including class power) relations in the society. Maxine Molyneux has eloquently shown how, within the world of underdevelopment, an economic, political, and social revolution has been a necessary requirement for the liberation of the majority of women and men.[31]

3. Besides the technological changes, the Report calls for the collaboration of those who may oppose the shift of priorities within the health care sector, for example the medical professions and the multinational drug industries. The report suggests that governments make these interest groups aware of the commonality of interest they have with the reformers. These interest groups need to be convinced that the proposed changes will be to their benefit as well. For example, the report notes that "physicians and other professionals will need to be persuaded that they are not relinquishing medical functions but gaining health responsibilities."[32] Similarly, the drug and medical industries need to be made aware of the enormous benefits that they can obtain from the changes:

"Opposition from the medical industries can be directed into positive channels by interesting them in the production of equipment for appropriate technology to be used in primary health care. Any losses from reduced sales of limited amounts of expensive equipment could well be more than counterbalanced by the sale to large untapped markets of greater amounts of less expensive equipment and supplies for primary health care."[33]

In other words, there is a lot of profit to be made from those changes. An assumption is made here, of course, that the powerful groups and the powerless ones (for whose benefit the reforms are supposed to take place) can share the same interests. This is in essence what is being said. What is not said, of course, is that the medical profession holds a class, gender, and professional position and reproduces an ideology and practice aimed at optimizing its class interests, which are in conflict with the interests of the working class and popular masses. This explains why the instruments of the medical profession have always—from the Bolshevik Revolution to Allende's Chile—opposed the socialization programs put forward by the working class.[34] Similar arguments can be made about the drug and medical industries. It is to their advantage to reproduce the current relations of forces within and outside medicine. Witness the current opposition of the multinational pharmaceutical industries to the establishment of national health services in the LDCs.[35] Let us not forget that the drug industry paid for the fascist Pinochet coup in

Chile, and that the Chilean Medical Association sent the first telegram of congratulations to Pinochet![36]

4. The Alma Ata Declaration also calls for community participation. By community, the report means an aggregate of individuals having common interests and aspirations (including health). Thus, community participation is defined as "the process by which individuals (and families) assume responsibility for their own health and welfare and for those in the community who develop the capacity to contribute to their and the community's development."[37] Community, then, is seen as an aggregate of individuals. But a community is *not* only an aggregate of individuals; it is more than that. A community is a set of power relations in which individuals are grouped into different categories, of which classes are the key ones. And power is distributed according to those categories.

A physician, for example, is not merely an individual. He/she is a member of a class (as well as a race and gender) whose power comes not only from his/her medical position but also from the position he/she occupies within the class and gender and race relations in that society. It is primarily one's class position that determines one's interests. The primary commitment of the medical profession, for example, is not the health of the people. The primary commitment of those in the medical profession is to the optimization of the interests of their class (as well as their race and gender).

These four positions are clear ideological and political positions, and all of them appear in the Alma Ata Declaration. These positions need to be criticized, not because they are limited (i.e. they do not go far enough) but because they are wrong. But let's continue our analysis of the WHO Alma Ata positions and see what other ideologies appear in them.

The health care system as the health system

5. The Alma Ata report uses the expressions "health," "health care," "health care sector," "medical care," and "health systems" interchangeably. On deeper analysis, it appears that what the report actually means by health system is basically a health care system built upon and organized around the medical care system, that is health care goods and services provided to individuals and families by

health professions and health workers. The report's main recommendation is to shift the emphasis more toward primary care. That shift is supposed to take place within a medical care system in which primary health care should be at the center:[38]

> "Primary health care is the hub of the health system. Around it are arranged the other levels of the system whose actions converge on primary health care in order to support it and to permit it to provide essential health care on a continuing basis. At the intermediate level more complex problems can be dealt with, and more skilled and specialized care as well as logistic support provided. At this level, more highly trained staff provide support through training and through guidance on practical problems that arise in connection with all aspects of primary health care. The central level provides planning and managerial expertise, highly specialized care, teaching for specialist staff, the expertise of such institutions as central health laboratories, and central logistic and financial support.[39]

It is clear from this quotation that the report is basically referring to a regionalized and modified medical care system which includes primary, secondary, and tertiary care services, giving major emphasis to primary care. Primary care is to include preventive as well as curative services, environmental as well as personal health services. The report is aware, of course, that health cannot be attained by the health sector alone.[40] It indicates that other interventions, such as anti-poverty programs, water, sanitation, housing, and education, contribute to health. Later on, the report refers to these interventions as *"supportive of the primary care sector."*[41] Agricultural, water, housing, public works, and communication interventions need to be designed *to support the tasks* of the primary health care sector, which is considered to be at the center of those endeavors.

In summary, the report uses health and health care interchangeably. Thus, when the report speaks about health for all by the year 2000, the report is actually promoting accessibility to health services for all by the year 2000. Moreover, by considering the primary health services as *"the* key to achieving an acceptable level of health throughout the world," the report singles out health services as *the* most important intervention to attain health.[42] The central role that accessibility and availability to health services plays in this strategy for health needs to be challenged. It represents an ideological and political position that, indeed, should be questioned.

I do not want to minimize the importance of a shift of priorities within the health care sector. Nor do I want to diminish the value of expanding the responsibilities of the health care sector. These are very important tasks. But to consider them as *the most* important interventions to achieve health for all is profoundly incorrect. Most improvements in health have been due to changes in economic, social, and political structures rather than in the health sector. Indeed, abundant empirical evidence exists to show that the most important changes in the health of the LDCs populations during the last twenty years have occurred in revolutionary socialist LDCs via changes in their economic, political, and social structures, independently of and outside the health care sector. It is worth mentioning that even the British pharmaceutical industry recognizes that the major changes in health have taken place in revolutionary socialist countries, referred to in its report as "command economies."[43] Those revolutionary changes have also enabled changes in the health sector that have assisted in the further improvement of health. But most of the changes have taken place because of interventions coming from *outside* the health care sector.

Empiricism or atheoretical pragmatism in the Alma Ata Declaration: The way of interpreting non-health sector-related interventions

6. The Alma Ata document recommends a series of interventions outside the health sector, such as food production and education, plus changes in public works and communications, housing, water, and so on.[44] All of these changes are needed to improve the health of the population. This listing of activities is presented in apolitical terms. However, this type presentation is itself political. It assumes that each of these interventions has an autonomy of its own. In sociological discourse this is called empiricism or atheoretical pragmatism, that is the analysis of the variables without reference to their structural determinants. A system, society, or community, however, is defined *not* by the individual elements and/or interventions that

exist within it but, rather, by the structural relationships among these elements and the powers they reproduce. Linear atheoretical pragmatism and empiricist thinking view interventions as independent of the structures and the power relations that determine them. For example, the discussion on whether "population control" or "technological transfer" or "the New Economic Order" is the solution to underdevelopment carries with it this type of thinking. The ways in which the questions are posed predefine the answers. The reality (which is dialectical rather than linear) shows, however, that to know whether population size is a problem or not, we have to understand the variable (size of the population) within its historical and political context. In other words, the size of the population may or may not be a problem, depending on the social, economic, and political structure in which that population is articulated.

In summary, what defines the effectiveness of an intervention (e.g. housing) is not that variable *per se* but, rather, (a) how the different interventions are structurally related; and (b) who and what are the agents of change, conflict, and resistance within those structures (both within and outside medicine). A specific intervention may be successful in Cuba but ineffective in El Salvador. Its analysis needs to be seen politically and historically. Empiricism and atheoretical pragmatism fail to do this; by not relating the parts to the totality, the totality remains unchanged. The Alma Ata Declaration fails in the same way. Its assumed "pragmatism" is only an indicator of its ideological functions.

Here, again, we find that the Alma Ata recommendations are not so much limited but, rather, incorrect. The mere listing of different types of interventions (both outside and within the health care system) is misleading, since the key question (whether they are or are not to be effective) depends on how these interventions are related within a structure and a set of power relations that give their meaning and importance. The avoidance of recognition of these structures and power relations is thus the main weakness of the report.

Concluding remarks

Contrary to widely held belief, health is a profoundly political issue. I have tried to show in this part of the essay how the Alma

Ata Declaration is not apolitical but rather profoundly political. WHO, through its technological-administrative reports, reproduces ideologies and political positions as well. The WHO Alma Ata Declaration is not an exception.

Let me quickly add that it is not my intention to castigate but, rather, to critique that report. It does contain, after all, a good major recommendation, the shifting of priorities within health care toward primary care and away from secondary and tertiary care. *But its interpretation of the major health problems in today's world, as well as its proposed solutions for them, is wrong.* Its recommendations reproduce, for the most part, the point of view of the development establishments. These views are part of the problem and not of the solution; they represent the perspective of the dominant classes in today's world.

The changes in the world structures and the power relations that explain them (greatly stimulated by the new liberation forces that are breaking with the Old Economic Order) will determine changes in the UN and in the "technical" agencies within it—including WHO. A sign of that change will be for WHO to (1) break with the medical ideology (the Flexnerian model) that sees health as an outcome of medical care, however that care may be redefined and expanded as health care and primary health care; and (2) embrace the systemic view of health that explicitly sees health in the world of under-development today as primarily an outcome of politically deter-mined structural economic and social changes.

This new understanding of what health and health struggles are should lead the WHO of the future to focus on:

(a) concrete assistance to the liberation movements in their strug-gles against institutionalized violence and disease;[45]
(b) analysis of the structural constraints to health and the class and other forms of resistance to basic change;
(c) change of all existing staff and consultant structures to better reflect the huge diversity of views on health, breaking with the dominant medical ideology; and
(d) research and storage of information on the international mobility of capital and labor and its possible implications for health.

Let me add that today, for example, there is no international agency that gathers information on the flow of capital (including toxic industries) among countries and continents, nor about the movement of workers (migrations) between countries and the health consequences of both. Similarly, there is no international agency which collects systematic information about structural economic changes and health, nor about employment (or lack of it) and health.

These are mere examples of areas and problems that need to be faced and that have not been faced, because they are seen as too "controversial" or "political." They are controversial because they threaten the interests of the dominant powers that define the acceptable items in the social agenda. They are not more political, however, than the current "technological" discourse that dominates WHO positions. They do respond to different interests than the dominant ones, the ones that establish the permissible boundaries of current discourse. Still, demands for change are increasing, augmented by the largest crisis that the world capitalist system has faced since the 1930s. New, bold and daring solutions need to be put forward that will transcend and leave behind the Alma Ata report. This new discourse will not be the one of the development establishments of the Western world, but will come from the authentic representatives of the majorities in the underdeveloped world who will justly proclaim their right to a place under the sun in their magnificent lands which could, under different systems, give to all what is now denied to most.

Notes

1 Alma Ata, International Conference on Primary Health Care, Alma Ata, USSR, Sept 6–12, 1978.
2 Cited in J. H. Bryant, WHO Program of Health for All by the Year 2000: A Macrosystem for Health Policy Making—A Challenge to Social Science Research, *Social Science and Medicine* 14A (1980): 382.
3 Cited in the Seventh General Programme of Work approved by the World Health Assembly, *WHO Chronicle* 36 (4) (1982): 132.
4 Cited in Bryant, *op. cit.*, p. 382.
5 Estimated Service Coverage for Sanitation in Developing Countries, 1970–1980, *Drinking Water and Sanitation 1981–1990. A Way to Health*, World Health Organisation, 1981, p. 2.
6 C. H. Wood, The Political Economy of Infant Mortality in São Paulo, Brazil, *International Journal of Health Services* 12 (2) (1982): 215.

7   This fact and many others, explaining the deterioration of the standard of living in many LDCs, is cited in V. Navarro's The Crisis of the International Capitalist Order and Its Implications in the Welfare State, *International Journal of Health Services* 12 (1) (1982): 185.

8   C. S. Haignere, The Application of the Free Market Economic Model in Chile and the Effects on the Population's Health States, *International Journal of Health Services* 13 (3) (1983): 389.

9   I am aware, of course, that the development establishment is not uniform. Many development establishments do exist. But they all share the basic positions outlined here.

10 E. F. Schumacher, *Small Is Beautiful: Economics as if People Mattered*, New York: Harper & Row, 1975.

11 I. Illich, *Tools for Conviviality*, London: Calder & Boyars, 1973.

12 *North and South. A Program for Survival*, Report of the Independent Commission on International Development Issues under the Chairmanship of Willy Brandt, Cambridge, Mass., 1980.

13 E. Elson, The Brandt Report: A Programme for Survival, *Capital and Class* 16 (Spring, 1982): 110.

14 The Commission included members from developed and less developed capitalist countries. Among those coming from LDCs was former Chilean President Eduardo Frei, a main opponent of Allende's government.

15 Willy Brandt Commission Report, p. 126.

16 *Ibid.*, p. 77.

17 W. D. Graf, Anti-Brandt: A Critique of Northwestern Prescriptions for World Order, *The Socialist Register* (1981): 33.

18 J. Petras, *Critical Perspectives on Imperialism and Social Class in the Third World*, New York: Monthly Review Press, 1978, p. 36.

19 K. Marx, *German Ideology*, Chicago, Ill.: Progressive Publishers, 1976.

20 V. Navarro, Work, Ideology and Science, the Case of Medicine, *Social Science and Medicine* 14C (1980): 191–205.

21 A. Gramsci, *Prison Notebooks*, New York: International Publishers, 1971.

22 N. Poulantzas, *State, Power and Socialism*, London: New Left Books, 1978.

23 *Medical Care in Developing Countries*, London: Office of Health Economics, 1972.

24 *Health*, Sector Policy Paper, World Bank, March, 1975.

25 Alma Ata report, pp. 11, 12, 13; also 44, 49.

26 *Ibid.*, p. 7.

27 *Ibid.*, p. 12.

28 V. Navarro (ed.), *Imperialism, Health and Medicine*, Farmingdale, New York: Baywood Publishing, 1981.

29 Alma Ata report, p. 16.

30 *Ibid.*, p. 16.

31 M. Molyneux, Socialist Societies Old and New: Progress Towards Women's Emancipation?, *Monthly Review* 34 (3) (1982): 56.
32 Alma Ata, p. 11.
33 *Ibid.*, p. 12.
34 V. Navarro, Deprofessionalization and Democratization in the Health Sector in the period 1917–1921, *Social Security and Medicine in the USSR. A Marxist Critique*, Lexington, Mass.: Lexington Books, 1977, p. 18. V. Navarro, Allende's Chile: A Case Study in the Breaking of Underdevelopment, *Medicine under Capitalism*, New York: Neale Watson, 1976.
35 *Medicines, Health and the Poor World*, Office of Health Economics, London, 1982, p. 21.
36 V. Navarro, Allende's Chile, *Medicine under Capitalism*, New York: Neale Watson, 1976.
37 Alma Ata report, p. 20.
38 *Ibid.*, p. 23.
39 *Ibid.*, p. 23.
40 *Ibid.*, p. 10.
41 *Ibid.*, p. 16.
42 *Ibid.*, p. 15.
43 *Medicines, Health and the Poor World*, p. 37.
44 Alma Ata report, pp. 16–18.
45 Although I am aware of the structural constraints under which WHO operates, still the reality is that other UN agencies are providing such assistance already.

Radicalism, Marxism, and medicine*

The radical reading of Marxism

Marx defined capitalism as the dictatorship of the bourgeoisie, understanding, as such, not a political form of government but, rather, an overwhelming dominance which the bourgeoisie has in all spheres of life. In the ideological instance, that dominance appears, not by monopolistic control and prohibition of opposition but by the establishment of an ideological competition so unequal as to give a crushing advantage to one side against the other. The US academic institutions are a clear example of this situation. Marxist works are continuously ignored in bourgeois practice and discourse. This reality takes its extreme form in medicine. Witness the chapter on "The State of the Art in Medical Sociology" prepared for the *International Sociological Association*[1] by a leading US sociologist; not one Marxist reference is even mentioned in that compilation of sociological studies of medicine. The dictatorship of the bourgeoisie in intellectual life is done more frequently, however, not by silencing Marxist contributions but rather by manipulating, caricaturing, and stereotyping them, practices that also appear with uncomfortable frequency among many US radicals. The absence of a mass-based Marxist movement and culture in the USA explains a limited acquaintance by many US radicals of Marxism, a limited acquaintance

* Written in 1983.

that enables them to consciously or unconsciously stereotype Marxist positions. A recent case in point is John Ehrenreich. In the introduction to a volume edited by Ehrenreich, *The Cultural Crisis of Medicine*,[2] he presents a distorted view of Marxism, taking my work as representative of that position. It should be said that in that introduction, no specific quotations are given. My position and that of others are abstracted to an unrecognizable whole. As I will show in this essay, this practice is far from unique. It is almost the trademark of many radicals' writings on Marxism. It is my intention in this essay to correct the misrepresentation of my and other Marxists' works done by Ehrenreich and other radicals and answer their critique with a presentation of alternate views and strategies to the ones presented by them.

Several points need to be made at the outset. One is that what we are involved in here is not a mere scholastic discussion of theory but, rather, a different understanding of practice. Agreeing with Gramsci, I do not believe that theory is innocent. It carries an understanding of practice that needs to be evaluated in the analysis of its theory.

Another point that needs clarification is that the frequent references to Marx in my text do not respond to a Talmudic exercise with calls for authority in sacred texts. Rather, it is a discussion of the relevance of Marx's and other Marxists' analyses to our understanding of medicine, an understanding that carries different theoretical and practical implications from radical ones. In this respect, I do not aim at merely contraposing a Marxist understanding of medicine to current radical ones but, rather, at providing the initial elements of a Marxist answer to the critical question of what is meant by socialist medicine. The answer to this question bears great implications in political praxis in both capitalist and socialist societies. But let us first start with an analysis and critique of the radical position, taking the most recent Ehrenreich work as a point of departure.

The two traditions within the US left

Ehrenreich, in his analysis of the US health Left, defines two traditions: the "political economy tradition" which considers medicine as primarily good and worth struggling for, and the "cultural critique tradition," which considers medicine as primarily bad, an instrument of social control.[3] He characterizes the former—"the conventional Marxist pattern of analysis"—as tracing the problems in medicine "to the private ownership and control of medical institutions, with the consequent existence of market relations which determine an unequal distribution of an otherwise admirable and beneficial medicine."[4] Based on that analysis, "political economist" strategists, including myself, are supposed to ask for the nationalization of medicine—statist medicine—and for the establishment of planning to enable a better distribution of medical services. According to Ehrenreich's view of the Marxist prescription, socialism focuses on the betterment of the distribution rather than of the production of services, since the latter, the production of medical services, is considered to be "fine and admirable" (the caricature terms used by Ehrenreich). The struggles in medicine by liberals and Marxists are thus limited to organizational struggles touching on the institutions but not on the practice of medicine.[5]

Ehrenreich opposes to that position, the cultural critique tradition which questions the value of medical institutions and practices.[6] He includes among its followers black community groups, feminists, radical psychotherapists, and health policy analysts. Instead of distribution, this tradition is said to focus on the production of medicine, understanding as such, the production of services considered to be more harmful than helpful. Thus, until the practice of medicine changes, the better distribution of what is seen as racist, sexist, ineffective, and harmful medicine is to be opposed rather than favored. According to Ehrenreich, the great merit of this cultural critique position is in questioning for the first time the goodness of medicine which Marxists are supposed to have uncritically accepted. He currently considers himself as belonging to this cultural critique tradition. His sympathies are not, however, without qualification. He finds *some* medical knowledge and skills good, needed and useful, and he considers parts of medical practice worth saving for current and future socialism.[7]

In the presentation of these two traditions, Ehrenreich recognizes that he is deliberately exaggerating the gulf between the two critiques (although not the critiques themselves) for the purpose of clarity.[8] What Ehrenreich does, however, is not so much to exaggerate but, rather, stereotype and distort the Marxist position. What Ehrenreich understands by Marxist analysis is actually a specific reading of Marxism as technological determinism, a current within Marxism that has been, from the moment of its occurrence, questioned and criticized by other Marxist currents. Indeed, according to that current, the forces of production (including science and technology) are intrinsically positive, and they are considered to be separate from the relations of production. This position is well stated in Stalin's famous booklet, *Dialectical and Historical Materialism*, which upholds the view that the growth of the forces of production is the main motor of history and that that growth requires a change in the relations of production (from capitalism to socialism) that could allow a full flourishing of those forces of production, including science and medicine. As I have indicated elsewhere, not only Stalin but also Lenin conceived science and technology as neutral entities, rather like tools, the function of which depended on who used them.[9] According to some present versions of that current within medicine, socialism is needed to nurture fully the potential of medicine.[10] The political implication of that understanding is that it is in the objective interests of scientists and professionals of medicine, the carriers of science, to ally themselves with the working class and join them in order to be able better to fulfill their social mission, "the truly high tradition of medical science."[11] Thus, the proposed alliance of the medical professions—"all the doctors"—with the working class.[12]

But that technological determinist current within Marxism was questioned from the very beginning of its existence. Other Marxist currents within and outside the Bolshevik circles questioned the presumed neutrality of science and medicine.[13] They defined "neutral" science as bourgeois science, contraposing it to working-class science in which a new knowledge and practice could be created in a new set of institutions controlled by the working class.

In brief, the existence of technological determinist Marxist currents within the history of the worker's movement has gone side by side with other Marxist currents and other Marxist voices that have questioned the supposed neutrality of science and medicine. I personally have criticized extensively the vision of the forces of production as being intrinsically positive, a vision that has existed both in the Second and Third Internationals. Indeed, my Marxist critiques of medicine in the USSR[14] and in the UK[15] were political interventions aimed at criticizing the visions of science, technology, and medicine which existed in some sectors of the communist and social democratic movements and which have led both traditions to an understanding of socialist medicine as statist medicine. It is more than an abrasive oversimplification; it is a travesty of truth that after six hundred pages of criticizing that statist understanding of socialist medicine I am catalogued by Ehrenreich as holding this very position, which I have criticized earlier and more extensively than he. It is not only ignorance of the history of the international workers' movements but also an ignorance of Marxist theory that leads Ehrenreich and other radicals to equate Marxism with technological determinism and statism. Moreover, their unfamiliarity with historical materialism—the Marxist method of analysis—keeps their analysis stuck in bourgeois terrain. Their profound intellectual debt to the "professional dominance" school and their seeming inability to break with their past "interest groups" position limits most seriously their understanding of medicine. Indeed, John and Barbara Ehrenreich's intellectual debts to Talcott Parsons and Eliot Freidson defined as "the most important contributors to the sociological description of medicine"[16] appear throughout their analysis of medicine. The choice they make not to criticize those two authors but, rather, build upon their work places their work within a tradition that hinders rather than facilitates the explanation of medicine. Let us focus on how these positions appear in John Ehrenreich's work and why they limit the value of his discourse and practice.

Social relations as interpersonal relations

Ehrenreich indicates that what is wrong with medical practice is not so much that the medical–patient relationship is—as Marxists are assumed to believe—a commercial transaction indirectly mediated by money but, rather, a *direct social relation* between two people unmediated by the commodity form.[17] The position that medical practice is a social relation is not unique nor new. Others, including myself, have written about it.[18] But what is unique about Ehrenreich and other radicals is that they see those social relations primarily as direct interpersonal relations between people with different power.[19] Social relations become synonymous with interpersonal relations—(relations for instance of dominance and subservience) —between individuals. Ehrenreich is not unique in this; other US radicals like Young and Figlio do the same.[20] But, as Hilary and Stephen Rose have shown, by defining social relations in that way—a very different way from which Marx uses the term— radicals transform the slogan of the French May of 1968 "the personal is the political" into its converse "the political is the personal."[21]

Seeing social relations in medicine as relations between individuals holding different degrees of power raises the question of the sources of power of the medically dominant individuals. For Ehrenreich, this is an unproblematic area.[22] Holding to Freidson's professional dominance position, he believes that the power of the medical individual comes from the professional monopolization of medical knowledge and practice. Medical power is assumed to come from control over science, a science that is considered useful but contaminated by racism and sexism of the upper class, white and male physicians, the holders of knowledge and power.[23] The proposed solution is the decontamination of medical knowledge and practice by reprofessionalization of medicine, changing the class, sex, and racial backgrounds of medical personnel and instilling new medical values in the medical profession aimed at strengthening the idea "that providing health care is a calling, attended by a strong ethic of service."[24]

In this analysis, knowledge and practice are seen as separate from institutions. Because of this Ehrenreich can propose a synthesis of the "cultural critiques" strategy (dealing with knowledge and practice) with the "political economist" strategy (dealing with institutions).[25] He believes that while control of institutions is needed, what is needed even more is a cultural revolution within those institutions to purify them, instilling new values in them. The area of intervention is in the area of professionals' and people's values, cultures, and practices calling "for an unleashing of people's imagination."[26] How is this going to occur? Ehrenreich remains silent except for a vague call for social mobilization towards an undefined end. The intervention is in people's culture, changing their practices in a process of renewal. The absence of any analysis of how those practices are reproduced and the material basis on which practices are based makes that analysis and the strategy deriving from it so insufficient.

Social relations as social relations of production

In order to understand the dominant/dominated relationships in medicine, we have to understand their place within the overall social relations of production. The power of the medical profession does not come primarily from its position in medicine, but rather, from its position within the whole society or social formation, that is from its position within the social division of labor, in turn determined by the social relations of production in that specific society or social formation. By social division of labor, I mean the distribution of different tasks which individuals have in a society and which they realize according to the place they occupy within the social structure and relations determined by the social relations of production. By relations of production, I mean "those relationships which are established between the owners of the means of production and the direct producers in a definite process of production, relationships which depend on the type of ownership, relation, possession, dispossession or usufruct which they establish with the means of production."[27] According to Marx, there are two fundamental types of social relations of production, depending on two forms of ownership of the means of production: (1) relations of exploitation; and (2) relations of reciprocal collaboration. The former exists when the owners of the means of production live off the labor of the direct producers. They include *relations of slavery* in which the master is not only owner of the means of production but is owner also of the labor power (the slave); the *relations of servitude*, in which the master is the owner of the land, and the servant depends on him and must work gratuitously for him a certain number of days of the year; and, finally, *capitalist relations*, in which the capitalist is the owner of the means of production and the worker must sell his labor power in order to live. Relations of reciprocal collaboration are established when there exists a social ownership of the means of production and when no sector of society lives off the exploitation of another sector. For example, the relations established between members of primitive communities or the relations of collaboration which, according to Marx, *characterize the communist mode of production.*

It is important to clarify at this point that (a) the mode of production is reproduced not only at the economic but also at the political and ideological levels; (b) medicine contributes to the reproduction of the mode of production, not only at the economic but also at the political and ideological levels; and (c) medicine is always articulated within a specific mode of production. Consequently, we cannot speak of medicine in general but, rather, we have to speak of feudal medicine, capitalist medicine, or communist medicine.[28] In this respect, a historical materialist analysis needs to include the study of ideological, political and economic levels within the specific type of medicine and the articulation of each level with the corresponding level in the mode of production of which it is a part. The unawareness of this method of analysis among many medical historians tends to *historicism* rather than history of medicine, that is the description rather than the explanation of history, a description of historical medical events in which their periodicity is defined in chronological or cyclical times without articulating and linking those events to the changes in that social formation.

Different social relations of production determine different modes of production (including medicine). These different modes may exist within the same social formation or society historically defined. At the start of the twentieth century, European capitalist societies, for example, were composed of elements of (a) the feudal mode of production; (b) the form of simple commodity production and manufacture; and (c) the capitalist mode of production in its competitive and monopoly forms.[29] Each mode had its corresponding medicine. Today's USA includes the capitalist mode of production in its monopoly form plus elements of other forms such as petty commodity production and others. The fact that different modes and forms of production may exist within the same social formation does not mean they are unrelated to each other. Rather, one mode (and one form within that mode) occupies a dominant position with a decisive influence on the others. The dominant mode is the one which gives each society its overall character (feudal, capitalist, etc.). Similarly in medicine, we have in today's USA, forms of corporate medicine (determined by the monopoly capitalist form) and cottage medicine (determined by the petty commodity form of capitalist relations). Each form of medicine has its own knowledge, practice, and institutions that are clearly related under the hegemony and dominance of the corporate medicine form.

Classes are antagonistic social groups defined by the place they occupy within the social division of labor determined by specific social relations of production.[30] It is important to stress that the place the social group occupies in the social division of labor—their class—determines their composition, hierarchy, status, income, etc. and not vice versa. In this respect, the petit bourgeois character of the medical profession is not determined by its class origin, composition, hierarchy, income, or status, but rather the opposite. These attributes are consequences of the place the medical profession occupies within the social division of labor determined by specific capitalist relations of production. Thus, the class character of medicine will not change by changing its composition. Contrary to a whole series of illusions, the class (as well as the race and gender) character of medicine will not change by changing the class (and race and gender) origin and composition of the medical personnel, nor by adding some new values (the noble call to service) to their education. Although these measures are not unimportant, they are secondary to the basic problem of transforming the relation of the knowledge, practice, and institutions of medicine to the working class and popular masses. In the absence of these transformations, the new personnel will end up reproducing the practices that flow from the structure and relations of capitalist medicine. There are abundant historical examples that testify to this.

The dual function of medicine within the capitalist social relations of production

Another point that needs to be stressed is that the place which a social group occupies within the social division of labor is what determines its functions, not vice versa. In this respect, the petit bourgeoisie, by the position it occupies within the social division of labor, has a dual function of (a) dominance and control (which Marx called the bourgeois function or global function of capital) and (b) a needed function. For example, the foreman in a factory has two functions.

One is to help coordinate the workers and the work process. The other function is to control that process, including the workers. The former function—the coordinating function—needs to be done in any society. The latter function, the control function, also carried out by the foreman, exists under capitalist relations of exploitation and serves the purpose of controlling the worker. It does not need to exist under relations of reciprocal collaboration.

Similarly, the medical profession has a dual function. One, needed under any mode of production, is to contribute to the care and cure of the (historically and socially determined) health and disease of the collectivity. The other function is the control function over the working class and popular masses. It is important to stress that:

1. These two functions do not exist side by side, but, rather the control function is done through the needed function. In other words, they do not exist in a relation of exteriority. Consequently, that controlling function could not take place unless there was a need for medicine and unless this medicine was effective in resolving, at least partially, the problems of disease. In this respect, capitalist medicine is controlling medicine because it is effective, not vice versa.[31] To think otherwise—as the anti-medicine positions do—is Hegelian idealism in its pure form. It is tantamount to believing that medicine is a complete falsification that people have swallowed in their ignorance.

2. This dual function of the medical profession is an outcome of the position of that social group within the social division of labor and does not depend on the will of its individual agents. A Marxist physician, for example, in the absence of a new relationship in medicine (a new social division of labor) will reproduce both functions—the controlling and the useful functions—independently of his motivation, purpose or commitment. The unawareness of structural constraints is what shows the limits of voluntarism, the prevalent political position among radicals. Calls for "new values" and "cultural revolutions" (without understanding the material structure on which bases those values are reproduced) will not do. Historical examples of the failures of voluntarism are indeed many.

3. In this dual function, the global function of capital (or the bourgeois control function) is the one that shapes the needed func-

tion. In this respect, it is important to understand the antagonistic nature of the relationship between capital and the working class. Capital exploits labor, not out of greed (a moral category) but out of necessity. Capital is exploited labor. Thus, capital needs to extract as much labor power as possible from labor. In order to do this, it must reproduce the dominant/dominated relationship (which exists at the level of production) at the political and ideological levels as well. Consequently, the capital/labor relationship is a dominant/dominated relationship on all economic, political, and ideological levels and spheres of society (including medicine). In that respect, it is wrong to define medicine as capitalist, because it is commercialized or because it is distributed according to the market or because it produces value. Medicine may be nationalized and not produce value and still be capitalist medicine. Medicine is capitalist because, as a consequence of its position within the social division of labor, it reproduces the dominant/dominated class relations in which the capitalist class is dominant. In other words, it is the position which the medical profession occupies within the social structure (in which the capitalist class is the dominant class) which makes medicine a capitalist or bourgeois medicine. As I have indicated elsewhere, contrary to widely held belief, it is not the medical profession which dominates medicine—it is the bourgeoisie.[32] The medical profession is, symbolically speaking, the administrator of medicine. To believe this is not to believe (as Figlio wrongly accuses me of doing) that the medical profession is a mere appendix of the bourgeoisie or that medicine is a mere transparency of bourgeoisie's power that has not an opacity of its own.[33] On the contrary, it means that however autonomous the knowledge and practice of medicine may be, and however independent the medical institutions may appear to be, they are all, in the last analysis, under the political dominance and ideological hegemony of the dominant class or bourgeoisie. Actually, most of the changes that have occurred in medicine have been in spite of the medical profession, not because of it. Bourgeois dominance always determines in the ultimate instance what occurs in medicine. I have shown elsewhere how that class dominance presents itself in medicine.[34]

Let me repeat that this dominance occurs not only in the practice and institutions of medicine but also in the knowledge in medicine.

Indeed, medical knowledge is not a class-free knowledge which is contaminated by racism and sexism and which needs to be liberated of those impurities in order to be fully useful. I am speaking here not of the control of the *use* of medical knowledge but of the *production* of that knowledge. Medical knowledge is not produced and reproduced in the abstract but through agents and relations which are bearers of power relations of which class is a determinant one. To say this is not to say that medical and scientific knowledge does not have an autonomy of its own. But that autonomy takes place within a set of power relations which determines not only how medical knowledge is used (the uses of medicine) but also what knowledge is produced and how that knowledge is produced. Thus, to the question: can science and medical science be autonomous from the dominant ideology? The answer is yes and no, understanding these two categories not as an either/or type of relationship (linear thinking) but, rather, as two mutually dependent instances in which one is dominant (dialectical thinking). The answer is "yes" in the limited sense that once established, medical science has an internal logic of its own, that is the internal structure of that branch of science. The answer is "no" in the major sense that medical knowledge is continuously growing under the dominance of bourgeois ideology. This dominant bourgeois ideology appears in medicine by the submission of medical knowledge to a positivist and mechanistic ideology which typifies science created under the hegemony of the bourgeoisie. Positivism and mechanicism appeared as the main ideologies of the bourgeoisie in the nineteenth and twentieth centuries in Europe with the works of Hume, Comte, and later, Durkheim. According to positivism, science (including medical science) must focus on specifics to build up the general, looking at social phenomena as natural phenomena subject to natural rules. Within that interpretation, causality is explained by association of immediately observable phenomena. Positivism appears in medicine in its definition of disease as a biological phenomenon which appears in the human body divided into different pieces (the organic basis for medical specialization—i.e. cardiology, neurology, etc.) and is caused by one or several factors which are always associated and observed in the existence of that disease.[35] That vision of medical knowledge appears in all bourgeois interpretations of medicine including its radical fringe.[36] Indeed, the addition of new causes—social and environmental—to old ones, does not break with the bourgeois vision of science.

Instrumentalism in medicine

The dual function of medicine: domination, and what we may call liberation (useful intervention aimed at freeing persons from disease) does not appear in two different types of knowledge, practice or institutions. There are not the medical services that are dominating on the one side and the other medical services that are liberating on the other. As I indicated before, the dominating function is carried through the liberating function. Therefore, it is not possible, as Ehrenreich believes, to save the truly scientific liberating parts of medicine and its unsexist and unracist components and throw out the rest. *Medicine is a social relation in contradiction, not an instrument that can be split in different parts.* In other words, we have to guard ourselves against the instrumentalist perception of medicine which considers medicine as a free standing power that is only afterwards utilized by the dominant classes in various ways. This also seems to be Figlio's position when he criticizes me for not seeing medicine as outside class relations.[37] He seems to be unaware that there is not medicine outside classes. Classes are not established first and take medicine afterwards, shaping medicine for their own purposes. Classes are in medicine from the very beginning, and they enter into the determination of medicine. Medicine is not an appendix to capitalism. Medicine under capitalism is capitalism. Needless to say, medicine (feudal medicine) preceded capitalism, but under capitalism medicine is permeated and determined by capitalism.

Another consequence of the instrumentalist vision of medicine appears in the theoretical analysis of medicine as constituted by different interest groups (doctors, drug companies, insurance companies)[38] that act upon medicine, spreading through the networks of power and taking shape in structures. As I have indicated elsewhere, this theoretical position—the most abundant among liberal and radical critiques of medicine—ignores the non-visible actors in medicine who define the set of rules, values, and parameters of intergroup struggles, and it reduces the analysis of medicine to

246 · Crisis, Health, and Medicine

conflicts among visible actors and individuals whose *behavior* and *motivation* determine the nature of the conflict.[39] The fact that those visible actors are groups or fractions of classes in struggle within a specific set of class relations is ignored, or dismissed as irrelevant.

Still another example of instrumentalism is frequently found in the radical tradition which flows from the Frankfurt school that views medicine as determined primarily and exclusively by the needs of the capitalist class. In this vision, medicine is seen as primarily playing a role in capital accumulation and legitimation of the capitalist system, a role defined exclusively by capital. In this theoretical position, medicine (and the other components of the welfare state) is seen as a set of instruments controlled by the bourgeoise. The working class is perceived to be "outside" that instrument, that is the state and medicine. Needless to say, the working-class demands may trigger the state response, a response that is perceived as contributing to the legitimation of the overall social system. The state in this position is perceived as having the function of creating social peace and consensus.[40] The limitations of this position are that (a) it considers class struggle as taking place outside the state, (b) it considers the state as an instrument of the bourgeoise, who use it to optimize its functions, that is capital accumulation and legitimation, and (c) it assumes that the working class is either dissatisfied (and asking for more medical services) or is satisfied (when it receives them). In this latter case, the state response is assumed to contribute to create a consensual social acceptance of the social order. This dichotomy excludes the possibility, however, that the working class may not be in consensus and that the social order may not be perceived as legitimate, but still the working class may not rebel because it does not see any alternative to the current order, or it does not see itself with the power to transcend it. In other words, the consensus-legitimation paradigm excludes the non-consensual acceptance of power[41] and it includes a functional-instrumentalist conception of the state that is faulty. *Whatever happens in the state (or in medicine) is not a mere outcome of what the bourgeoisie wants.* It is indeed far from self-evident that the bourgeoisie is the only force determining medicine or that it can freely tailor medicine to its requirements. It is also far from clear that medicine emanates in its entirety from the will of the dominant class or "from that of its hired politicians." On the contrary, the dominance of medicine by the bourgeoisie takes place within a set of power relations in which the bourgeoisie is not the only power that plays. A dominant class requires a dominated class which is never absorbed and subsumed under the dominant one. Classes do not exist independently of class struggle. In that respect, to define *medicine as capitalist or bourgeois medicine does not mean that medicine is an instrument controlled by the bourgeoisie but, rather, that it is a medicine determined by the class struggle, a process in which the bourgeoisie is dominant.* Medicine is not a thing but a social relation in which class relations are key. Thus, the working class is always in medicine and its struggle with the bourgeoisie always appears in medicine. Thus, the primary determinant of medicine is class struggle, a struggle that takes place under the dominance of the bourgeoisie. In summary, the knowledge, practice, and institutions of medicine are the synthesis of power relations, in which class relations and struggles are key ones.

The unawareness of this fact also limits Stark's critique of US radicals.[42] Indeed, the normative aim that he advocates of creating autonomous spaces outside the state and outside medicine implies that the working class (or any other dominated social agent, e.g. women) can indeed be outside the state. Actually, Stark believes that the non-existence of a national health service in the USA is more an outcome of the strength rather than of the weakness of the US working class. This position, however, reproduces the instrumentalist conception of the state that sees the state primarily as an instrument of control and/or mystification. Thus, the expansion of the state and of medicine is seen primarily as an expansion of control. The expansion of the state (and of medicine) however, has to be seen as an outcome of class (and other forms of) struggle in which the state is the synthesis of that struggle, carried out under a set of dominant/dominated relations, in which the dominated classes and groups are also determining the form and nature of that expansion. The welfare state is an outcome of the strength of the working class. Its underdevelopment in the USA is an outcome of the weakness rather than strengths of the US working class, a weakness that explains that, in spite of the continuous demands for an expanded welfare state by the instruments of the US working class, they have not obtained it.

Class struggle in medicine

How does the class struggle appear in medicine? How does the working class appear in medicine? Here, several notes of clarification are called for. The presence of the working class in medicine does not appear, as instrumentalists seem to believe, in capturing parts of medicine. Indeed, it is worth repeating that medicine is not a capturable thing that can be divided into bourgeois parts (e.g. hospital medicine and/or curative medicine) and working-class parts (e.g. occupational medicine and/or preventive medicine). Nor, for that matter, can the bourgeois state be divided into bourgeois parts (e.g. repressive apparatuses) and socialist parts (the National Health Service or Social Security). Medicine is the specific material condensation of a relationship of forces among classes and class fractions given in a specific conjuncture. For example, the origins of bourgeois medicine were an outcome of the process of class struggle in the nineteenth century, in which different visions of medicine linked to specific class interests were profoundly engaged in struggle, a struggle that was primarily a class struggle. Contrary to the bourgeois position, the history of medicine is not a linear evolution starting with previous discoveries. Bourgeois medicine was not a linear successor of previous discoveries (blood circulation by Harvey in 1628, microscope by Van Leeuwenhoek in 1683, etc.), as bourgeois history of medicine would have it. These discoveries did not create scientific medicine. Rather, it was the victory of the industrial bourgeoisie which established the positivist conception of science and medicine. The fact that those previous discoveries were presented as the origins of scientific medicine was due to changes in the correlations of forces and subsequent victory of the bourgeoisie as the dominant class under industrial capitalism.[43] In this respect, scientific medicine was not the linear growth of previous knowledge; rather, and to use a Kuhnian term,[44] a shift of paradigm took place. The new paradigm which carried a new, a positivist, vision of disease, represented a shift or break that was determined in the last instance by the new correlation of social forces in that society. The unawareness of this determination, incidentally, limits Kuhn's and also Feyerabend's work.[45] Neither Kuhn nor Feyerabend touch on the socio-economic and political determinants of the scientific breakthroughs, a key subject which leaves their positions wanting. A further fault of Feyerabend's work is the determinant role he gives scientists in initiating or stopping changes. For example, in examining the situation of blacks, chicanos, and American Indians, he writes that "much of the spiritual misery of the remnants of non-Western culture in the United States is due to this uninformed intellectual fascism of most of our leading philosophers, scientists, philosophers of science."[44] The roots of the problems, however, are much deeper than Feyerabend seems to realize. He does not touch on the key issue of why those "fascist" ideas are the ruling or leading ideas.

Class struggle and the institutions of medicine

The expansion of state medical expenditures and state health regulations, components of the welfare state, in the post-World War II period is an outcome of the strength of the working class that has forced the bourgeoisie to provide those services and interventions. The fact that the bourgeoisie is the dominant class in that class struggle explains that those services and interventions have (in addition to being useful and having a liberating function which makes them wanted) a controlling function, a function, incidentally, of which the working class is frequently aware.

In summary, the dual function of medicine (and of the welfare state) takes place within a set of class forces continuously in struggle. The working class asks for an effective social and medical service to ameliorate their suffering. Because of bourgeois dominance, those services are provided with a dominating intent and character. While for the working class the primary reason for asking for medicine is their need for it, for the bourgeoisie the primary reason for giving it is one of domination. To see medicine primarily as control is to believe that the working class in its demand for a national health service, for example, is asking for more control. It is not surprising that the radical message is perceived as highly irrelevant by the working class. It has cost the working class sweat and tears to get these services. And when the current Reagan administration intended to cut those services and government interventions (like OSHA), the working class demonstrated on the streets of Washington on Solidarity Day of 1981 in one of the largest demonstrations ever known in the capital of the USA. The working class seems to be more dialectical than radicals are. The linear thinking of the latter limits their comprehension of the former.

A last point that needs to be stated is that the expansion of medicine does not follow a *will* by the bourgeoisie to mystify the working class or hide the reality of oppression. The bourgeoisie does not lie. Nor does the medical profession. To lie means to know the truth. And neither social group knows it. Bourgeois domination cannot be viewed as the conspiracy or individual will of the capitalist. Rather, it has to be seen within the structure of class relations in which the interests of the bourgeoisie explain their vision of reality, a vision of reality that is presented by that class as universal and valid for all groups. This point needs to be made due to the frequency of analysis in which the bourgeoisie is seen as continuously coopting and manipulating the working class by using seductive and cooptive instruments like medicine. This vision reduces class power relations to interpersonal relations and motivations and the acceptability of an instrument or left-wing strategy is evaluated by its potential for cooptation.

Class power and sex and racial power

Needless to say, not all power relations in medicine are class relations. If I have focused here on class relations, it is because in the USA—in the absence of a Marxist culture or tradition—most liberal and radical critiques of medicine have ignored, minimized, dismissed, or stereotyped the Marxist and class critique of medicine. Instead, an entire series of "interest groups" analyses have appeared with a discourse in which class relations do not appear or are misrepresented. Examples are the continuous references to class as one more "interest group" or as category of hierarchy, income, or status.

There is yet another reason to focus on class relations. This is because in class-divided societies, the motive force is class struggle and class power is the cornerstone of power.[47] Other forms of power, like race and gender power, are invested in class power and are mediated and reproduced as class relations. Class power traverses and utilizes other powers, assigning to them specific political significance. Racism and sexism, for example, are used by the bourgeoisie in order to strengthen and reproduce their class dominance in all spheres of life, including medicine. Racism and sexism in medicine appear through the bourgeois knowledge, practice, and institutions of medicine. Racism and sexism do not appear independently from each other, but, rather, reinforce each other through class-dominated medicine.

In brief, there is no set of exploitations (class, race, and gender exploitations) that occurs independently of each other, with each one reproducing itself separately from the other. All forms of exploitation feed off one another and ultimately benefit the same class, the dominant capitalist class.

Another point worth stressing is that Marxism does not deny that all forms of power are, indeed, created and reproduced throughout society. But it is important not to leave unanswered that theory of power, much in vogue today, according to which there is a "pluralism of micropowers" that exists everywhere. This position introduced by Foucault and the new philosophers in France,[48] is a French recycling of an old and still-prevalent theoretical position in the USA in which power is perceived as widespread without any social group organizing the reproduction of power relations in society. In political discourse, this theoretical position appears embodied in the definition of the USA as a pluralist system in which a set of checks and balances exists with no one group dominating the others. By atomizing power and dispersing it, this theory of power denies the central role that class power plays in reproducing all power relations in society and negates the possibility of transcending capitalist society. Indeed, by perceiving that all types of powers are equally important in the determination and reproduction of the system, this theoretical position does not enable us to focus on the agents and leverage for change, nor on the type of interventions required to transcend the current order. Nowhere is the capitalist order as strong as in the USA where the great variety of mini-rebellions co-exists with the absence of a class-conscious working-class and Marxist movements. This is, as Manuel Castells put it, the "poverty of Pluralism."[49]

Under capitalism, power exists everywhere but all power has a class significance. This is why the working class is the decisive and needed force to break with capitalism. Misunderstanding of this reality leads to populism in which the elements of class struggle are diluted in a scenario of people against corporations and/or medical profession, in which the people include all rebellious groups and their potential and actual constituencies. The agency for change is considered to be an ill-defined community, an undifferentiated category which appears as an abstract agency upon which calls are made for mobilization. The disappearance of classes and their absorption by the broad categories of "people" leave many radical positions wanting.[50]

Let me add that I am aware that this position will be dismissed by US radicals as class reductionism, implying that I am holding the view that all power can be reduced to class power. I want to further stress that I am not saying that. I am fully aware that the power position of an individual is given by the position of that individual within a matrix of dominant/dominated power relations of which class is only one parameter. Race, gender, nationality, etc. are, of course, also categories of power. But these categories of power are not related to each other in conditions of exteriority, that is one is not independent or outside of the other. In class societies, class is the organizer of the power matrix in which these other forms of power exist. The unawareness of this reality explains how a US radical, Linda Gordon, can see the creation of Flexnerian medicine as outcome of a "male takeover" of the institutions of medicine.[51] It was indeed more than that. Actually, it was not so much a "take-over" but the creation of a medicine within a social formation in which a class (besides a gender) dominated that process of transformation. Gender and class were not two additive characteristics of that process of dominance. How gender domination appeared in medicine had indeed a clear class significance.[52]

State and socialism

The lack of awareness of class power as explanation of reality is accompanied in many radical analyses by the unawareness of the state as a constitutive force of the relations of production and the power that it realizes at every level of society, including medicine. Indeed, independently of medicine's being private or public, the state plays a key role in reproducing the power relations in medicine, power relations that appear in the knowledge, practice, and institutions of medicine. Forgetting the role of the state leads to two erroneous political practices. One is the call for changing medicine by changing the culture and values of medicine—via mass mobilization in medicine. This strategy—the cultural strategy—carries with it a great charge of subjectivism and voluntarism, asking, as Ehrenreich does, for changes in the culture and ideology of medicine by calls to people's imagination, but ignoring the constitutive role of the state in the reproduction of that ideology and culture.

The other erroneous strategy is an old one which tries to develop institutions outside the state by ignoring it.[53] This tradition, whose inheritance comes more from Bakhunin than Marx, sees the development of "relaxed and autonomous communities" as the solution to our problems. The point that needs to be raised, however, is how are we going to reach that goal? It was Marx, not only Lenin, who spoke of the need for the working class to seize the state in order to establish socialism.[54]

These two traditions dismiss the Marxist tradition as one that leads toward *statism*, that is the state taking over all spheres of collective and individual life. According to this reading of Marxism, a political party takes over the state and becomes the state. The fact that this possibility has become a reality in some countries does not mean, however, that this practice is unavoidable or that it can be blamed on Marx or Marxism. To condemn Marx because of Stalin (a self-proclaimed inheritor of Marx) is like condemning Christ because of Franco (a self-proclaimed inheritor of Christ). To recognize the key role that the capitalist state plays in reproducing social power relations and, therefore, the importance of seizing state power in any revolutionary strategy does not transform Marxism into statism, nor into a position that "nothing can be changed until the revolution takes place."[55] This abusive interpretation belongs to the realm of sectarian polemics rather than rigorous debate. To understand the great importance of state power in reproducing social power relations does not mean that all revolutionary activities should focus on the state or that all meaningful changes need to be postponed until the day of the revolution. A limited understanding of what capitalism, socialism, and communism are, and a limited awareness of the problems of the transitions between the modes of production and forms of medicine, lead to radicals' easy stereotyping of Marxist positions.

Socialist medicine

To define socialist medicine, we have to understand first what is meant by capitalism, socialism, and communism, and the transition from one to another. According to Marx, socialism is not a mode of production. Socialism is a social formation or society in transition from the capitalist mode of production to the communist mode of production. And by communist mode of production, Marx meant one determined by relations of reciprocal collaboration, not exploitation, relations that are established when there is social ownership of the means of production and when no sector of society lives off the exploitation of another.[56] Socialism as a social formation includes both capitalist and communist modes of production. Capitalist medicine is medicine determined by capitalist relations of exploitation, while communist medicine is medicine established under conditions of reciprocal collaboration. Socialist medicine in a socialist society has forms of capitalist and communist medicine, two forms of medicine that exist in antagonistic contradiction.

Two points need to be stressed in the transition from capitalism to communism. One is that this transition takes place within a given social formation or society.[57] The transition from capitalism to socialism, however, follows a different logic than the transition from feudalism to capitalism. In the womb of feudalism, capitalist relations grew to a point where the capitalist forces and relations of production (the infrastructure) forced a change in the ideological and political structures so that the state would better respond to the needs of that new capitalist infrastructure. In France, for example, the transition from feudalism to capitalism occurred in its economic base prior to the 1789 Revolution. The capitalist mode of production was already the dominant one in France before the French Revolution. The seizure of state power by the bourgeoisie which occurred in that revolution was to consolidate the bourgeois dominance already existing in the economic base or infrastructure. In that transition, *the political followed the economic change.* Bourgeois medicine as part of the capitalist mode of production followed a similar evolution.

Capitalist relations in medicine grew with capitalism, and bourgeois medicine was already the dominant (over feudal medicine) form of medicine prior to the seizure of state power by the bourgeoisie.

The transition from capitalism to communism, however, is different. Communist relations of production cannot be born within the womb of capitalism. Indeed, to have some factories managed or even controlled by workers does not mean that they are communist islands in a capitalist sea. What is produced in those factories, and how it is produced still depends on the division of labor defined by capitalist relations dominant in that capitalist social formation. For the transition from capitalism to communism, there is a need for the working class of that social formation to seize state power and force the change in the relations and forces of production towards a communist mode of production. For that transition, *the political relations in the state are the first ones to be established.* The seizure of power by the working class and its allies establishes the basis for changes in the relations and forces of production towards communism. The transition from capitalism to socialism is thus a transition in which revolutionary political action precedes changes in the relations of production. In the new social formation—socialism —we will find different modes of production and the capitalist mode will certainly still exist. Under socialism, various modes and forms of production can exist in balance without any of them being specifically dominant. This transition may take centuries, as did that from feudalism to capitalism. The direction of that transition in the socialist social formation depends primarily on the class struggle within that social formation. *The key criterion to define a social formation as socialist is whether there is control by the working class and allied forces of the political instance in that formation.* The expansion of the capitalist mode of production during NEP in the Bolshevik Revolution did not mean that social formation was returning back to capitalism. The socialist character of the Bolshevik Revolution was not determined by the "size" of the mode of capitalist production in that social formation, but rather, by the degree of control by the working class over the state. In other words, the key issues for understanding and defining socialism or transition to communism are (a) how does working-class control over the state take place; and (b) how does that control shift the balance among the different modes of production to enable the eventual dominance of that society by the communist mode of production?

In summary, in the transition from feudalism to capitalism, the political and ideological relations arise to confirm and support the relations of production which have arisen spontaneously—through the law of capital accumulation—from the infrastructure. The transition from capitalist relations of production to communist relations of production does not happen spontaneously. In that socialist transition, the political relations are the first to be established. The working class and its allies have to seize and hold state power and have to direct that economic transformation. Let me clarify several points here. One is that by holding state power, I do not mean that a group or elite or party holds it on behalf of the working class, however much that group may legitimize its state power by administering society according to workers' expectations.

Nor do I understand political control as merely a juridical category, that is the nationalization of the means of production. State control over economic relations is not merely defined in the sphere of juridical property but also in the sphere of possession of those means, that is the capacity to put them to work. In other words, the working class, through the state, has to not only own the means of production but also possess them, to control both the means of production and the labor process. That cannot be done immediately at the moment of state seizure. There are agents in that labor process, technicians, administrators, etc. who are needed but who are reproducing capitalist relations in that process. The working class, through its control of state power, can direct the changes in that labor process continuously, redefining the social and technical relations of production that respond to new relations of production. Whether or not the socialist state will control the economic relations depends primarily on the correlations of forces—outcome of the class struggle—that will exist in the political, ideological, and economic levels in that socialist society. A necessary condition for that control to take place is for the working class to take state power.

It follows from the above that communist medicine (or medicine based on relations of collaboration) cannot exist under capitalism, a system based on relations of exploitation reproduced by the capitalist state. In order to establish communist medicine, it is necessary to seize state power and establish a socialist state under which the socialist form of medicine will contain both capitalist and communist forms of medicine. It will depend on the correlation of forces within the process of class struggle whether communist medicine will become the dominant and hegemonic form. The transition from capitalist to communist medicine is likely to be a long process.

There is a need at this juncture to clarify several points.

First, the transition from capitalist to socialist medicine does not mean the negation (or smashing) of the knowledge, practice, and institutions of medicine but, rather, their transformation from capitalist forms to communist forms. This transformation will mean not only a change from a type of medicine where priority is given to curative, hospital-technological based, individual, clinical, and somatic-mental interventions to another one where the priority is given to preventive, occupational, environmental, and social interventions. The change from capitalist to communist medicine means not only a change of priorities in the distribution of resources but, most importantly, in the production of those resources. Communist medicine will imply a change not only in the distribution but, most important, in the production of health, where health, disease, and medicine will not be ontologically defined by a dominant class, and administered by "experts," but rather they will be defined and reproduced by a collectivity of unexploited agents, within a division of labor in the production of knowledge, practice, and institutions that will not be exploiting nor exploited.

Second, communist medicine cannot become the dominant and hegemonic one under socialism, immediately after the seizure of power by the revolutionary forces. There will unavoidably be in socialist medicine knowledge, practices, and institutions that reproduce bourgeois medicine but that are still needed until new types of medical knowledge, practice, and institutions corresponding to communist relations are established. Communist forms of medicine, however, can and need to be established early in the revolutionary process, and that can be built on pre-communist forms already established under capitalism.

Third, in this process of transformation, a class struggle exists under socialism between capitalist medicine and communist medicine. They are two antagonistic modes of medicine that respond to two antagonistic types of relations, relations of exploitation against relations of collaboration. Class struggle in medicine (and in the entire society) will exist in all socialist societies.

Fourth, an important mystification which occurs at the level of ideological class struggle (upheld by the bourgeois vision of medicine) is that medicine is a non-class-related instrument that can be held by either class for its own uses. I have already criticized elsewhere that neutrality of medicine and the instrumentalist conception from which it derives. A most frequent penetration of bourgeois ideology within the labor movement has been, as indicated before, the acceptance of the neutrality of forces of production, including science and medicine. As a consequence, socialist medicine has been perceived as a better distributed medicine (bourgeois medicine perceived as neutral). This position leads to the reproduction of *class relations within medicine*. Let me stress that the reproduction of that ideology has a material basis, that is it reproduces the power relations within medicine to the advantage of the medical professionals and other elements of the petit bourgeoisie, regardless of what they are called (e.g. medical workers) or how much they are paid. And it reproduces that social order in which a new and/or old class became dominant. In conclusion, they reproduce the class relations in the societal whole.

Fifth, the transformation from bourgeois medicine to communist medicine is not done by a mere change of personnel (class, race, and sex of new workers), or by adding new values to their formation, or by changing the priorities within medicine. It is done by deliberately, consciously, and politically changing the relations in medicine, submerging the knowledge, practice, and institutions of medicine under the direct control of the working class and popular masses, not mediated by indirect representations or delegation. Thus, communist medicine is not bourgeois medicine better distributed but, rather, a qualitatively new form of medicine created by new relations of collaboration and cooperation in the process of production and reproduction of health. Similarly, socialist medicine is a new form of medicine existent under socialism that, while containing two types of medicine—bourgeois and communist medicine—is under the control of the working class and popular masses, a control that occurs primarily by direct process of participation and control over the collective creation of knowledge, practice, and institutions of medicine. In this respect, socialist medicine would be the fullest expression of democraticized medicine whose initial primitive forms can already appear under capitalism.

Sixth, class struggle under socialist medicine is articulated with class struggle at the social formation level. Therefore, the power of the professional groups in medicine, education, transportation, and other services is a power that does not come primarily from control over knowledge or practice of medicine, education, and so on, but rather from the position they occupy within the class structure and relations under socialism.

Seventh, the transition from capitalist to communist medicine under socialism is not a predetermined transition that occurs spontaneously with the growth of the forces of production. It is a political and ideological class struggle in which the working class can be defeated.

The transition from capitalism to socialism

The initial issue in this transition is to take state power. But what does this mean? The instrumentalist vision of medicine held by some radical and Marxist currents appears also in their instrumentalist vision of the state. The state is a *thing* that can be seized, taken over, and smashed. As we saw with medicine, the state, however, is not a *thing*. It is a relation. In that respect, by seizing state power, I mean the transformation of the power relations that appear in the ideologies, functions, and apparatuses of the state, a transformation that is not limited to changes of state personnel or changes in government, but includes changes in the relation of forces within the state. This transformation is a process that cannot be synthesized in a specific date or event. This process can already take place within the capitalist state as an outcome of changes in the relation of class forces within the state, changes that determine not the appearance of socialist islands within the capitalist state—as the instrumentalists believe—but, rather as a shift of class forces toward strengthening the working class, making that class better able to get more advantages and benefits from that state. In this way, the working class strengthens its power within the state which may lead to a series of breaks and transformations of which the break with the state apparatus of repression will be a key one.

Needless to say, these struggles need to be carried out within and outside the apparatuses of the state, carrying the struggles for democratization and control to all instances in society, including medicine. Socialist politics is the broadening and deepening of the concepts and praxis of both politics and democracy, not limiting the concept of democracy to the level of politics but, rather, expanding it to include all areas of political, economic, social, ideological, and cultural spheres; and not limiting the concepts of politics to the participation by "experts" or representatives in the realm of representative or indirect democracy, but rather expanding them to include all forms of direct democracy—such as workers' councils, neighborhood committees, and others—where the collectives and individuals affected by decisions participate actively and not merely passively in the genesis and implementation of those policies. This expansion and deepening of democracy is what I have called *mass democracy*.[58] Similarly, in medicine, there is a need to democratize medicine by changing the relations of forces in the production of knowledge, practice, and institution of medicine. Let me clarify that while the full massive democratization of medicine—the dominance of medicine by the working class and allied forces—is not possible under capitalism, still important changes in those relations of forces can occur under capitalism that may allow the establishment of more democratic forms of medicine that, while limited, can be highly relevant and beneficial to the majority of the population. This democratization needs to take place by carrying the struggle not only in the realm of representative democracy, but also in the areas of direct participation and control of knowledge, practice, and institutions of medicine, and of all other knowledge, practice, and institutions that have a bearing on health. In the area of occupational health, for example, *there is a need to complement the struggles for changing the correlation of forces within the state, producing progressive legislation to protect the workers, with struggles carried out at the work-place aimed at developing forms of workers' collective control over the labor process.*[59] A very important form of mass and direct participation, for example, is the active and direct participation which takes place in struggles around workers' control in many countries aimed at establishing forms of workers' control in which the working class and popular masses rebel against the totalitarian nature of work and relations in life. An outcome of these struggles has been the establishment of workers' councils, directly elected by the workers in those factories, councils which represented centers of power for the workers who see those councils as autonomous, independent, and conflictive with management of those factories. They are based on a clear awareness of the intrinsic conflict which exists between workers and managers at the place of work. Their objective has been to carry the class struggle into the process of production itself. The aim of the workers' councils (as has been the aim of many previous workers' councils' experience under capitalism in the history of labor), has been to limit managers' control and to change the power relations at the point of production. They have won veto power in the establishment of new conditions of work, new equipment, new labor policies, changes of personnel, and new investments. *Needless to say, it is still a defensive strategy, but a most effective one.*

Workers' councils as expressions of workers' struggle offer a form of mass participation aimed at transforming the relations of power in the factory. This transformation undoubtedly will reach a break or series of breaks in that unit—breaks which will not successfully occur, however, in just that unit unless other breaks occur in other areas of the social fabric as well. Thus, workers' control struggles have to be seen as political movements which extend to all other areas of work and life. Gramsci stressed the need to carry struggles from the work-place into the communities. The struggle for democracy has to overcome the alienation of the individual, not only as a producer, but as a consumer and citizen. Gramsci proposed the creation of other forms of mass democracy—neighborhood committees—elected directly by the different mass movements based in those communities. The working class has, in moments of popular rebellions against the bourgeoisie, always linked these two types of struggles; at work and in the community. Community struggles to control community institutions such as schools, health institutions, post offices, transportation, etc. are also forms of mass democracy which represent an expansion and deepening of the concept of democracy. These forms of democracy cannot be seen as mere decentralizations of representative institutions. If the neighborhood committees, for example, are mere agencies of the municipalities, they are likely to be mere administrative outposts of the municipalities, pre-empting any form of direct and autonomous participation by the residents of the neighborhoods in the direct running of those institutions. In this respect, mass democratization is to be distinguished from the decentralization of regional or municipal administrations or from the municipalization of all local institutions. Mass democratization should be the direct participation in the running of those institutions (including medical institutions) and activities by those who are affected or served by them and who work in them. Direct participation would take place within the margins established by the municipalities and/or other forms of representative democracy. In this respect, I do not consider mass democracy to be the same as what Ingrao calls *base democracy*, by which he defines the decentralization of representative democracy at the very local levels.[60] By mass democracy, I include both forms of representative and direct democracy with great reliance in the local levels, for example, schools, medical and public health services, markets and places of trade, means of communications, and other places in forms of direct democracy where individuals elected to the governing bodies—workers and users—of those institutions do not become full-time representatives but combine their responsibilities as representatives with the ones they have as workers, students, residents, patients, or potential patients, and where the institutional decisions are taken, not by a committee on whom authority has been delegated, but by the entire assembly of workers and users of those institutions, decisions that are reached after collective discussion and individual (and secret) vote. Mass democracy, then, is an expansion and deepening of the process of democratization by adding forms of direct to indirect democracy and by adding those types of participation in all areas which affect people's lives.

Class struggle and mass democracy

Needless to say, mass democracy will not occur without the deepening of class struggles in all areas of life. And that class and mass struggle will differ, depending on the area and subject of the struggle. Community struggles, for example, are different from work-place struggles. The former, for example, can apply only a limited type of pressure, that is there is no strike weapon. Also, there can be more variations of interests within the community than within the working place. And the community struggles usually do not have the type of structures and organization that usually exist in struggles around the work-place. These differences require different types of struggles and thus these struggles require a certain autonomy in their operations.[61]

These different forms of struggles do not necessarily lead to the development of a pre-revolutionary situation. These experiences in the USA, where many mass movements based on direct popular participation have existed for short periods, show that. The existence of autonomous and separate movements, each one acting as a pressure group for its own specific interests, leads to corporativism in which the struggle for power is perceived as competition among unrelated groups. This atomization of the struggle, together with the existence of multiple minirebellions unrelated to each other, is easily isolated and does not represent a threat to the global capitalist order. That is the serious weakness of Foucault's position and other radical positions. The proper concern of these issue-oriented movements in becoming trapped by the practices of a political party may lead to, as Poulantzas rightly indicated, the opposite extreme, into the realm of minicorporate struggles in which all rebellious movements share the common absence of revolutionary political consciousness.[62] For mass forms of participation to have a pre-revolutionary impact, they have to be *political, that is to change from being power pressure groups to political forces aimed at a socialist project.* As indicated before, revolutionary politics means the breaking of the monopolization of politics by the politicians and the massive politicization of the diverse mass forms of participation in search of socialist projects. In other words, politics cease being the realm of experts on politics —the political representatives—and become the practice of daily struggles inside and within mass movements. Similarly, medicine ceases to be the realm of experts and becomes a struggle for the collective production of health. This position is to be distinguished from the self-care movement that, for the most part, is individually oriented and takes place outside the struggle within the state. The project I am advocating is the collective—as opposed to individual —struggle that realizes itself, both outside and within the state, with the articulation of mass and political struggles. This diversity of struggles and movements, conscious of the need for socialist projects, provides the educational experiences for the popular masses to be the agents, and not the objects of change, and that provides a diversity of political movements for socialism. To paraphrase Gramsci, revolutionary politics means breaking down the distinction between political and civil society. Or, as Althusser put it more recently, "to break down the exclusive identification of politics with the state."[63]

This mass struggle carried out in its many different forms also needs, however, to be carried out in the area of representative politics by instruments such as political parties which can present and articulate the demands made by these movements. The absence of this component is, in my opinion, the primary limitation of an otherwise excellent analysis of mass movements carried out by André Gorz in France and F. Piven and R. Cloward in the USA. Political parties need to represent, articulate, and mediate the social movements. Articulation, however, does not mean direction, or simply making the mass movements into transmission belts for the parties. Historically this has simply destroyed those movements. The effectiveness of left-wing parties will depend on the degree to which they can listen to, articulate, and represent the demands of those movements.

This observation of parties should not be taken to mean that the left parties should be the group of "experts" whose politics take place only in the realm of representative politics, and whose aims are to seize, hold, and *become* the state power. This is indeed, the genesis of Stalinism, the government by "experts," a position also shared, incidentally, by Fabianism and other forms of social democracy. Rather, the role of the working-class parties is to support and encourage the forms of mass democracy which will be essential for the breaking and transformation of state power, towards building a new state and a new society in which the average citizens and, paraphrasing Lenin, including the cooks, will be able to control the state and all forms of collective life. The role of the left-wing parties is to articulate, synthesize, and represent the diverse mass movements in the realm of representative democracy; to carry on, side by side, with the mass organizations, the struggle for the breaking and transformation of the state and all institutions and relations in society; and to support and politicize those mass movements offering globalizing and competing projects to build socialism.

A note of warning needs to be made here. Support and politicization of mass movements does not mean their infiltration and control. As many instances on both sides of the Atlantic show, this control is the quickest road to their collapse. Support can be both from outside and within the movements—in the latter case, by the involvement of party militants in those movements. But these militants need to feel their primary loyalty to the mass movements and not to the party. The development of *dual militancies* allowing feminist militants of left-wing parties to work within feminist organizations and be primarily responsible to those organizations is a very positive step towards the broadening of the understanding of politics by left-wing parties. Also, these militant feminists would sensitize the parties towards the feminist cause, helping to transform them into instruments for the liberation of women as well as of men. In that way, the left-wing parties, for example, do not become *the* feminist parties but help the feminist cause by supporting it through mobilizations, through interventions in representative and direct organs of democracy, and through militants in those organizations. Conversely, all these types and forms of involvement would help the parties to develop a program of socialist transformation that would include a theory and praxis for human liberation.

In summary, there is a great urgency that the increasing number of rebellious movements, raised against the increasingly clear capitalist exploitative relations, be sensitized to the need to transcend capitalism. To stress this is not to repeat the widely held belief that there is a great urgency and possibility for having a revolutionary working class ready to undertake a revolutionary project. I do not believe that. The historical record shows that no modern social revolution has ever been made by a unified class subject demanding a completely new social order. Revolutions have occurred and have been made when various forces with different immediate reformist demands —peace, bread, land, end of repression, social security, etc.—have come together to face a divided and weakened bourgeoise unable to respond to those demands satisfactorily.[64] The continuous demands for these reforms within an order incapable of satisfying all of them has lead to the revolutionary transformation of that order. In other words, revolutions are not done by a conscious revolutionary class but rather by non-revolutionary forces who push for the resolution of their demands, even at the cost of breaking and transforming that order. It is the task of the organized socialist forces to stimulate and support those forces and to assist in their linkage—unity—that will make that project of transformation possible. The increased inability of the current capitalist order in resolving and responding to the increasing demands of the working classes and popular forces makes that transformation today historically possible.

Notes

1 A. C. Twaddle, From Medical Sociology to the Sociology of Health: Some Changing Concerns in the Sociological Study of Sickness and Treatment, in T. Bottomore, S. Nowak, and M. Sokolowska, *Sociology: The State of the Art*, International Sociological Association, London and Beverly Hills: Sage Publications, 1982.
2 J. Ehrenreich (ed.), *The Cultural Crisis of Modern Medicine*, New York: Monthly Review Press, 1978.
3 Ehrenreich, Introduction: The Cultural Crisis of Medicine, *op cit.*, p. 2.
4 *Ibid.*, p. 16.
5 *Ibid.*, p. 3.
6 *Ibid.*, p. 4.
7 *Ibid.*, p. 29.
8 *Ibid.*, p. 2.
9 V. Navarro, Work, Ideology and Science: The Case of Medicine, *Social Science & Medicine* 14C (1980): 197.
10 J. Tudor Hart, The Point Is to Change It, *Medicine in Society*, p. 4. For a critique of J. T. Hart's position, see V. Navarro, "The Point, However Is *How* to Change It . . . , *Medicine in Society* 5 (1979).
11 Hart, *op. cit.*
12 *Ibid.*
13 See D. Lecourt, *Proletarian Science*, London: New Left Books, 1976, for a discussion of early debates among Marxists on this point.
14 V. Navarro, *Social Security and Medicine in the USSR: A Marxist Critique*, Lexington, Mass.: Lexington Books, 1977.
15 V. Navarro, *Class Struggle, the State, and Medicine*, Oxford: Martin Robertson, 1978.
16 B. and J. Ehrenreich, Medicine and Social Control, in Ehrenreich, *op. cit.*, p. 43.
17 Ehrenreich, *op. cit.*, p. 17.

18 Navarro, Work, Ideology and Science.
19 Ehrenreich, *op. cit.*, p. 17.
20 J. Young, Science Is Social Relations, *Radical Science Journal* no. 5 (1977); K. Figlio, Sinister Medicine, *Radical Science Journal* no. 9 (1979).
21 H. Rose and S. Rose, Science, Ideology and the Real World, *Science Bulletin* 22 (1980): 14.
22 The interpretation of medical power, assumed to be rooted in the control of the medical skills and knowledge by the medical profession, is also the main weakness of another radical interpretation of medicine, B. Ehrenreich and D. English, *For Her Own Good: 150 Years of the Experts' Advice to Women*, London: Pluto Press, 1979. To see the primary conflict in medicine as the conflict between the "expert" and the "women" is, as Ludi Jordanova rightly indicates, to avoid the key questions of "who are the experts, by whom are they designated, who accepts the label, who reads what they write." (See Ludi Jordanova, Conceptualizing Power over Women, A review *For Her Own Good*, *Radical Science Journal* no. 12 (1982): 125.)
23 Ehrenreich, *op. cit.*, pp. 15, 29.
24 *Ibid.*, p. 29.
25 *Ibid.*, p. 24.
26 *Ibid.*, p. 25.
27 M. Harnecker, *Los conceptos fundamentales del materialism historico*, Siglo XXI, 1977, p. 43.
28 Each mode of production has its own knowledge, practice and institutions of medicine. Somewhere else I have defined the characteristics of capitalist medicine—its biologism, positivism, mechanicism and individualism—and how (a) its appearance in history meant a break—not a linear succession—with feudal medicine; and (b) its hegemony and dominance was determined by the victory of the bourgeoisie over the feudal aristocracy in a struggle that took place in the transition from feudalism to capitalism. See: How Bourgeois Ideology Appears in Medical Knowledge, in Navarro, Work, Ideology and Science, pp. 198–203.
29 See V. Navarro, The Limits of the World Systems Theory in Defining Capitalist and Socialist Formations, *Science and Society*, Spring, 1982, for a further expansion of this point.
30 N. Poulantzas, *Classes in Contemporary Capitalism*, London: New Left Books, 1974.
31 M. Carpenter wrongly attributes to me the opposite position without ever mentioning quotes or specific references. See review of Marxists and radical works by M. Carpenter, *Capital and Class*, Summer, 1979, p. 145.
32 V. Navarro, *Medicine under Capitalism*, New York: Neale Watson, 1976.
33 Figlio, *op cit.*, p. 33.

34   Navarro, Work, Ideology and Science.
35   Bourgeois Dominance, Ideology and Knowledge in Medicine, in Navarro, Work, Ideology and Science.
36   Ehrenreich, *op. cit.*, p. 13.
37   Figlio, *op. cit.*, p. 32.
38   Ehrenreich, *op. cit.*, p. 25.
39   Navarro, *Medicine under Capitalism*, p. 190.
40   C. Offe, Some Contradictions of the Modern Welfare State, *Critical Social Policy* 2 (2) (1982).
41   See good discussion of this point in G. Therborn, *The Ideology of Power and the Power of Ideology*, London: New Left Books, 1980, p. 109.
42   E. Stark, Limits of Radical Health Criticism, *International Journal of Health Science* 12 (3) (1982): 441.
43   Navarro, Bourgeois Dominance, Ideology, and Knowledge in Medicine.
44   T. Kuhn, *The Structure of Scientific Revolutions*, Chicago, Ill.: University of Chicago Press, 1962.
45   P. Feyerabend, *Science in a Free Society*, London: New Left Books, 1978.
46   *Ibid.*, p. 207.
47   N. Poulantzas, *State, Power and Socialism*, London: New Left Books, 1980, p. 44.
48   M. Foucault, *La volonté de savoir*, Paris: Gallimard, 1977 and G. Deleuze, Ecrivan non: un nouveau cartographe, *Critique*, 1975.
49   Personal communication.
50   Figlio, *op. cit.*
51   L. Gordon, The Politics of Birth Control, 1920–1940, in Ehrenreich, *op. cit.*
52   See Stark, *op. cit.*, pp. 449–551, for a good discussion of this point.
53   J. Eyer, Stress Related Mortality and Social Organization, *Review of Radical Political Economics* 9, no. 1 (1977): 1.
54   K. Marx, Carta a J. Weydemeyer, 5 Marzo, 1852 in *Obras Escogidas*, II, p. 456.
55   This critique of Marxists is one of the most frequent that appear in radical critiques. M. Carpenter, K. Figlio and J. Ehrenreich indulge extensively in this critique.
56   Harnecker, *op. cit.*
57   This section is abstracted from V. Navarro, The Limits of the World Systems Theory in Understanding and Defining Capitalist and Socialist Formation, *Science and Society*, Spring 1982: 77–90.
58   V. Navarro, The Nature of Democracy in the Core Capitalist Countries: Meanings and Implications for Class Struggle *The Insurgent Sociologist* 10 (1) (Summer, 1980): 3. Components of this part are abstracted from that article.
59   G. Assennato and V. Navarro, Workers' Participation and Control in

Italy: The Case of Occupational Medicine, *International Journal of Health Services* 10 (2) (1980): 217.

60 P. Ingrao, *Crisis y Tercera Via*, Barcelona: Saia, 1980.

61 M. Castells, *Ciudad, Democracy, Socialismo*, Siglo XXI, 1978.

62 N. Poulantzas, L'état, les mouvements sociaux, le parti, *Dialectiques* no. 28 (1979).

63 Interview with Louis Althusser on the Problems of the State by Rosanna Rossanda, *Viejo Topo* 20 (1978): 4.

64 Therborn, *op cit.*, p. 110.

Name index

Subject index